THE DESIGN OF RESEARCH LABORATORIES

Extension to the Agricultural Research
Council's Animal Research Station,
Cambridge, an experimental building designed
by the Nuffield Foundation's Division for
Architectural Studies. View from the west.

THE DESIGN OF
RESEARCH LABORATORIES

The Report of a Study carried out by the

Division for Architectural Studies of the Nuffield Foundation

LONDON

Oxford University Press

NEW YORK TORONTO

1961

Oxford University Press, Amen House, London, E.C. 4

GLASGOW NEW YORK TORONTO MELBOURNE WELLINGTON
BOMBAY CALCUTTA MADRAS KARACHI KUALA LUMPUR
CAPE TOWN IBADAN NAIROBI ACCRA

PRINTED IN GREAT BRITAIN
AT THE UNIVERSITY PRESS OXFORD
BY VIVIAN RIDLER
PRINTER TO THE UNIVERSITY

THE NUFFIELD FOUNDATION
DIVISION FOR ARCHITECTURAL STUDIES

CONTROLLING COMMITTEE

Chairman: Leslie Farrer-Brown, C.B.E.

Members: Sir Ernest Rock Carling, F.R.C.P., F.R.C.S., HON. LL.D.*
Dr. F. M. Lea, C.B., C.B.E., D.SC., F.R.I.C., HON. A.R.I.B.A.
Sir William Holford, M.A., F.R.I.B.A.,† M.T.P.I., F.I.L.A.
Sir Edward Playfair, K.C.B.
Sir William Slater, K.B.E., D.SC., F.R.I.C., F.R.S.
Richard Llewelyn Davies, M.A., F.R.I.B.A. (*Director of Division*)

* Died July 1960.   † P.R.I.B.A. 1960–62.

INVESTIGATION TEAM
FOR THE LABORATORY STUDY

Richard Llewelyn Davies, M.A., F.R.I.B.A.
John Musgrove, B.ARCH., A.R.I.B.A.

Michael Smith, B.ARCH., A.R.I.B.A.

Jack Nightingale

Ruan McWilliam, B.A.

Christine Adnitt, Patricia Barber, Janet Blatcher, Susan Clay, Gillian Heigham Davis, Esther Dittmar, Walter Goddard, Susan Hunt, Dilys Ingold, P. Kaikini, Ann Kay, Sarah Kydd, David Moizer, John Page, D. J. Petty, Rachel Phillipson, Jean Walker

Statistical Adviser: Dr. N. T. J. Bailey, M.A., D.SC.

ADVISORY PANEL
FOR THE LABORATORY STUDY

Chairman: Leslie Farrer-Brown, C.B.E.

Members: N. C. Barford, M.A., B.SC.
A. R. Gilson, M.A.
Dr. W. P. Grove, D.SC.
Prof. H. D. Kay, C.B.E., D.SC., PH.D., F.R.S.

FOREWORD

AN investigation into the function and design of research laboratories was proposed to the Nuffield Foundation by the Agricultural Research Council in 1953. The Division for Architectural Studies was set up by the Foundation in 1954 and the laboratory study was its first project. The Agricultural Research Council supported the work by making a contribution towards its cost and by giving the team access to all its research establishments.

The Building Research Station of the Department of Scientific and Industrial Research collaborated with the Foundation's team in the study and some of the research reported in this book was carried out at the Station.

We are particularly indebted to the Directors and Staffs of the Agricultural Research Council's establishments; and to Messrs. Imperial Chemical Industries Limited, Glaxo Laboratories Limited, and The Distillers Company Limited, in whose premises the laboratory survey was carried out.

The cost studies would not have been possible without the valuable work carried out by the Ministry of Works which provided the great bulk of the cost data. Help in collecting cost data was also given by the Ministry of Agriculture, Fisheries and Food, The Engineering Division of Messrs. Courtaulds Limited, Messrs. Johns, Slater and Haward, and by Messrs. G. N. Haden and Sons.

Acknowledgements and thanks are due to all of these and to many other public bodies, private firms, and individuals who have given advice and assistance to the team in all stages of this work.

LESLIE FARRER-BROWN
RICHARD LLEWELYN DAVIES
Nuffield Lodge, London, 1960

CONTENTS

LIST OF FIGURES

LIST OF TABLES

AN HISTORICAL INTRODUCTION

Early laboratories

ALCHEMY flourished in Alexandria in the third and fourth centuries A.D., but probably had its origins some centuries earlier in the chemical industry which had sprung up in the Mediterranean countries to meet the demand for cheap dyes, imitation pearls, and alloys which looked like gold and silver (1). In Egypt practical work was fostered by the priests and the earliest laboratories were built adjoining the temples (2).

Greek scientific philosophy was expounded and reappraised by Roman writers just before and just after the beginning of the Christian era. Rome added little that was new to Greek ideas but developed and applied them, especially in the fields of medicine and agriculture. In some centres, such as the Greek settlements in Italy, development probably continued during the changes and upheavals of the Dark Ages, but there are no records of buildings used as laboratories during this period. Alchemy was practised, however, from the eleventh century onwards, when ancient Greek learning again began to influence thought in western Europe.

In the middle of the thirteenth century Albertus Magnus, a Dominican, taught alchemy in Hildesheim, Regensburg, Cologne, and Paris (3). Roger Bacon, sometimes regarded as the intellectual originator of experimental research, taught in Oxford. In the court of Frederick II, King of Sicily, a school of practical anatomy was established between 1200 and 1250, and subsequently, an anatomical school was instituted at Bologna (4). In these two schools we hear for the first time of students working in laboratories.

Although there were probably active schools of scientific method in the fourteenth and fifteenth centuries, practical experimental work was left to the alchemists, engrossed in their search for the Philosopher's Stone or the Elixir. James IV of Scotland set up John Damian, an alchemist of French or Italian origin, in a laboratory in Stirling Castle in 1501 (5). This laboratory was probably similar in appearance to those illustrated in contemporary woodcuts and in paintings of the Dutch School (Figs. 1 and 2). The alchemist was usually depicted in a gloomy interior, surrounded by the paraphernalia of his calling. The environment was calculated to enhance the esoteric mumbo-jumbo with which the alchemist surrounded his work.

A hundred years later, however, Andreas Libavius was unwilling to work under these conditions. In his *Alchymia* (6), he published a project for a complete chemical institute (Fig. 3), which, though never executed, is of particular interest as the earliest record of laboratory planning. On the ground floor, rooms opening off a central hall included a main laboratory, an analytical laboratory, and a private laboratory for the director. There was a chemical store, a preparation room with benches and fittings, a crystallizing room with vats, storerooms, and a room for the assistants. The laboratory was to be supplied with water, and charcoal stoves were to be used for heating. Outside the building were plots for making saltpetre, vitriol, and alum. The upper story contained living quarters, a study, and a library.

Up to the middle of the seventeenth century, the ideas of the Middle Ages were being extended and developed. A number of books appeared, notably Agricola's *De Re Metallica* (1556), and these together with the traditional skills handed down by craftsmen in the mines, foundries, and glassworks, particularly in Germany, provided a large part of the data on which chemical science was founded, and were a direct source of inspiration to the French chemical schools of the eighteenth century.

During this transitional period before the advent of modern chemistry, there was little development in the design of buildings for practical experiments. Towards the end of the seventeenth century, however, scientific advance was accelerated. The laboratories and lecture rooms of the Jardin du Roi (for the culture of medicinal plants) had been formally opened in 1640. Here William Davidson of Aberdeen became the first professor of chemistry in France (7). The Royal Society was founded in 1660, its first aim being to promote the new experimental philosophy and to bring the benefits of science to industry. Thereafter, laboratories began to appear in the universities. One of the earliest of these (1682) was in the University of Altdorf in Germany (Fig. 4). The building was 36 ft. long, 15 ft. wide, and 14 ft. high,

DEBENT   IGNARI   RES   FERRE   ET   POST   OPERARI   QVATVOR   INSERTA   NATVRIS   IN   NVBE   REFERTA
IVS   LAPIDIS   CARI   VILIS   SED   DENIQ3   RARI   NVLLA   MINERALIS   RES   EST   VBI   PRINCIPALIS
VNICA   RES   CERTA   VILIS   SED   VBIQ3   REPERTA   SED   TALIS   QVALIS   REPERITVR   VBIQ3   LOCALIS

Fig. 1. The alchemist at work, *c.* 1560. From an early engraving by Cock, after P. Brueghel.

Fig. 2. The alchemist. From a painting by Ostade, 1661.

Fig. 3. Plans for a chemical institute by Libavius, 1606.

1. South-east front.

2. North-east front (with the chimney-stack of the main laboratory).

3. North. 4. West. 5. East. 6. South.

A. East entrance with small door. B. Main room with galleries. C. Spiral staircase. D. Garden. E. Drive. F. Vestibule of the laboratory. G. Chemical laboratory. H. Private laboratory with spiral stairs to the study. J. Small analytical laboratory. K. Chemical pharmacy. L. Preparation room. M. Bedroom for the laboratory assistant. N. Store room. O. Crystallization room. P. Wood store. Q. South store room. R. Fruit store. S. Bathroom. T. Aphodeuterium (closet). V. Vegetable cellar. X. Wine cellar. Y. Laboratory cellar. Z. Water-supply.

aa. Doors to the laboratory cellar. bb. Entrance to the wine cellar. cc. Steam-bath. dd. Ashbath furnace. ee. Waterbath. ff. Distillation apparatus for upward distillation. gg. Sublimation apparatus. hh. Ordinary fireplace. ii. Reverberatory furnace. kk. Distillation apparatus. ll. Distillation apparatus with spiral condenser. mm. Dung-bath. oo. Coal store. pp. Philosopher's furnace in the private laboratory. qq. Assay furnaces. rr. Analytical balances in cases. ss. Tubs and vats. tt. Distillation 'per lacinias' (table with vessels). xx. Equipment and benches for preparations. yy. Water tanks. zz. Space for preparing saltpetre, alum, and vitriol.

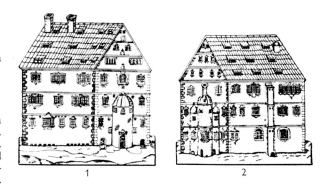

1

2

3

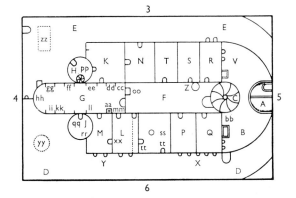

6

designed in late baroque style. At each end of the laboratory there was a large furnace with a draught hood. A table was placed in the middle of the room which was used for lecturing as well as practical work.

In this country John Francis Vigani, an Italian, began to give lectures in chemistry at Cambridge in 1680. He was given the use of a room for his lectures and experiments at Queen's College. At Trinity College, Dublin, the authorities ordered the building of a chemical laboratory which was opened in 1711 (8). In Edinburgh the Surgeons' Incorporation acquired a hall which Alexander Monteith equipped as a chemical laboratory, where apprentice apothecaries might receive training (9), and in the university, Dr. James Crawford was elected Professor of Physic and Chemistry in 1713, two rooms being allotted to him for teaching. In 1747 Dr. William Cullen, who was lecturing in medicine at Glasgow University, persuaded the university to fit up a chemical laboratory. An expenditure of £52 was sanctioned, later increased to £136, and a grant of £20 annually made for the maintenance of the laboratory. At Marischal College, Aberdeen, George French received permission to fit up a laboratory in a 'low mean-looking building with a tiled roof' which appears to have been the kitchen of the Grey Friars' monastery, and at King's College the chemistry class was held in a room 18 ft. square and 9 ft. high where 'from 60 to 80 students were cooped up' (10). Instruction still took the form of lecture-demonstrations where students might take their stand round a circular bench. Forty years were to elapse before the appearance of teaching laboratories in which undergraduates could carry out their own experiments.

Figs. 5 and 6 show typical arrangements in private chemical laboratories in the eighteenth century. In Fig. 5 the work-bench is a strongly constructed table, and there is a large draught hood. The laboratory shown in Fig. 6 is believed to have been instituted by Boyle in Maiden Lane, Southampton Street, at the end of the seventeenth century, continuing under Godfrey and Cook, manufacturing chemists, throughout the eighteenth until the middle of the nineteenth century (11). The print shows examples of laboratory furniture and racks for glassware; the flues from the furnaces call to mind the fume cupboard ducts of much later laboratories. To some extent, however, the cloak of the alchemist was inherited by the pharmacist whose laboratory was usually a large room or shop, opening into a smaller room or private laboratory at the rear (Fig. 7).

The laboratories used by Priestley and Lavoisier (12) in the second half of the eighteenth century are shown in Figs. 8 and 9, the former obviously part of a normal domestic room given over to the purpose. In Lavoisier's laboratory, furniture and fittings appear now to be of the simplest and most unpretentious kind, although Douglas McKie considers this laboratory to have been unequalled in its equipment 'until the rise of modern research institutions' (13).

1800–1920

In this country the founding of the Royal Institution in 1799 with its theatre, model-room, and workshops, was an important milestone in laboratory design. In 1803 this laboratory was thought to be 'equal or indeed superior to any in this country and probably to any on the continent' (14). Fig. 10 shows Faraday's laboratory at the Institution as it was in

Fig. 4. Chemical laboratory at Altdorf University, Germany, 1682.

1852. Ideas on laboratory design developed rapidly in the first half of the nineteenth century, and in spite of extensive alterations, the Royal Institution failed to keep pace with these ideas. This was made clear in 1873 by a lecturer who said:

> In the opinion of those best qualified to judge our chemical laboratory was badly ventilated, badly lighted, badly drained, and quite unfit to be occupied for many hours daily. It was probably the very worst, and certainly all but the worst chemical laboratory in London. The physical laboratory had remained for nearly seventy years in its original state. At first it was said to be equal to any laboratory; but then there were hardly any in existence in this country; and during the last few years such splendid edifices have arisen in London, Oxford, Cambridge, Manchester, and in Glasgow, and elsewhere, that the laboratory of Davy of Faraday and of Tyndall was much inferior to the private laboratories of the professors who carry on their course of instruction in public rooms of still greater size and extent.... The main purpose of our laboratories is research, and instead of offering by their excellence an inducement to professors to come and stay, the one was a makeshift and the other a noble relic.... By the construction of new laboratories[1] this material disadvantage will be removed (15).

Meanwhile, in France it was realized that if science

was to survive after the Revolution, it must be fostered by every means at command. A number of leading scientists (Lavoisier, Bailly, and Cousin) had fallen to the guillotine and the Académie des Sciences had been closed (16). Following the Revolution, Vauquelin organized a course of instruction and, later, Gay-Lussac and Thenard also taught in their own laboratories, in which conditions were said to be exceedingly cramped. Little support for the teaching of science came from the State in the early nineteenth century and the fees a laboratory student had to pay were 'exorbitant' (17).

At the beginning of the nineteenth century chemistry was still looked upon by the natural philosophers in Germany as an experimental art, not a science. Those interested in science went to study in laboratories abroad. Friedrich Wöhler travelled to Sweden to work under Berzelius in Stockholm. In an account of his experiences given to the German Chemical Society, Wöhler describes Berzelius's laboratory:

> At that time I was the only one in the laboratory; before me came Mitscherlich and H. and G. Rose, and I was followed by Magnus. The laboratory comprised two ordinary rooms fitted in the simplest way; there were no furnaces or ventilating hoods; no service of water or gas. In one room stood two common long tables, made of deal; Berzelius worked at one of these, I at the other. On the walls there were some cupboards with the reagents; in the middle stood the mercury-trough and the table

[1] The new Davy-Faraday Research Laboratory at the Royal Institution was opened in 1896. (See p. 10.)

5

6

7

Fig. 5. Chemical Laboratory in the middle of the eighteenth century.

Fig. 6. Boyle's laboratory, *c.* 1670. From an early print. Boyle is said to have instituted the laboratory illustrated at Maiden Lane, Southampton Street, London.

Fig. 7. Laboratory of the pharmacist d'Ailly. From a painting by Johann Jelgershuis, 1818.

Fig. 8. Apparatus used by Joseph Priestley during his experiments on different kinds of air, *c.* 1774.

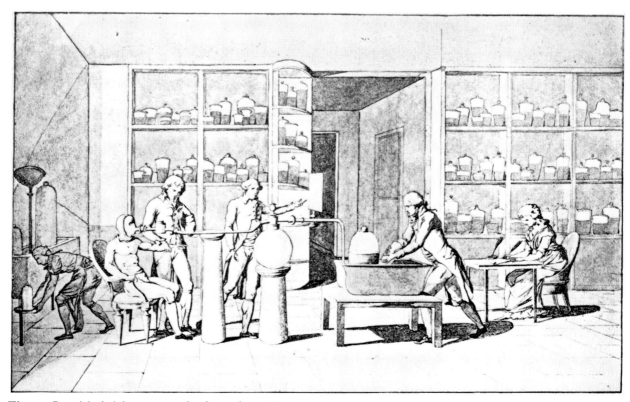

Fig. 9. Lavoisier's laboratory at the Arsenal, *c.* 1789.

Fig. 10. Michael Faraday's laboratory at the Royal Institution in 1852.

blowpipe, the latter under an oilskin hood communicating with a flue. Besides this, there was the washing-up place, consisting of a stoneware cistern with a tap, standing over a tub. Here the severe Anna, Berzelius' cook, used to clean the apparatus every day. The other housed the balances and some cupboards containing instruments and apparatus; in an adjoining small workshop there was a lathe. Close by, in the kitchen where Anna cooked the meals, stood a small furnace, seldom used, and a sand-bath, always kept hot (18).

Liebig returned from Paris to organize the first real school of practical chemistry at the University of Giessen in 1824. His laboratory, which was to be the model for numerous teaching laboratories built in the nineteenth century, comprised a workroom with just sufficient space for twelve workers at benches under the windows (Fig. 11). Behind the workroom was a room crammed full of equipment and supplies; behind this again a room in which apparatus for glass-blowing was kept, and where anvils and balances were set up. Opening into a corridor which led into the latter room was Liebig's own work cabinet and a small private laboratory with space for two or three persons (19). The most striking feature of the main laboratory is the appearance for the first time of benches provided with cupboards, drawers, and shelves for reagent bottles. The bench tops were removable and were fitted with sinks; piped water was laid to the benches. As far as is known, this was the first laboratory so equipped. The serviced benches were placed around the walls and in the middle of the room were ordinary tables. At one end of the room there was a metal fume cupboard with a movable glass front, under which was a coal-fired furnace.

In France, in the second half of the century, progress was slow, as is shown by Pasteur's forceful article written for the *Moniteur* in 1868:

I implore you, take some interest in those sacred dwellings meaningly described as *laboratories*. Ask that they be multiplied and completed. They are the temples of the future, of riches and of comfort. There humanity grows greater, better, stronger; there she can learn to read the works of nature, works of progress and universal harmony, while humanity's own works are too often those of barbarism, of fanaticism and of destruction.

Some nations have felt the wholesome breath of truth. Rich and large laboratories have been growing in Germany for the last thirty years, and many more are still being built; at Berlin and at Bonn two palaces,[1] worth four million francs each are being erected for chemical studies. St. Petersburg has spent three and a half million francs on a Physiological Institute; England, America, Austria, Bavaria have made most generous sacrifices. Italy too has made a start. And France? France has not yet begun . . . (20).

As a direct result of this article, Pasteur and other leading scientists gained an interview with Napoleon III, and in the following year Wurtz presented his report on German laboratories to the French Minister of Education, in which he insisted upon the necessity of establishing properly equipped laboratories for practical instruction in chemistry (17). From 1870

[1] University laboratories. A detailed description of these laboratories is given in A. W. Hofmann's report to the British Government in 1866.

Fig. 11. Liebig's laboratory at Giessen. From a drawing by Trautschold, 1842.

onwards there was a gradual improvement in laboratory accommodation in French schools and universities.

In the United States the earliest institutions where students undertook their own experiments were the Rensselaer Polytechnic Institute at Troy, New York, and the Massachusetts Institute of Technology in Boston. At the former laboratory work was probably carried on by students from its foundation in 1824 (21).

Interest in science in the British universities continued to grow. Thomas Thomson, Professor of Chemistry at the University of Glasgow, opened the first chemical laboratory where students could undertake their own practical work in 1820. By 1831 the number of students and research workers had so increased that a new chemistry department was erected in Shuttle Street and this continued in use until 1870. This building, now used as a warehouse, is still unmistakably a laboratory. The top floor is lit by means of roof-lights; there are a number of fitted ventilators, and many gas-pipe junctions still to be seen (22). It was here that Greville Williams produced his *Handbook of chemical manipulation* (1857) in which he puts forward suggestions for the design of a laboratory to be used solely for research work. Also at Glasgow, in 1846, one of the earliest physical laboratories for students was set up by William Thomson. On taking over he found 'apparatus of a very old-fashioned kind, much of it was more than a hundred years old, little of it less than fifty years old, and most of it was worm-eaten mahogany. . . . There was absolutely no provision of any kind for experimental investigation' (23). To meet his re-

quirements the Faculty allotted him a wine cellar, part of an old professor's house, the rest of which had been converted into lecture rooms. The bins were removed, and a water supply and a sink installed. This room served as a physical laboratory for several years, and is described as follows by Professor Ayrton, a student of Thomson's in the sixties:

In my time Thomson's laboratory consisted of one room and the adjoining coal-cellar, the latter being the birth-place of the siphon recorder. . . . There was no special apparatus for students' use in the laboratory, no contrivances such as would to-day be found in any polytechnic, no laboratory course, no special hours for students to attend, no assistants to advise or explain, no marks given for laboratory work, no workshop, and even no fee to be paid. But the six or eight students who worked in that laboratory felt that the entrée was a great privilege. . . . Thomson's students experimented in his one room and the adjoining coal-cellar, in spite of the atmosphere of coal dust, which settled on everything, produced by a boy coming periodically to shovel up coal for the fires. If for some test a student wanted a resistance coil, or a Wheatstone's bridge, he had to find some wire, wind the coil, and adjust it for himself. It is difficult to make the electrical student of to-day realise what were the difficulties, but what were also the splendid compensating advantages of the electrical students under Thomson in the sixties. . . . But oh! The delight of those days! Would we have exchanged them, had the choice been given us, for days passed in the most perfectly designed laboratory of the twentieth century without him? No! For the inspiration of our lives would have been wanting (24).

In 1870, Glasgow University opened a new chemistry building of 'Glastonbury Kitchen' design, a

Fig. 12. The laboratory of the Pharmaceutical Society in Bloomsbury Square, 1845–60.

copy of the Abbot's Kitchen at Glastonbury Abbey (1304–41).[1] The Glasgow laboratory has recently been demolished, but a similar building at Oxford is still in use. Built in 1855, it adjoins the Science Museum. As a result of a competition, two designs were selected, one in Gothic style by Benjamin Woodward and one in the Renaissance style by Barry. Ruskin strongly advocated the Gothic design and this was chosen. After a visit to the laboratory Ruskin said, in a letter to Professor Acland, that he felt no architecture other than vaultings and strong buttresses could yield itself to the crucible and the blast of the furnace. Referring to the interior, he wrote:

The more active and workmanlike our proceedings the better, fresh air blowing in from the windows, and nothing interfering with the free space for our shelves and instruments on the walls. I am not sure that much interior imagery or colour, or other exciting address to any of the observant faculties, would be desirable under such circumstances. You know best; but I should not more think of painting in bright colours beside you, while you were dissecting or analysing, than of entertaining you by a concert of fifes and cymbals (25).

In London, practical chemistry was first taught in

1844 in a room belonging to the Pharmaceutical Society on the second floor of No. 17 Bloomsbury Square, and in the following year the Royal College of Chemistry was founded.

The Pharmaceutical Society's first laboratory was replaced in 1845 by a larger room in the basement which extended into the garden to meet the increased demand for teaching accommodation (Fig. 12). The work-bench was divided into twelve compartments, six on either side, each student having one to himself. A lead gutter ran down the middle of the bench to collect the waste water from the sink in each compartment. Immediately over the gutter, and extending the whole length of the bench, was a horizontal duct with an opening with sliding doors opposite each work place. The duct was connected directly to the chimney. This worked well in carrying off gases and fumes. An airtight cupboard connected to a sewer was used for getting rid of sulphuretted hydrogen and other heavy gases; a furnace hood was used for light gases (26). In 1860 the laboratory was found to be too small to house all the students and a new one was built and fitted with benches for seventy students and later increased to provide one hundred places. In the new laboratory the bench tops were of slate (felt pads were provided to prevent breakages) but there were no sinks and no water supply. Burners were placed on a table at the end of the bench and

[1] The kitchen at Glastonbury, with four fireplaces, is 40 ft. square, 72 ft. high, and is built of stone. The roof is divided by eight stone ribs rising to a circular ring supporting a lantern 12 ft. across used for ventilation as well as lighting.

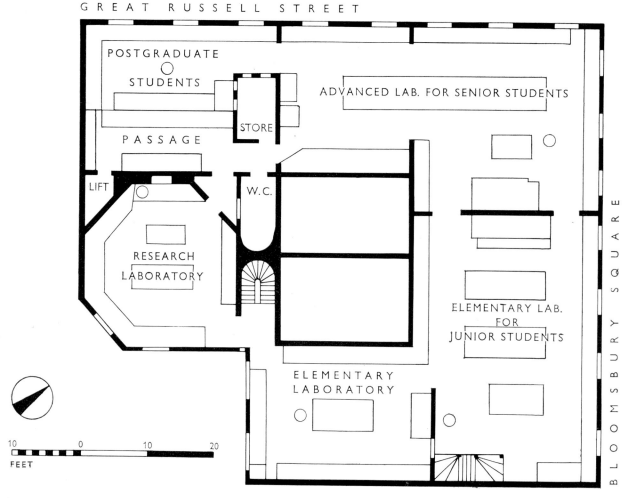

GREAT RUSSELL STREET

POSTGRADUATE STUDENTS

ADVANCED LAB. FOR SENIOR STUDENTS

STORE

PASSAGE

LIFT

W.C.

RESEARCH LABORATORY

ELEMENTARY LAB. FOR JUNIOR STUDENTS

ELEMENTARY LABORATORY

BLOOMSBURY SQUARE

10   0   10   20

FEET

Fig. 13. Plan of the chemical laboratories of the Pharmaceutical Society, 1903. These laboratories with certain changes were in use from 1860 to 1956.

there was a communal sink at the end of the room (Figs. 13 and 14). The research laboratory as used in 1905 is shown in Fig. 15. In 1908–9 the benches were fitted with teak tops and sinks, and water was laid on (27).

The Royal College of Chemistry in Oxford Street had a frontage of 34 ft. with a depth of 53 ft. The whole of the first floor was occupied by the students' laboratory while on the ground floor were a private laboratory for the Professor, a balance room, and a lecture room. The basement contained furnaces, a steam-boiler, and stores (28). It was here that William Perkin studied from 1853 to 1856 under Hofmann. He describes the facilities as follows:

We had to make our H_2S in a small square chamber connected with the chimney flue. There were no stink closets except the covered part of a large sand bath heated with coke. There were no Bunsen burners but we had short lengths of iron tube covered with wire gauze. For combustions we used charcoal. A bench and cupboard containing reagents and use of the above chamber was all we practically had and a charcoal combustion furnace in addition for advanced students . . . (29).

In the middle years of the nineteenth century, however, more and better-equipped laboratories came into use in the universities. Attention began to be paid to ventilation and lighting. In the new building for physical science at Glasgow University (1870), for example, pure air was drawn down a shaft in the tower by fans worked by a small steam-engine. The air was passed through a dry chamber containing hot water pipes and then mixed with a controlled quantity of fresh cold air before being supplied to the laboratory. The air entered at the top of the room and was extracted through ducts built below the floor (30). One of the features of the physical laboratory of Owens College, Manchester (1898), was the planned system of ventilation combined with an attempt to exclude dust. The plenum system, much used in laboratories at this time, was rejected because it took up too much basement space, was ineffective in excluding dust, and because the noise and mechanical shaking from the fans would seriously interfere with the work of the laboratories (31).

The Davy-Faraday Research Laboratory at the Royal Institution was opened in 1896. It was unique of its kind, being the only public laboratory in the

Fig. 14. Chemistry laboratory for advanced students of the Pharmaceutical Society, 1903.

Fig. 15. Chemistry research laboratory of the Pharmaceutical Society, 1905.

Fig. 16. The first research laboratories at Ardeer, 1876.

world solely devoted to research in pure science (32). The new laboratory comprised rooms for research in organic, inorganic, and physical chemistry, special rooms such as balance rooms and photographic rooms, a large library, and a museum.

Parallel with the rapid development of science in the universities came the new idea of industrial research. The progress in applied work was slow at first, and was not to reach fruition until after the First World War. Nevertheless there were early beginnings. J. B. Lawes, inspired largely by Liebig, started field manure experiments in 1834 on his estate at Rothamsted (later to become a research institute under the Agricultural Research Council), and the first artificial fertilizer, superphosphate, was manufactured commercially in 1844 in his factory at Deptford. The original laboratory consisted of a converted bedroom in the Manor House at Rothamsted, but by 1843 it had been transferred to a barn. Two years later a fund raised by the local farmers enabled Lawes to erect a new laboratory which was used until 1914. The present building on the same site was completed in 1917 (33).

When William Perkin made his discovery of mauve in 1856, he was working in 'half of a small but long-shaped room with a few shelves for bottles and a table'. His description of his own first private laboratory continues:

In the fireplace a furnace was also built. No water laid on or gas. I used to work with old Berzelius spirit lamps and in a shed I did combustions with charcoal. It was in this laboratory I worked in the evenings and vacation times and here I discovered and worked out my experi-

ments on the mauve. The little back garden was afterwards used to conduct larger operations. . . .

By the end of the following year the new dye was being supplied from his factory at Greenford Green. Here Perkin had 'a proper laboratory built in the works with balance room also stink closet and most of the appliances of the day which were very few but no gas' (29).

Among the oldest industrial research laboratories in this country are those of the Nobel Division of Imperial Chemical Industries Limited founded by Alfred Nobel in 1873 at Ardeer. The first laboratory consisted of one large room which served also as a drawing office (Fig. 16). It was a single-storied building attached to another of two stories which afterwards became the manager's house. Later, the work was transferred to another building and a second laboratory was built next to it. Both were in use in 1881 and the later building (Fig. 16A) was used until 1927, when the present buildings were opened (34).

The Reichsanstalt was founded in Charlottenburg by Werner von Siemens and von Helmholtz during the years 1884–7. It was probably the first national research laboratory. In this country, at the instigation of a committee headed by Lord Rayleigh, it was decided to set up a State research laboratory in 1899. Work on the National Physical Laboratory was originally begun at Kew Observatory, but in December 1900 Queen Victoria gave over Bushy House for the purpose, and a grant of £14,000 (afterwards increased to £19,000) was made by the Treasury

Fig. 16A. The research laboratory at Ardeer, 1890.

towards the initial alterations, additional buildings, and equipment at Teddington. The basement and ground floor at Bushy House were used for the physics laboratory, and for the engineering laboratory a building 80 ft. by 50 ft. was erected. The National Physical Laboratory was at first entrusted to the Royal Society, but in 1918 was transferred to the Department of Scientific and Industrial Research.

The latter department was formed in 1916, largely as a result of the war, which had shown the dependence of this country upon scientific development abroad. In the next five years the programme of the department was gradually defined, and by 1925 six research stations had been founded. Also, the department launched a scheme for the establishment of research associations which it was anticipated would

depend for some considerable time on the facilities of the universities and the larger technical colleges. At the end of the First World War, however, the universities had to devote the greater part of their energies to teaching, and the research associations had to consider at once the establishment of their own laboratories. Up to this time, although laboratories had been built for the universities, few new buildings were erected in this country specifically for research, either by the Government or private firms. Usually, when new lines of research were begun, large houses were taken over and converted to laboratory use. By the nineteen-twenties, however, the inconvenience of such buildings for highly specialized work was realized, and the research laboratory began to emerge as a distinct building type.

REFERENCES

(1) WHETHAM, afterwards DAMPIER, Sir William C. *A history of science and its relations with philosophy and religion.* 4th edition revised and enlarged. Cambridge, 1948, p. 50.

(2) MEYER, Ernst von. *A history of chemistry.* 2nd edition. London, 1895, p. 9.

(3) Ibid., p. 31.

(4) THOMSON, William, *Baron Kelvin.* 'Scientific laboratories.' *Nature, Lond.* **31**, 1885, pp. 409–13.

(5) READ, J. *Humour and humanism in chemistry.* London, 1947, p. 18.

(6) LIBAVIUS, A. *Alchymia.* Frankfurt, 1606.

(7) READ, J. *William Davidson of Aberdeen.* Aberdeen, 1949. *Aberdeen University Studies,* no. 129.

(8) WHEELER, T. S. 'The Dublin Schools.' *J. Inst. Chem.* **77**, 1953, p. 64.

(9) COMRIE, J. D. *History of Scottish medicine.* 2nd edition. London, 1932, **I**, pp. 253, 289.

(10) STRATHEE, R. B. 'The University of Aberdeen.' *J. Inst. Chem.* **77**, 1953, pp. 220–31.

(11) PILCHER, R. B. 'Boyle's laboratory.' *Ambix*, **2**, 1938, pp. 17–21.

(12) PARTINGTON, J. R. 'Evolution of the chemical laboratory.' *Endeavour*, **1**, 1942, pp. 145–50.

(13) McKIE, D. *Antoine Lavoisier, scientist, economist, social reformer.* London, 1952, p. 195.

(14) *Nature, Lond.* **7**, 1873, p. 223.

(15) *Nature, Lond.* **7**, 1873, p. 264.

(16) WHETHAM, *afterwards* DAMPIER, Sir William C. *A history of science and its relations with philosophy and religion.* 4th edition revised and enlarged. Cambridge, 1948, p. 288.

(17) MEYER, Ernst von. *A history of chemistry.* 2nd edition. London, 1895, p. 591.

(18) READ, J. *Humour and humanism in chemistry.* London, 1947, p. 236.

(19) GOOD, H. G. 'On the early history of Liebig's laboratory.' *J. Chem. Educ.* **13**, 1936, p. 557.

(20) VALLERY-RADOT, R. *The life of Pasteur.* London, 1920, p. 152.

(21) CAJORI, Florian. *A history of physics in its elementary branches including the evolution of physical laboratories.* New York, 1929, p. 392.

(22) KENT, A. 'The Shuttle Street Laboratories.' *Glasgow University Gazette*, no. 25, 1956.

(23) THOMSON, William, *Baron Kelvin.* 'Scientific laboratories.' *Nature, Lond.* **31**, 1885, pp. 409–13.

(24) THOMPSON, S. P. *The life of William Thomson, Baron Kelvin of Largs.* London, 1910, **1**, p. 297.

(25) COOK, E. T., and WEDDERBURN, A. *The Oxford Museum.* London, 1905, p. 223. *The Works of Ruskin*, **16.**

(26) *Pharm. J.* **5**, 1845–6, pp. 314–24.

(27) WALLIS, T. E. Personal communication.

(28) TILDEN, Sir William A. *Chemical Discovery and invention in the twentieth century.* London, 1916.

(29) CLIFF, W. H. 'The dyemaking works of Perkin and sons.' *J. Soc. Dy. Col.* **73**, 1957, pp. 313–14.

(30) BOTTOMLEY, J. T. 'Physical science in Glasgow University.' *Nature, Lond.* **6**, 1872, p. 29.

(31) *Nature, Lond.* **58**, 1898, pp. 621–2.

(32) *Nature, Lond.* **55**, 1896, pp. 208–9.

(33) ROTHAMSTED EXPERIMENTAL STATION. *Guide to the experimental farms.* Harpenden, 1954.

(34) MILES, F. S. *A history of research in the Nobel Division of I.C.I.* Birmingham, 1955.

Chapter 2

CURRENT PRACTICE IN LABORATORY DESIGN

WITH only a few exceptions, such as the Royal Institution Laboratories, buildings specially designed for research purposes only did not appear until the nineteen-twenties. Study of the design characteristics of laboratories erected in the last forty years reveals widely varying judgements on broad principles of planning. The pattern of research undertaken by the team was in large measure determined by means of a preliminary survey of current practice. Also, descriptive analyses of a few of these research buildings provides a background to the studies described in Part II.

British research laboratories since 1920

To some extent, the research institutes built in the nineteen-twenties set the pattern of design for research buildings in this country. Generally, research rooms with serviced benches, offices, special rooms of various kinds and the usual ancillary accommodation are planned in shallow units (14 ft. to 16 ft.

from window wall to back of room) on either side of a central corridor. Laboratories vary in size from the one-man room to large open laboratories. They are normally separated by permanent structural partitions. Bench arrangements of every conceivable kind can be seen. In small rooms, serviced benches are arranged around the perimeter. Service pipes are usually embedded in or attached to structural walls and floors, with the result that in many large rooms, benches placed in the middle of the laboratory area cannot be serviced. Almost without exception these buildings were planned around fixed routines at a time when research techniques were not developing and changing as rapidly as they do now. The Molteno Institute for Research in Parasitology at Cambridge (1920–1) is typical of this period. It is a compact three-story rectangular block. Rooms are planned on each floor on either side of a central corridor (Fig. 17). Research rooms, 14 ft. deep and roughly square in

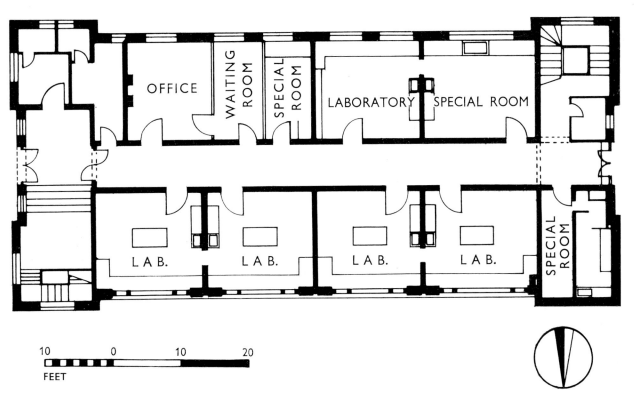

10   0   10   20
FEET

Fig. 17. Ground floor plan of the Molteno Institute for Research in Parasitology, Cambridge, 1920–1.

Fig. 18. A room in the main research laboratories, Nobel Division, Imperial Chemical Industries Ltd., Ardeer, 1927.

shape, occupy the north side, while common rooms, libraries, offices, &c., occupy the south side. Benches are arranged along the window wall with short returns on the side wall in some cases, each room having about 17-ft. run of bench. The laboratories are well lit by natural daylight, having large windows and a ceiling height of about 10 ft.

The British Cotton Industry Research Association Laboratory (1920–2) incorporated some design ideas which were not carried forward until very much later. It is a single-story building with laboratories 22 ft. deep planned on either side of a central corridor. Rooms are of two or three sizes, built up of standard bays, 10 ft. 6 in. wide. A 5-ft. deep service duct was placed under the corridor and a 3 ft. 6 in. void formed below the floor, so that service lines could be carried to any point and taken up through the floor where required. This method of servicing was not fully explored and developed until quite recently in the Wellcome Research Laboratories at Beckenham.

During the late twenties and early thirties the larger private companies found that their own small works laboratories, and the facilities offered by the research associations, did not completely meet their needs. Large concerns were anxious to improve methods of production and to develop new products, and so needed research facilities under their direct

control and in contact with their own production activities. The small works laboratory, therefore, began to grow into the central research department. The main laboratories of the Nobel Division, Imperial Chemical Industries, in use today at Ardeer, were first occupied in 1927 and 1928. Fig. 18 shows the interior of a typical laboratory room.

Although isolated earlier efforts had been made to arrive at economic planning arrangements (for example, the central research laboratories of the United Steel Companies opened in 1934 contained rooms 28 ft. deep), it was not until the late thirties that the first attempt was made to rationalize laboratory planning. Serge Chermayeff's design for the research laboratory of the Dyestuff's Division of Imperial Chemical Industries at Blackley was an important development in this respect (Fig. 19). To fit the building to the work Chermayeff designed a repetitive unit to accommodate one worker, and built up laboratories of various sizes by combining different numbers of units. The original building[1] is two stories high and has two wings designed on different dimensional modules and placed at right angles to each other. One wing contains offices, and the other

[1] Two other wings have been added since the original building was completed. These have laboratories on both sides of the corridor instead of on one side only as in the original building.

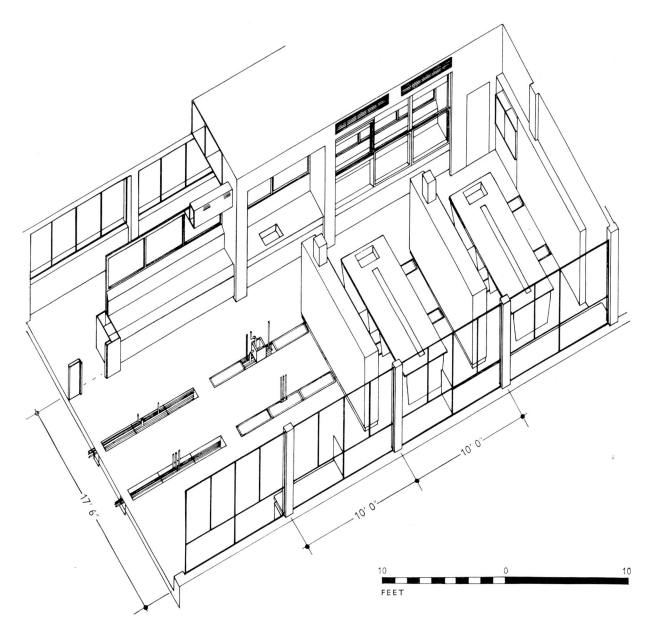

Fig. 19. The standard laboratory unit at the research laboratories of the Dyestuffs Division, Imperial Chemical Industries Ltd., Blackley, 1938.

a series of research rooms on one side only of a connecting corridor. A typical laboratory room housed eight research workers at four island benches, each bench being screened from its neighbour by shelving. No serviced benching was placed along the window wall and communal accommodation, such as washing-up sinks, fume cupboards, &c., were placed on the corridor wall. The laboratories were artificially ventilated from ducting in the corridor ceilings, and the corridor walls carried fume cupboard ducts and services to sinks, &c. Shallow floor ducts with removable covers ran longitudinally along the middle of the laboratories carrying sub-mains to the bench positions. Windows occupied the whole of the external wall down to desk level. The fume cupboards, which formed the dividing wall between the laboratories and the corridor, were glazed on both sides so that the back of the laboratory received light through the corridor.

The Blackley building contained the germ of certain ideas in laboratory planning which have been considerably developed in the United States (see below, pp. 19–21) and to a lesser extent in a few industrial laboratories in this country, for example, Courtauld's Acetate and Synthetic Fibres Laboratory at Coventry (Fig. 20), and the Imperial Chemical Industries' Pharmaceuticals Laboratory at Alderley Park (Fig. 21). These ideas can be summarized as follows:

1. Overall planning was based on a structural module derived from an assessment of the space needed by each individual worker, i.e. bench length, bench width, and the clearance between benches.

Fig. 20. A deep laboratory room at the Acetate and Synthetic Fibres Laboratory, Courtaulds Ltd., Coventry, 1954.

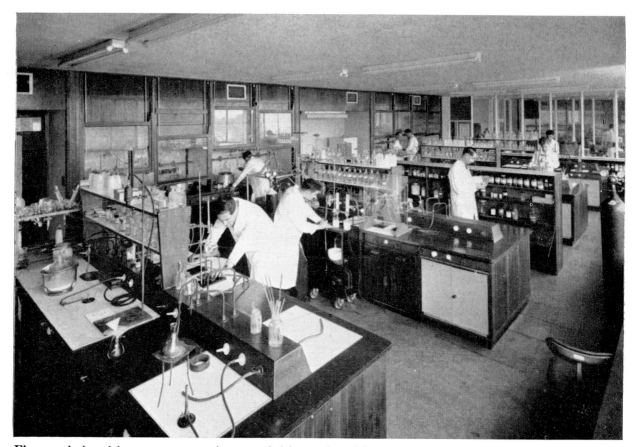

Fig. 21. A deep laboratory room at the research laboratories of the Pharmaceuticals Division, Imperial Chemical Industries Ltd., Alderley Park, 1957.

2. Laboratory benches were placed at right angles to the window wall for ease of servicing and access from a longitudinal corridor.

3. Straight unimpeded runs of benching were provided for each worker.

4. Attention was given to the problem of lighting rooms greater in depth from window wall to corridor wall than had been used hitherto.

5. Office accommodation was provided in a separate wing, the office wing being based on a different dimensional module, thus avoiding the use of expensive serviced laboratory space.

At Blackley no flexibility was provided between rooms. Probably the earliest attempt to do this was in the London, Midland and Scottish Railways' research laboratories at Derby (1935), where the cross walls between laboratory rooms were made demountable, and main services were run around the outside walls of the building.

The lead given by Chermayeff in the thirties has not been followed in many subsequent buildings and some recently built establishments bear close resemblance to the research institutes of the twenties. Nevertheless, the influence of Chermayeff's building can be seen in a few post-war laboratories, for example, the British Nylon Spinners Laboratory at Pontypool (1952) where each graduate chemist and his assistant are given one structural bay, 10 ft. wide and 25 ft. deep, with two straight lengths of bench at right angles to the window wall (Fig. 22). Most of the laboratories face north-east in order to avoid sunlight penetration. Offices of less depth (9 ft. $4\frac{1}{2}$ in.) are placed opposite the research rooms, though some desk space is provided in the laboratory. All services are carried above a false ceiling in the corridor and piped overhead to the benches.

The rapid development of scientific techniques in the last ten years has emphasized the need for research buildings which can be quickly and easily adapted to meet specialized demands as they arise. Moreover, there is a changing pattern of research organization, even within quite small establishments. In recent laboratory buildings there are two main trends in design both of which reflect the need for adaptable buildings. First, there is the trend towards open serviced floor areas which can be divided up with demountable partitions, the aim being to give each scientist or group of scientists a serviced area which may be divided up to provide any combination of rooms as and when required. Secondly, there is the trend towards a simplified, functional arrangement of benches in long unimpeded lengths, spaced and arranged in such a way to rationalize bench servicing. The former approach to laboratory design has received most attention in this country, the latter has received more attention in the United States and on the Continent.

The laboratories for Imperial Chemical Industries' Plastics Division at Welwyn (1953) went a great deal further in providing overall flexibility by means of demountable partitioning than had been attempted previously. The building is planned on a 4 ft. grid and partitions can be put up anywhere on the grid whilst services are available at most grid points from floor ducts carried in deep floors constructed on lattice beams. Each department was free to plan its own special arrangement of rooms: one such arrangement is shown in Fig. 23. The depth of the building is such that many of the rooms are internal and rely on artificial lighting and ventilation.

One of the few examples of a building designed around rationalized bench and services layout in this country is Courtauld's Acetate and Synthetic Fibres Laboratory at Coventry (Fig. 24). The laboratory space is designed on a grid 11 ft. 9 in. by 28 ft., and multiples of this basic unit are used to give rooms of various sizes. Main services run vertically in ducts placed at each grid point along the corridor wall. Offices are provided in a separate wing, but a minimum amount of office space is allowed in the main laboratory area, opening directly off the laboratories.

Recent American laboratories

In recent American research buildings emphasis has been less on overall flexibility than on the development of a planning principle which would permit great flexibility of room use without recourse to structural modification. The laboratories of the Bell Telephone Company, built in 1941, had considerable influence on subsequent work. Fig. 25 shows the plan of a typical laboratory unit in this building. Small rooms for offices are placed in separate short wings, at right angles to the main laboratory block. The laboratory layout is based on an assessment of the space needed for a two-man team. This results in rooms approximately 20 ft. deep, and 12 ft. wide. Some large laboratories with island benches are provided for routine work and these are of greater depth (25 ft.) in order to allow for extra circulation

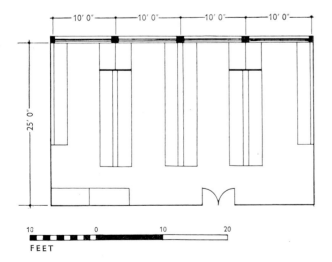

Fig. 22. Four-graduate chemistry laboratory at the British Nylon Spinners research laboratories, Pontypool, 1952.

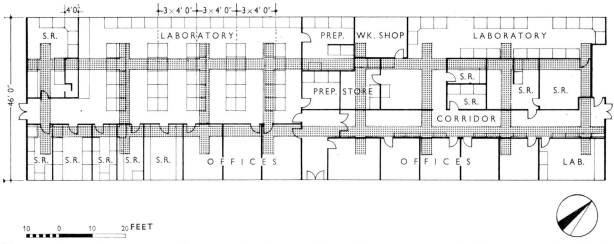

Fig. 23. A typical arrangement of rooms, using demountable partitions, in the research laboratories of the Plastics Division, Imperial Chemical Industries Ltd., Welwyn, 1953.

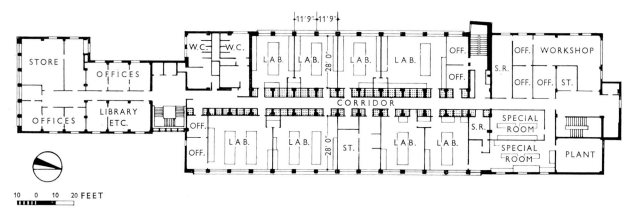

Fig. 24. Third-floor plan of the Acetate and Synthetic Fibres Laboratory, Courtaulds Ltd., Coventry, 1954.

space without seriously reducing the unimpeded runs of benching. The 20 ft. deep rooms are placed on one side of the main corridor, the 25 ft. deep rooms on the other, making a laboratory block of over 50 ft. in depth. Vertical service ducts are placed at 6 ft. centres on the outside walls. Horizontal branches under the windows link each bench run to the vertical sub-mains. Island benches are serviced by means of short floor ducts (Fig. 26). Serviced benches are at right angles to the outside walls, the clearance between benches being from 5 ft. to 7 ft., according to the furniture used. Movable tables, 5 ft. by 2 ft., placed against the serviced wall or spine are used instead of fixed benching.

Further developments in this type of planning can be seen in the B. F. Goodrich Research Centre, New Jersey, and in the standard laboratory unit designed by the United States Department of Agriculture for its regional research laboratories, and in the Johns-Manville Laboratory, New Jersey. A single bay room in the latter is shown in Fig. 27.

It is accepted practice in America to plan on the basis of a dimensional module related to the space needed for an individual worker or teams of known size. The modules used vary in width from 10 ft.

to 13 ft., depending on the space allowed between benches (4 ft. to 7 ft.). The clear bench run needed for the work, and the length of serviced wall space to accommodate standing equipment, fume cupboards, &c., determines room depth, as all service runs to the benches are perpendicular to outside walls. Most of the buildings since 1939 have rooms from 20 ft. to 30 ft. deep, with vertical sub-mains placed at each grid point. In deep rooms of this kind it is uneconomical to service benches under windows, and it may be essential to provide access between rooms near the outside walls as a safety measure in some cases. Also, as Haines points out (1), bench units on outside walls interfere with normal heating arrangements, the cleaning of windows in high buildings, &c. Fume cupboards or hoods are usually placed adjacent to corridors so that trunking can be taken directly into the vertical ducts. Figs. 28, 29, and 30 show alternative arrangements of laboratory space.

In multi-story buildings lighting at the back of deep rooms is normally supplemented by artificial means, and artificial ventilation and air-conditioning are common. Special rooms such as constant-temperature rooms, instrument rooms, &c., are planned internally and have no natural lighting.

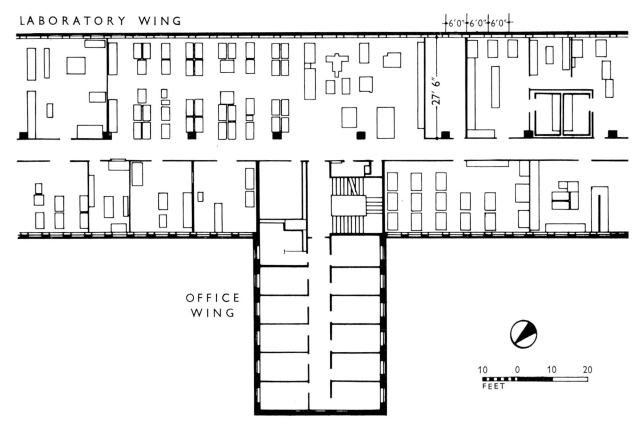

LABORATORY WING

OFFICE
WING

10 0 10 20
FEET

Fig. 25. Part plan of the laboratory wing and office wing at the Bell Telephone Company research laboratories, New Jersey, 1941.

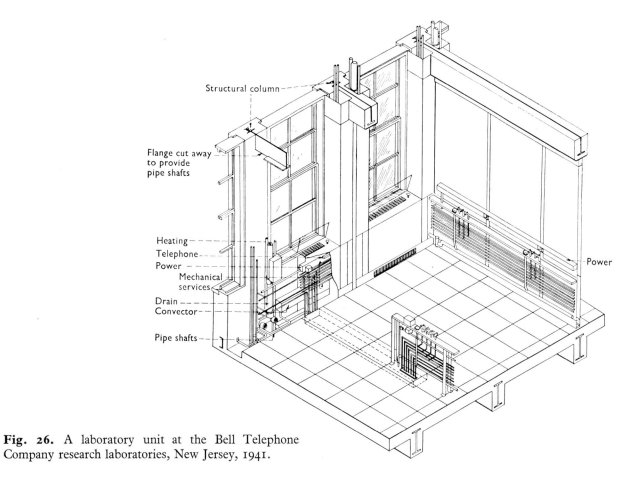

Structural column

Flange cut away
to provide
pipe shafts

Heating
Telephone
Power
Mechanical
services
Drain
Convector

Pipe shafts

Power

Fig. 26. A laboratory unit at the Bell Telephone Company research laboratories, New Jersey, 1941.

21

Fig. 27. Single laboratory unit at the Johns-Manville research centre, New Jersey, 1945. The unit is 10 ft. 6 in. wide by 26 ft. deep.

Recent European laboratories

In Europe the most advanced laboratories from the point of view of functional design were found in Sweden, Denmark, and Germany. In recently completed buildings laboratories were found to be comparatively deep (19 ft. to 25 ft.) and usually placed on each side of a central corridor. Users of the buildings are convinced that long bench runs at right angles to the windows are functionally efficient and essential to flexibility of use. The structural grid is without exception determined by bench spacing, and services distribution to the benches is along the grid lines. Vertical sub-mains on the corridor wall or on the outside wall are used even in buildings of two or three stories, because of the comparative ease of maintenance. Bay widths for research buildings (generally 9 ft. to 10 ft.) are somewhat smaller than those recommended in this report (see Part II, Chapter 1, p. 50). This is mainly due to a reduced bench width which is standardized in Denmark and Sweden at 55 cm. (1 ft. 10 in. approx.).

There is a broad acceptance of the principle of limited but adequate flexibility based on a services grid. In some laboratories the partitions between the bays are demountable in order to allow rapid rearrangement but only in multiples of one whole bay.

Fig. 31 shows such an arrangement in the Shell laboratories near Stockholm. The small unit benches can also be seen in this illustration. They are placed against a serviced wall or a service spine but are not attached in any way and can be removed or rearranged at will. A further development of this principle is shown in Fig. 32. In these laboratories at the Danish Atomic Energy Research Establishment at Risø, permanent vertical members are placed at about 4 ft. centres on the grid lines and can be wholly or partially filled in with solid panels as required. The vertical members incorporate a patent screw-fixing system on which bench tops, cupboards, service pipes, and even sundry pieces of movable equipment such as small refrigerators, ovens, &c., are supported.

Ceiling heights generally are from 9 ft. to 10 ft. except in Germany where there are binding regulations controlling the minimum volume of air per person. The microbiology department of the University of Munich (see Fig. 33 and also Fig. 60 in Part II, Chapter 3) illustrates one of the few examples found by the team in which bench services are carried from vertical sub-mains across the whole depth of a laboratory in floor ducts, and in which some degree of services adaptability is maintained.

In Europe there has also been an attempt to combine the idea of limited flexibility with some degree of adaptability based on possible combinations of a fixed bay size. The preference amongst users and architects alike is to improve the systems of servicing rather than to spend money on excessive flexibility, which is rarely if ever used. It is of some interest that the Battelle Institute in Frankfurt which undertakes all kinds of research for private firms, on a repayment basis, has adopted a rather different approach to flexibility. The laboratory accommodation must be capable of changing over to an entirely different kind of work, possibly two or three times in the course of a year. Industrial finishes have been used throughout the building: internal walls are constructed in lightweight concrete blocks and are left unplastered. All services are carried at high level, completely exposed, and drop to bench positions where needed (see Fig. 61, Part II, Chapter 3). The concrete-block partitions are capable of carrying cupboards, shelves, &c., and can be quickly taken down and rebuilt in a new position. In a building life of some five years, almost every internal wall had been taken down and rebuilt. The electrical services are carried in a plug-in trunking system in the corridors. The trunking is carried at high level in the corridor; plug-in points are available at about 1-ft. intervals along the trunking. Heavy metal plugs are used to pick up electrical supplies from the main power lines in the trunking and carried in P.V.C. covered cables to any point where required in the laboratories. The system is a proprietary one and although expensive is considered essential to flexibility of use in the Battelle building.

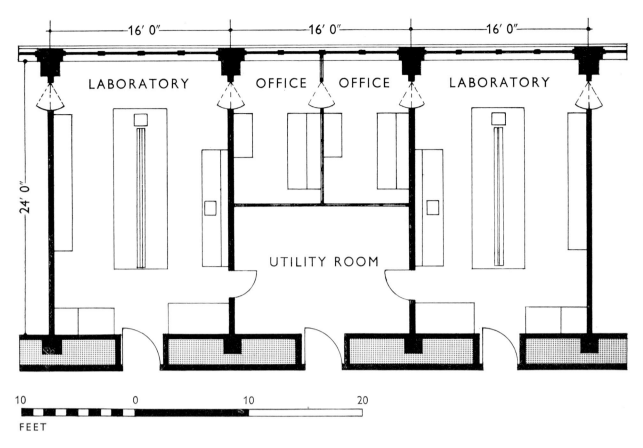

Fig. 28. Plan of the standard laboratory unit adopted in the regional research laboratories of the United States Department of Agriculture.

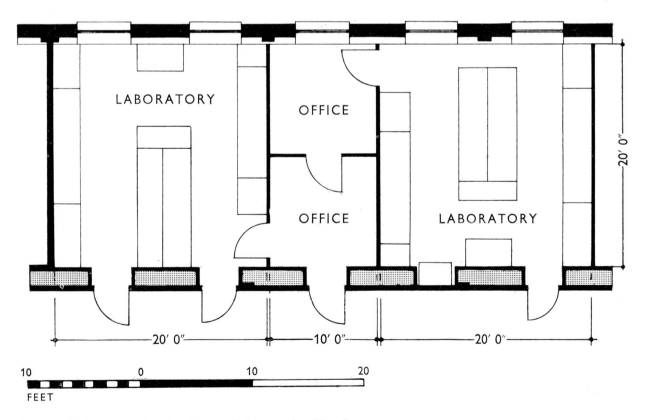

Fig. 29. Laboratory unit, Merck research laboratories, New Jersey.

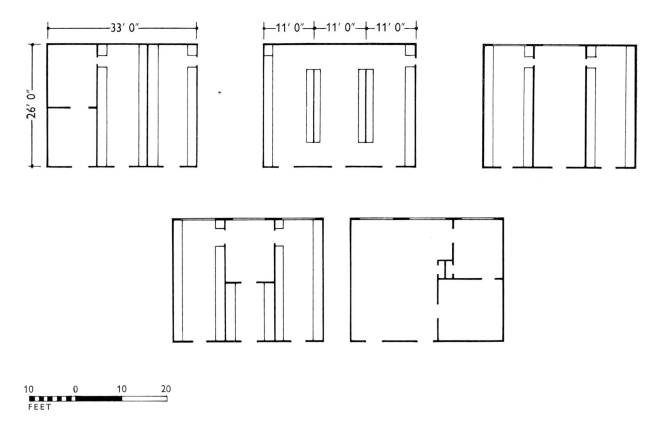

Fig. 30. Laboratory units, Johns-Manville laboratory, New Jersey.

Aspects of design

From the study of recent buildings there emerged certain aspects of design which are of special importance in laboratories. These are discussed in greater detail below.

Office accommodation

The provision of office space for laboratory workers has a marked effect upon building economy as well as working efficiency. Serviced laboratory space is expensive and must therefore be used intensively, and it follows that if large areas of serviced space are given over to office use, it cannot be economical in terms of building cost. In many of the older laboratories no special provision was made for offices, except perhaps a private office for the director and an area given over to administrative use. It will usually be found in buildings of this kind that desks and tables have found their way into laboratory rooms. In buildings such as the I.C.I. Nobel Division Laboratories at Ardeer, there is quite often sufficient space to place a writing-table in the middle of the laboratory without seriously impeding the work carried out on benches around the perimeter (Fig. 18).

More recently it has been realized that reading and writing take up a considerable amount of the scientist's time. It is also inevitable that an increasing amount of administrative work falls upon senior scientific staff, and work of this kind cannot conveniently be carried out within the laboratory. Three main methods of providing office space are used, and in some cases two or more of these methods are combined in the same establishment.

1. Offices opening directly off the laboratory, usually occupied only by staff working in the laboratory immediately adjacent. An example of this kind of arrangement can be seen in Fig. 28 (the standard laboratory unit of the U.S. Department of Agriculture).

2. Offices planned within the laboratory block but separate from the laboratories themselves, for example, opposite to the laboratory rooms on the other side of a corridor. There are several recent examples of this kind of planning, such as the laboratories for the British Nylon Spinners at Pontypool and the Höganäsmetoder Laboratories near Hälsingborg in Sweden.

3. Offices planned in a separate wing of the building as in the Bell Telephone Laboratories (Fig. 25) and I.C.I. Dyestuffs Laboratory at Blackley.

Where separate office accommodation is provided (methods 2 and 3), it is inevitable that a certain amount of writing will still be carried out in the laboratory, and it is of some interest that at the Höganäsmetoder Laboratories some graduate staff have preferred to move out of their offices on the opposite side of the corridor and return to much less adequate accommodation in the laboratories themselves. From the

31

32

Fig. 31. Demountable partitions and removable unit benches at the RASTA laboratory (Shell), Lidingo, Sweden.

Fig. 32. Vertical steel service channels and suspended bench units at the Danish Atomic Energy Research Establishment, Risø.

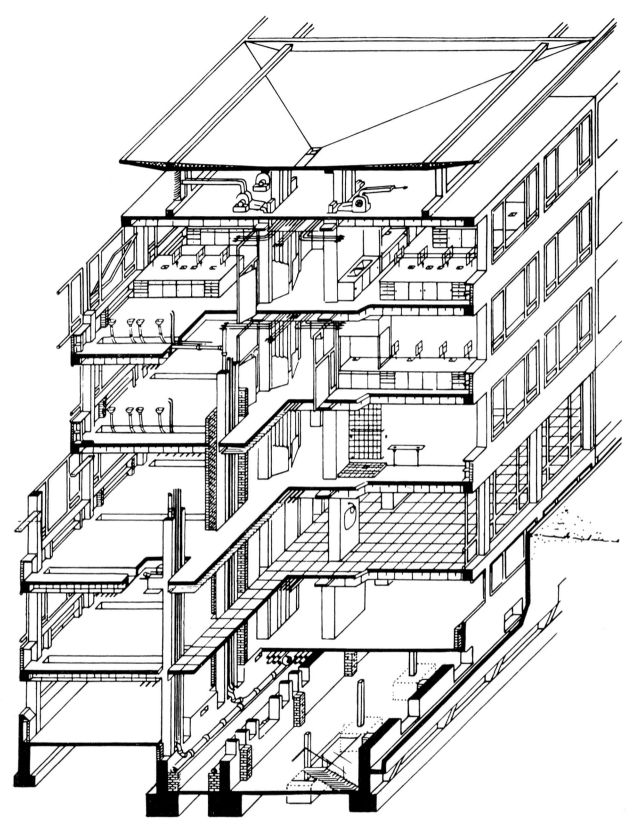

Fig. 33. Bench services carried from vertical sub-mains across the width of the laboratory in floor ducts at the University of Munich.

point of view of building economy it is obviously cheaper to provide office space in a separate wing. The offices can usually be built with a lower ceiling height, have less expensive finishes, and, of course, do not require the complex servicing of the laboratory areas. Many organizations, however, will not permit this kind of arrangement except for the purely administrative non-technical staff. They prefer the scientist to be near the laboratory, if not actually in it. There are obvious difficulties in supervising junior technical staff from a remote office.

The proportion of overall laboratory area to be devoted to office space should be related to the amount of time the scientists spend in reading and writing, and the method of provision should be related to the relative amount of time spent thus by different grades of worker. These aspects of laboratory office accommodation are discussed fully below in Part II, Chapters 2 and 6.

Lighting

The tendency described above to design laboratory rooms of greater depth has brought with it problems of lighting. In America permanent artificial lighting to supplement natural daylight is accepted. In the few laboratories in this country which have rooms of depths greater than 16 ft., artificial lighting is, of course, used, but no attempts have been made to arrive at rationalized standards of lighting for laboratories related to the visual characteristics of the work. Recent advances in natural and artificial lighting techniques have enabled the team to study laboratory lighting in some detail in collaboration with the Building Research Station (see Part II, Chapter 4).

Servicing systems

More detailed analyses of current methods of laboratory services distribution are given in Part II, Chapter 3. In many recent laboratories much greater attention has been paid to ensuring that the servicing systems as well as the building itself incorporate some degree of adaptability. Older laboratories, where service lines are inaccessible, have failed to meet the changing demands of modern scientific techniques.

There is an increasing tendency, especially on the Continent, to regard laboratories as workshops, in which the service lines are an integral part of the equipment. The completely exposed services of the Battelle Institute in Frankfurt have already been mentioned and there are other similar examples such as the Atomic Energy Research Establishment at Risø in Denmark. The criticisms levelled at exposed piping in the past are now largely invalid. Corrosion problems can be overcome with modern applied coating (see Appendix II), and dust collection becomes less of a problem where proper ventilation is installed.

REFERENCE

(1) Haines, C. 'Planning the scientific laboratory.' *Archit. Rec.* **108**, 1950, p. 111.

BIBLIOGRAPHY

Architectural Record. *Buildings for research.* New York, F. W. Dodge Corporation, 1958.

Coleman, H. S. *Laboratory design.* New York, Reinhold Publishing Corporation, 1951.

Haines, C. S. *Recent trends in the design of American industrial research facilities.* Institute of Physics. *The design of physics laboratories.* London, Chapman and Hall Ltd., 1959.

Lassen, F. *Laboratorien: Planung Bau Einrichtung.* Darmstadt, Verlag Das Beispiel, 1957.

Schramm, W. *Chemische und biologische Laboratorien: Planung Bau und Einrichtung.* Weinheim/Bergstr, Verlag Chemie GmbH., 1957.

National Research Council of Canada Division of Building Research. *An annotated bibliography on laboratory buildings.* Ottawa, 1959.

Chapter 3

THE SCOPE AND METHODS OF THE INVESTIGATION

Scope of the study

CONSIDERATION of current practice in laboratory building as described in the previous chapter reveals the need for more precise information on several important aspects of design. The investigation, of which this book is the outcome, was planned to meet that need.

In the first place it was necessary to define the scope of the study, which could not of course explore all aspects of the problem. The terms of reference of the project confined the inquiry to research laboratories, and excluded laboratories intended primarily for teaching, or for the routine control of production. Although much of the field work was carried out in the laboratories of one of the research councils, the study and the results can be held to apply generally to research laboratories, whether under public control, in universities, or in industry. The present investigation is the first systematic attempt to study laboratory design, and it has been focused on certain types of accommodation of general interest.

A good many research buildings house large, heavy items of equipment, particularly where work in engineering or nuclear physics is involved. Such buildings present individual problems in each case, and must be designed to fit the equipment. They are not very susceptible to general study, nor are they repeated sufficiently often to warrant it. The design problems of this group of buildings were therefore excluded from the investigation. It was also decided to exclude buildings used for pilot-scale experiments, as they approximate more to factories than to laboratories. Factory buildings are currently under examination by a team at the Building Research Station (1).

The scope of the investigation has been, in the main, limited to laboratories of the common type, where the work involves equipment of small or moderate scale. It has covered the laboratory area proper, where general research work is carried on, and a range of other facilities such as special-purpose rooms, offices, and stores.

Over the field thus defined it was possible to attempt comprehensive coverage, and to plan a study which would take all major aspects of design into consideration. The results of the study taken separately each represent some contribution to one or other aspect of the problem. Put together, they suggest a general approach to the design of laboratories. This approach has been embodied in an experimental building designed by the team, a new laboratory for the Animal Research Station at Cambridge. The results have also been used in the design of two other buildings—the new laboratories for the Imperial Cancer Research Fund, Lincoln's Inn, and for the Agricultural Research Council at Letcombe Regis.

Methods employed

As the study was designed to be comprehensive within the limits described above, a considerable range of different methods was employed in carrying it through. Some of the problems which required investigation could only be tackled by inventing new techniques of study and carrying them out with the team's own resources. Others required joint attack by the team and the staff of the Building Research Station. In other cases the necessary information was already available in one form or another and simply needed to be unearthed. Often it was necessary to apply a technique developed for another purpose to some problem in laboratory design.

The results of the various inquiries undertaken by the team are reported in Part II. Where use is made of material published elsewhere, or where the methods employed are already well known, no attempt has been made to describe the research techniques other than by giving appropriate references to published sources. There are, however, three studies which broke new ground, and where the methods used, in whole or in part, are new. These are: a survey of user requirements; a study carried out at the Building Research Station into laboratory lighting; a comparative study of cost covering eight recently completed laboratories. Some discussion of each of these studies is included in the present Chapter as a contribution to the methodology of architectural research.

The survey of user requirements

Purpose of the survey

If a building is to function efficiently its design must be related as closely as possible to the work or other human activities which it has to house. These activities can be observed by a variety of techniques several of which have already been used in connexion with the design of other buildings (2). None of the techniques which had been previously employed was found to be appropriate, because of the absence of standard routine in scientific work. Not only does the work vary between individuals, but each man engages in widely different activities over a period of years. The life of laboratory buildings outlasts their occupation by any individual scientist and far outlasts any individual piece of work on which a man is engaged. Efficient design therefore must aim at providing the sort of building which will satisfy the needs of a range of scientific workers over a number of years. To guide design in the first instance, a general picture of the fluctuating needs of scientific work is required. It is necessary to know how far the needs of a chemist differ from those of a physicist, and how the needs of each can be expected to vary over a period of time. The technique chosen for building up such a picture is the random sample survey with statistical analysis.

The laboratory survey described here is believed to be the first example of this approach applied to a problem in architecture, although it is likely that similar techniques would yield useful results in other fields of building design. It was principally directed to the requirements of general laboratory space which occupies a substantial proportion of floor space in nearly all research establishments. The laboratories of the Agricultural Research Service, in which the survey was conducted, are mainly engaged in normal, small-scale work requiring serviced benching or equipment of similar size.

The survey was designed in terms of the individual scientific worker. Each man was separately observed and the use he made of space and services was recorded. In practice, scientists sometimes work as individuals, sometimes as a team, sometimes with one or more assistants. There is little in the way of fixed organizational structure; two, three, or more men may work together from time to time on a particular project. A statistical technique whereby the survey data relating to the needs of individuals can be combined to give a picture of the needs of various groups was therefore used.

The survey was planned primarily to yield information on the amount of space and the service facilities used by scientists. In addition, it was found possible to collect by means of the same survey technique, information about the proportion of time spent on reading and writing activities, and to make assessments of the physical characteristics of laboratory work for the purpose of formulating rational lighting criteria.

Allocation of space

Three principal factors determine the space needed by the scientist for his bench work. They are the length and width of the bench and the free floor-area around it. Bench width is determined within fairly narrow limits by the length of human arm reach, and free floor area is determined by the need to allow movement and circulation between the benches. Bench length is directly related to the work in progress, whereas bench width and free floor area can be varied within limits for any given task. The latter two aspects were therefore studied by other techniques (see Part II, Chapter 1, pp. 44–47). Bench length only could then be used as the principal measurement of space for the purposes of the survey.

Apart from working space in the laboratory, scientists need the use of office space, and it is necessary to assess how large this space should be, and to determine how near it should be to the laboratory. Whilst it was realized that a final decision on this point may often depend upon the method of staff organization, it was thought that it would be useful to determine the proportion of a scientist's working time spent in reading and writing. Here the aim was to provide information which could be used to determine the extent of the problem, and enable informed decisions to be made.

The provision of services

The scale of provision of piped services to the bench is a major issue in laboratory design. Information is needed both on the number of outlets to be provided per man or per unit run of bench, and on the sizing of the pipes or cables. In order to arrive at an economical pipe or cable size, it is necessary to predict the load it will carry when the building is in use. The survey was therefore planned to yield data on services use which, when analysed, would provide a guide to the number of bench points required, and information which would be of help in pipe-size calculations.

The assessment of lighting criteria

Although certain lighting standards have been laid down on the basis of good practice, no objective information was available on the visual characteristics of laboratory work. This information is essential in determining lighting levels and it was decided that observations would be made on laboratory task characteristics as part of the survey.

The pilot survey

Before embarking on the main survey which, if it was to cover a sufficiently long period of time, was likely to be a fairly lengthy operation, a pilot run was undertaken in order to develop practical methods of collecting and analysing the information.

The pilot survey took place during April, May, and June of 1954. It was carried out in two stations engaged in agricultural research, the Rothamsted Experimental Station and the National Institute for Research in Dairying, near Reading. These stations were chosen because they were easily accessible from London, covered between them a very wide range of scientific work, and were believed to be reasonably well provided with space and services. In the pilot survey, selected individuals were observed at work in the laboratory for periods of one hour each. No individual knew in advance that he was going to be observed. The total number of scientific workers observed was 232—too few to enable any significant differences to be distinguished in the needs of the individual scientific disciplines. Results from the pilot survey were, however, analysed according to staff grading—Scientific Officers, Experimental Officers, and Assistants. The comparatively long period of each observation—one hour—adopted in the pilot survey, enabled the observers to see scientific work as a process, and to pick up points of particular importance in the interpretation of results.

The results showed that, on the whole, there was not much change in the pattern of work during the period of observation. This suggested that the presence of the observer had negligible effect. It also meant that the main survey would be carried out more efficiently by means of the 'snap-round' technique, under which each individual is observed instantaneously at a number of separate times rather than continuously over a period. An account of the pilot survey and samples of the analysed results were published immediately it was concluded (3). Broadly, the pilot survey showed that it would be practicable to collect the necessary data, and that the analysis of the data would present no insuperable difficulties.

The main survey

The main survey was designed to cover the full range of scientific work carried on within the Agricultural Research Service. It was necessary to examine the needs of each scientific discipline and each grade of worker separately, and also to compare the needs at different times throughout the year in order to discover seasonal fluctuations, if such existed. The survey, therefore, was designed to cover a considerable number of individuals for a period of at least twelve months.

The first task was to classify scientific staff according to grade and discipline. Grade presented little difficulty, as staff were already classified in the records of the Agricultural Research Council as Scientific Officers, Experimental Officers, and Assistants. Within the Scientific Officer grade there are several ranks, e.g. Senior Principal Scientific Officer, Principal Scientific Officer, Senior Scientific Officer. For the survey these were grouped together, but heads of stations, and other staff whose work included a substantial proportion of administration, were excluded. It was fully realized that the use of these staff categories would inevitably mean that the

survey results were related to the particular staff organization used in the government scientific service. Private concerns and other research organizations use several grades which are not strictly comparable but it was thought that some interpolation would be possible, as the qualitative delineations between the government grades are generally well known and quite rigidly defined.

Classification into scientific disciplines was more difficult. A man may be qualified in one discipline whilst actually engaged in the laboratory on another kind of work. It was decided to ask the directors of all establishments included in the survey to classify their scientific staff by discipline. A list of discipline groups was circulated as a guide, but directors were asked to comment on the list and add to it as they thought necessary. It was suggested that the classification should be based on the work on which the man was actually engaged, rather than on the nature of his qualifications, or the name of the department in which he worked. The original list was amended in the light of their comments and eventually all scientific staff were classified under the following heads:[1]

Chemistry	Animal Physiology
Physics	Plant Physiology
Biochemistry	Botany
Biophysics	Zoology
Microbiology	Pathology
Entomology and Helminthology	

It was decided to observe, if possible, ten people chosen by random sample from each grade/discipline class (i.e. $3 \times 10 = 30$ in all) making a total of 330 individuals for the 11 disciplines. The standard numbers in each group were subsequently increased to 11 scientific officers, 11 experimental officers, and 13 assistants, to allow for losses during the survey, due to staff turnover, illness, or other causes. Some groups contained less than the standard number because of deficiencies in the numbers actually available.

The following stations were included in the survey:

John Innes Horticultural Institution, Bayfordbury, Herts.

Institute of Animal Physiology, Babraham, Cambridge.

Unit of Insect Physiology, Department of Zoology, University of Cambridge, Cambridge.

Molteno Institute of Biology and Parasitology, University of Cambridge, Cambridge.

Field Station, Compton.

East Malling Research Station, East Malling.

Research Station, Department of Agriculture and Horticulture, University of Bristol, Long Ashton, Nr. Bristol.

Rothamsted Experimental Station, Harpenden.

[1] Assistants were classified as working in the discipline of the scientist for whom they worked.

National Institute for Research in Dairying, University of Reading, Shinfield, Nr. Reading.

National Vegetable Research Station, Wellesbourne, Warwick.

Macaulay Institute for Soil Research, Craigiebuckler, Aberdeen.

The Rowett Research Institute, Bucksburn, Aberdeenshire.

Poultry Research Centre, Edinburgh.

Animal Diseases Research Association, Moredun Institute, Edinburgh.

Hannah Dairy Research Institute, Kirkhill, Ayr.

Scottish Plant Breeding Research Station, Scottish Society for Research in Plant Breeding, Pentlandfield, Midlothian.

For stations in England the survey ran for twelve months from June 1955, and in Scotland from September 1955.

It was impossible with the time and resources at the disposal of the team to cover any other major group of scientific establishments, but it was felt that some comparison was necessary with scientists engaged in comparable work in industrial research laboratories. Three industrial establishments, engaged in microbiological work, were therefore included in the survey. It was hoped that comparison of microbiological work in industry with similar work in agricultural research laboratories might be of interest, although it was fully recognized that the necessarily small sample of data from industry could not be expected to establish any general parallels. The following industrial laboratories were surveyed, by courtesy of the companies concerned:

Imperial Chemical Industries Limited, Akers Research Laboratory, Welwyn.

Glaxo Laboratories Limited, Greenford, Middlesex.

The Distillers Company Limited, Research and Development Department, Epsom.

Since the survey was completed and the results analysed, Imperial Chemical Industries Limited have applied the same survey technique to a specialized laboratory design problem in their Heavy Organic Chemical Division at Billingham. In the latter case only a small number of observations were made over a short period of time. But the results of this study and the survey data on industrial microbiological laboratories show that for similar disciplines the results of the main survey carried out in Agricultural Research Council laboratories may be regarded as having wide application to bench scale laboratories.

DATA COLLECTED

The following data were recorded at each visit for each individual observed:

1. Presence or absence of individual at observation.

2. Site of work, i.e. in laboratory or elsewhere.

3. Whether engaged in reading or writing.

4. Whether sitting or standing at work.

5. Bench length in current use, measured to the nearest foot. Bench in current use was defined as 'space occupied by experiment in progress but may include space occupied by apparatus not actually in use at the time of visit'. Bench length included all improvised benching, equipment on the floor where it would have been on a bench had bench space been available, and also bench length in use in the corridor, other laboratories, or elsewhere outside the laboratory, again subject to the provision that these lengths would have been used within the laboratory had there been room. Fume cupboards were not counted as bench length when they were being used for their proper purpose.

6. Sink and draining board. Combined length of sink and draining board in use including any bench space used as draining board. (These observations referred only to sinks used for washing-up, not to cupsinks or other sinks used only for drainage from apparatus. Measurement was to the nearest foot.)

7. Electric services. (a) Amperage. Total amperage being consumed at time of observation. This includes current consumed by scientific equipment of all kinds, but excludes normal lighting and heating. (b) Number of electric plugs in use at observation.

8. Cold-water supplies. Number of taps turned on at observation.

9. Hot-water supplies. Number of taps turned on at observation.

10. Gas supplies. Number of taps turned on at observation.

11. Drainage. Number of cupsinks, or sinks used as cupsinks, in use at time of observation.

12. Fume cupboards. Number of cupboards including fume hoods in use for their proper purpose at time of observation.

13. Visual characteristics of laboratory task at observation. This was recorded in terms of a simplified version of the task categories given in the Illuminating Engineering Society's *Code for lighting in buildings*.

The data collected give a picture of the facilities in use at the time the observations were made. This was sometimes less than the space or service directly available and sometimes more. In the case of bench length, for example, working space in use outside the laboratory or in any other improvised form was included. Similarly, services or supplies taken from neighbouring benches, &c., were counted in the survey measurements. The validity of using this data to assess the requirements for future laboratory buildings depends to some extent upon whether the facilities available in the laboratories surveyed were reasonably adequate for the work in progress. If, for example, the establishments were grossly underprovided, the scientists concerned might have been unable to improvise additional space or services and, under these circumstances, the survey would not give a true picture of the needs.

Although it was generally known that the establishments included in the survey were not grossly underprovided, and that scientific work of first-class quality was in progress in all of them, it was not possible to check the scale of provision in any way until some of the data had been collected. Once some of the data was available, however, the frequency distributions of facilities in use could be checked against facilities available. For example, if the laboratories had been substantially underprovided there would have been a strong tendency for the frequency distributions to have a sharp cut-off. In fact, analysis showed distributions with long tails, giving decreasing percentages of user time for longer lengths of bench. Similar patterns were found for the other facilities, and it may therefore be concluded that the facilities in use were, in the large majority of cases, adequate for the job in hand. The analysed results can thus be regarded as giving a reasonably accurate picture of the scientists' needs for a given discipline. The team also took the precaution of ensuring that the laboratories surveyed were using scientific techniques and methods commonly used in that particular kind of work.

TECHNIQUES OF OBSERVATION AND RECORDING

Forty observations were made of each individual in the survey. Observations were arranged in four groups, one in each quarter of the year, and each lasting one week. During the week each individual was observed twice a day, once in the morning and once in the afternoon. At each station visits were made to individuals under observation in random order, so that the person observed was not aware when the visit would take place. Bench length in use was measured by the observer, the length in use being indicated by the scientist himself. Service points in use were observed directly. Electric current was occasionally measured by meter, but more commonly estimated from the ratings of the pieces of equipment in use. Heavy starting loads set up by certain types of equipment were not specially recorded.

All data were recorded at the time of observation, direct on to a Hollerith mark-sensing card. The cards were later punched automatically by electric sensing of the pencil marks. This technique of recording eliminated intermediate records and transcription forms, thus considerably reducing the work on the survey and eliminating several possible sources of error in the results. The punched cards formed the permanent record of the survey. All the basic analyses of the survey data were carried out mechanically on a Hollerith Sorter Counter.

The cards were sorted according to the discipline and grade of the individual observed, and also by the quarter of the year in which the observation took place. This gave 132 groups which were then sorted for each item of data as set out above.

METHOD OF ANALYSIS

The basic data from the cards were tabulated under the same broad categories, e.g. according to discipline, grade, and quarter of the year. The results were then treated statistically and tables prepared showing the distributions. The latter were then studied with a view to further grouping of the data in order to reduce it to more manageable proportions.

From the distributions it appeared that the results averaged over the whole year would give sufficiently accurate figures, so that seasonal variations could well be eliminated. Further, it was found possible to combine scientific disciplines in a comparatively small number of groups. In the case of bench length, for example, disciplines could be grouped into three classes—high, medium, and low bench-length users. The differences between the observed data for Scientific Officers and Experimental Officers were found to be insignificant. These two grades were therefore grouped together, and have been included under the one heading of 'Scientists': the other group remains as previously defined under the heading of 'Assistants'.

The next stage in the analysis was the preparation of tables to show the level of satisfaction obtainable with a given standard of provision. For example, in the case of bench length, only a moderate length of bench is required for most of a man's working time, and only occasionally is a very much longer run of bench used. Generally, it was found that the larger the amount of any facility which had been measured as 'in use' at the time of the observation, the less frequently it occurred in the tables. In other words, it was difficult or even impossible to place absolute upper limits on the facilities which might at some time be demanded. It can be deduced, however, that the greater the provision, the greater will be the satisfaction (suitably defined) to the user. Similar considerations apply to most of the other facilities and services. It became clear, therefore, that some criterion of efficiency or satisfaction was needed. There are two simple methods of defining such criteria, either of which is suitable for certain specific circumstances.

Consider, for example, the provision of electric current. If a man has available to him a single outlet from a ring-main he can use up to a maximum of 13 amps. When he demands more than this, part at least of his demand will remain unsatisfied. Indeed, if his only requirement in excess of 13 amps. is when he wants to use a piece of apparatus running at 25 amps., this latter demand will be *totally* unsatisfied. It seems best, therefore, to calculate the *proportion of time* that a man's demand is satisfied for specified levels of maximum current available. This *proportion of time satisfied* has been adopted as a measure of efficiency for ELECTRIC CURRENT, BENCH LENGTH, and SINK LENGTH, the latter two facilities also appearing to require the same kind of criterion.

Certain other items, however, seem to be more flexible in use. For example, if a man requires six electric points, it may be most convenient to have six independent outlets available. On the other hand, if there are only four, it will usually be possible to make up multiple connexions which will do the job nearly as well, at any rate if excessively heavy currents are not required. Thus when six outlets are demanded, and only four are supplied, two-thirds of the demand is met directly. This state of affairs would, however, contribute *nothing* to the satisfaction if the definition outlined in the previous paragraph were used. It seems more appropriate in this case, therefore, to employ a definition based on the *proportion of demand met*. This is easily done by working with man-point units and comparing the total supplied with the total demanded. This definition has been adopted for ELECTRIC POINTS, COLD-WATER TAPS, GAS TAPS, and FUME CUPBOARDS, to all of which similar arguments can be applied.

Although the *proportion of demand met* is straightforward in application and interpretation, the *proportion of time satisfied* can be measured in two different ways. It can be based either on the whole of a man's time or on that part of his time during which the facility in question is actually being used. If the facility is in use most of the time, say 90 per cent., there is no great difference between the alternative methods of measurement, but if a facility is used infrequently, it is best to employ the second method. Thus, although sinks are essential, if a man uses one for only 5 per cent. of his time, then failing to provide him with a sink will still give 95 per cent. efficiency if we base the calculation on the whole of his time. For this reason the analyses have been tabulated for both methods.

Finally, there is the question of the efficiency levels which should be aimed at. In the absence of any method of attaching a cost to failure to provide what is required, such decisions must be arbitrary, and to some extent will depend upon the degree of economy required by the building owner. The above method of analysis allows some degree of choice in the assessment of facilities to be provided for a given type of research work. It also provides a rational basis on which to make such a choice and to a large degree makes the building owner responsible for determining the level of provision. Where possible, therefore, tables derived from the survey material give a range of efficiencies to choose from, but in some instances the number of observations was too small to give sufficiently accurate estimates of provision needed for efficiencies over 95 per cent.

In some cases, e.g. sinks and hot-water taps, where the scale of use in terms of numbers of appliances is small over the whole sample, distribution tables only have been prepared, the tails of the distributions being too small to allow further analysis in terms of satisfaction levels.

Studies on physical environment

An important part of the team's work has been carried out in collaboration with the Building Research Station. The pattern of collaborative studies has become well established over the last ten years and great importance is attached to this architect-scientist co-operation. It has made possible, for example, development of new techniques in the application of natural and artificial lighting criteria as well as the establishment of the criteria themselves. Fundamental research has been closely allied to the team's architectural studies. Also, close liaison with the Building Research Station has made it possible to apply principles previously established in relation to other types of building, to the particular problems encountered in laboratories.

Lighting was found to be a critical factor in the design of laboratories, and the scope and methods of the lighting studies are described in some detail below. The approach to studies based on existing data are briefly described under the appropriate headings in Part II.

Lighting studies

The natural and artificial lighting studies were of two kinds. First it was necessary to determine the amount of light (either natural or artificial) needed for the efficient performance of the range of visual work normally done in bench-scale laboratories, and secondly to carry out studies of a more subjective kind on the application of the quantitative criteria and to determine the relationships between visual comfort, brightness contrasts, and the use of colour.

The laboratory survey described earlier in this chapter included a series of observations on the visual difficulty of laboratory work. The results were used to assess previous recommendations for natural and artificial lighting levels (see item 13, p. 31 and a brief description of the application of the survey technique to the lighting studies Part II, Chapter 4, pp. 99–104). Early work on the application of lighting criteria to practical design problems was published at an interim stage in the team's work (4). This was followed by a study of deep rooms, which was indicated early in the study as likely to prove desirable on functional grounds.

It has been found by experience in collaborative lighting studies that it is best to derive general principles by investigating the characteristics of individual rooms, preferably rooms in a proposed building where the findings can be checked when the building is complete. Accordingly the laboratory room designed by the team for the experimental building for the Animal Research Station at Cambridge was made the subject of a series of studies at model scale.

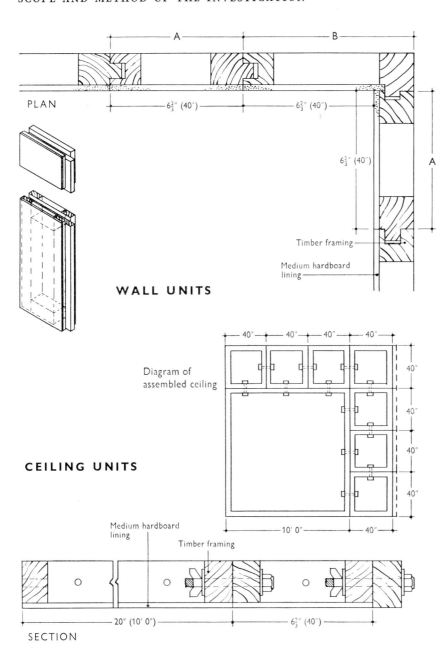

Fig. 34. Construction of model used in laboratory lighting studies.

PLAN

WALL UNITS

Timber framing

Medium hardboard lining

Diagram of assembled ceiling

CEILING UNITS

Medium hardboard lining

Timber framing

SECTION

For this purpose a model building system was designed so that rooms of any size and shape, one-sixth full size, could be built quickly and easily. The wall and roof units were lined with hardboard so that coloured papers could be pinned or stapled into position. A table fitted with removable panels enabled observers to look at the interiors from a normal viewing position. A detailed description of the system has been previously published (5). It is illustrated in Figs. 34, 35, and 36. The model was used for measuring lighting levels for subjective studies on daylight environment, and for the assessment of artificial and natural top-lighting to supplement the daylight from a single window. Also, a simple cardboard model (scale $\frac{1}{2}$ in. to 1 ft.) was used for heliodon studies of sun penetration, and for rapid daylighting measurements. This is illustrated in Fig. 37.

The larger scale model was of considerable use to the architect members of the team in enabling them to assess the general architectural quality and atmosphere of the proposed rooms. As the rooms are of unusual shape, both in plan and in section, the opportunity to visualize the whole volume by the use of the model was very helpful. The advantage of the unit system of model construction is that a single kit can be used repeatedly to construct rooms of any desired size and shape. The kit is therefore a useful tool for any research or development group engaged in the study of rooms of unconventional size or shape. The scale, one-sixth full size, has been found by experience to give the best results. It seems easier to 'imagine up' a room to full size from this scale than it is with models either much larger or much smaller.

Fig. 35. Units used for construction of model in lighting studies, one-sixth full size.

Cost studies

The purpose of the studies

Building costs influence design at almost every point. Because design problems can be solved in many ways, the solution chosen often depends upon the amount of money available.

The development of cost studies in building design is of recent origin. In the past, first estimates of cost were based on the experience of the architect or the quantity surveyor, in buildings of similar type. This method of informing the client of his probable liability in advance of a firm estimate of cost, based on drawings and bills of quantities, is unsatisfactory in many ways. In a period of fluctuating prices, assumptions have to be made, and estimates are often inaccurate. Further, very little help can be given to the client in telling him where economies can be made, and it is not possible to consider cost at a sufficiently early stage in the process of design.

Analytical studies of building costs were first undertaken some ten years ago in order to overcome these difficulties, and in an attempt to provide the architect, and through him the building promoter, with information which would allow selective adjustment of design in relation to cost.

To provide a basis for cost planning of future buildings the costs of buildings already erected and

Fig. 36. Table fitted with removable panels to enable observers to look at interiors from a normal viewing position in lighting studies.

35

Fig. 37. The half-inch scale model used for the sun penetration and daylighting studies.

paid for must be analysed. This process, for so complex an entity as a complete modern building, requires some simplification and grouping of the numerous items of structure and equipment involved. Amongst the earliest and most successful cost analyses were those carried out on the basis of the Ministry of Education *Building bulletin* no. 4 (6). The method of grouping building elements adopted for studying laboratory building costs is based on this work.

The reliability of future cost planning for laboratories will depend entirely upon the amount and accuracy of the information available on the cost of buildings already completed. For schools, a very large number of buildings has been subjected to the Ministry of Education process of cost analysis, and from the information gained in this way, it has been found possible to adjust the cost of individual elements and to control the overall cost of school buildings. The team has been fortunate in having the assistance of the Ministry of Works and the Ministry of Agriculture, Fisheries and Food, in addition to the co-operation of private architects in collecting data on existing completed buildings. Nevertheless, the analyses published here are merely a beginning, and many more cost analyses of typical laboratory buildings must be carried out before reliable laboratory cost planning is possible. Therefore, it was only felt possible to draw rather tentative conclusions from the analyses. It is hoped that many other laboratory

buildings will be subjected to this kind of analysis, and that the results will be published. By this means, the design and construction of laboratories can be made progressively more economical.

When first estimates of cost are based on the experience and knowledge of the architect and quantity surveyor, they are usually expressed in terms of cost per square foot of floor area or per cubic foot of space enclosed. If the overall cost of an earlier similar building is known, the architect makes adjustments to allow for price fluctuations and differences in standards of finishing, quality of fittings, and method of structure. Such estimates of cost, however, make no attempt to show why one design costs more or less than another. When economies are required by the client, very little help can be given in determining which parts of the building may be cheapened with least detriment to function.

The aims of cost studies, therefore, are as follows:

1. To determine the proportion of total cost allocated to the various elements in the building in terms of the accommodation and facilities provided.

2. To make possible the assessment of cost differences when the same facilities are provided in different ways.

3. To enable the client to prepare a building programme with some knowledge of the costs of

the facilities required and enable the architect to translate these requirements into element costs.

4. To facilitate selective cost adjustments.

Items 1 and 2 come under the broad heading of cost analysis, items 3 and 4, cost planning. The two stages are complementary, and the accuracy of the latter depends upon the spread of information available for the former.

The user of a building is interested in accurate cost estimating in relation to the space provided in the building and the facilities for carrying out his work. The designer is responsible for translating these requirements into building elements. It is in the field of cost planning that the greatest contribution to the subject can be made. From the analyses it was found that the proportions of actual laboratory area in relation to total floor area varied considerably from building to building, as did other design factors not directly related to building structure. In order to provide a basis for cost planning at an early stage in the design process, it is necessary to find some means of relating these factors to cost. Whilst it is fully realized that the amount of data on which the team was able to work is severely limited, an attempt has been made to do this. The cost figures were subjected to statistical treatment in the form of a regression analysis, the results of which are given as a formula in Part II, Chapter 6 in a general discussion on building cost in relation to the other aspects of the team's work. While the number of examples available for study are too small for the actual figures used in the formula to be regarded as very meaningful, the results suggest that when more data are available it may be possible to develop a new form of yardstick for the comparison of building costs. Such a formula which can take into account a variation in function between two similar buildings may overcome the difficulty of applying a standard in terms of cost per square foot to a range of buildings, which though generally similar, are not identical in function. Cost per square foot may be a reasonable standard when considering three-bedroomed houses or primary schools; it could not be so easily used to make comparisons between two laboratories or two hospitals. Cost adjusted on the lines of the suggested formula to allow for certain defined differences in function may, however, prove to be a practical method both for the comparison of different approaches to design and for the establishment by building owners of target building costs.

Scope of the cost studies

Cost analyses are given in Appendix I for eight laboratory buildings. Seven of these are full analyses based on data made available to the team by the Ministry of Works, the Ministry of Agriculture, Fisheries and Food, and Courtaulds Limited. In addition, one laboratory cost analysis, previously published in the *Architects' Journal* (7) has been used, the architects of the buildings having supplied the team with supplementary information as required. Cost planning is discussed fully in Part II, Chapter 6, in relation to the team's work and with reference to the comparative analyses given in Appendix I.

Comparative costs of laboratory servicing systems

It was not found possible to make valid comparisons between the different methods of services distribution in existing buildings. Even if it had been possible to do so, there remains the imponderable factor of maintenance costs, about which no significant information is available. An attempt was made, therefore, to arrive at comparative initial costs for different methods of distribution on a theoretical basis. In order to make this as realistic as possible, a firm of laboratory servicing contractors was asked to prepare cost figures for servicing a single bay, in buildings of two, four, and six stories, using three types of distribution systems.

REFERENCES

(1) DEPARTMENT OF SCIENTIFIC AND INDUSTRIAL RESEARCH. *Modern multi-storey factories.* London, 1959. *Factory building studies,* no. 1.
DEPARTMENT OF SCIENTIFIC AND INDUSTRIAL RESEARCH. *The lighting of factories.* London, 1959. *Factory building studies,* no. 2.

(2) NUFFIELD PROVINCIAL HOSPITALS TRUST. *Studies in the functions and design of hospitals.* London, 1955.

(3) LLEWELYN DAVIES, R., NIGHTINGALE, J. W., and BAILEY, N. T. J. 'Laboratory design. Survey of space and services requirements in two agricultural research laboratories.' *Nature, Lond.* **176,** 1955, pp. 999–1001.

(4) MUSGROVE, J., and PETHERBRIDGE, P. 'Lighting: A study of laboratory daylighting.' *Archit. J.* **126,** 1957, pp. 368–74.

(5) MUSGROVE, J., and PETHERBRIDGE, P. 'Lighting: Model construction for appraisal of building interiors.' *Archit. J.* **125,** 1957, pp. 215–20.

(6) MINISTRY OF EDUCATION. *Cost study.* London, 1951. *Building bulletin,* no. 4.

(7) *Archit. J.* **127,** 1958, pp. 359–74.

Introduction

When an architect plans a building he has to consider all aspects of the design problem and must try to make a balanced solution. This will often mean weighing one consideration against another, and sometimes the requirements seen from one point of view will be contradictory to those seen from another. The first purpose of the following chapters is to provide the laboratory designer with methods whereby he can get as clear a picture as possible of some of the factors which should influence his design. The size and shape of the rooms which he plans will depend on the present and possible future needs within the scientific disciplines for which he is designing. It is neither possible nor desirable to propose standard laboratory plans. Nevertheless, the results of the present investigation point to a general approach to laboratory planning which differs significantly from much of current design in this country as described in Part I of this report. Certain design principles applying to a wide range of laboratories can be established, and these are given in each chapter, and in more general form in Chapter 6.

Chapter 1

GENERAL LABORATORY SPACE

THE most useful way in which to consider the size of a laboratory room is in terms of the number of staff it is to house, as this is often the only information available to the architect at the early stages of design. For laboratories with serviced benches it is possible to establish some broad standards of space requirements in relation to the number of scientific workers. Where very large-scale equipment is in use, standards based on the number of workers are of little value, as the size of the equipment controls the space required in the building. These conditions, however, operate principally in heavy-engineering or pilot-scale laboratories which are outside the scope of this report (see Part I, Chapter 3).

General laboratory space may be regarded as a scientist's working base and, for the purpose of planning, it forms the centre of laboratory activities. With the exception of men engaged exclusively in the direction or administration of research, every scientist needs this kind of space, which must be supplied with services and may or may not be equipped with conventional laboratory benches. The approach to planning discussed below is aimed at providing standards around which this basic accommodation may be designed. Other accommodation, such as special rooms, which are usually shared, offices, stores, &c., must of course be provided in addition to the general laboratory space and this is dealt with in relation to overall planning in Chapter 2 below.

The floor area needed in the laboratory for an individual worker is defined by two dimensions: *length* and *width*. *Length* is the total length of benching, sink, fume cupboards, &c., which he needs for his work. *Width* is established by the width of his benching, plus the clear floor space needed for movement whilst working and for circulation between the benches. These dimensions define a rectangle, the area of which is the working area needed for one man. There is, however, a difference between the area needed for an individual worker in a room by himself, and the area he will need if he is in a room with others. In practice, rooms for one man are the exception in laboratory planning, and nearly all rooms are designed to provide for two or more workers. Space requirements for an individual in a room housing several workers are substantially less than would be needed in a one-man room, because in larger rooms circulation space, and to some extent working space are used in common. Further, facilities such as washing-up sinks and fume cupboards are nearly always shared. Economy of space is achieved therefore as soon as two or three workers share a room or a working area. Raising the number of workers in one room to four or five or more, results in a relatively small decrease in the area needed per man. Therefore, in working out the area per man required in laboratories it is reasonable to assume such standards as would be applicable to rooms designed for two or three workers. Where these standards are applied to big laboratories housing many scientists, they may be slightly too generous. But there is an advantage in providing space to this standard as it ensures that any future subdivision of the large laboratory will not unduly reduce the working area available for each man. In the discussion which follows, a unit of space appropriate to a group of two or three workers is considered.

The unit is equally applicable as a room for two or three or as part of a large laboratory.

Bench length

Let us consider first the dimension of length. Here and elsewhere in the report it is referred to as 'bench length'. This does not necessarily imply that fixed benching, or indeed any benching at all is provided. The term 'bench length' is used for *the length of serviced wall or service spine against which benches, laboratory rigs, or other items of laboratory equipment can be placed, and where the normal services are available.*

Tables 1, 2, and 3 present the basic material on the use of bench length arising from the laboratory survey undertaken by the team.[1] It will be seen that the variation between the different scientific disciplines is not very marked. Statistical examination showed that the disciplines could be grouped as follows:

High bench requirement: Biochemistry

Medium bench requirement: Chemistry, Physics, Biophysics, Microbiology, Entomology, Animal Physiology, Pathology.

Low bench requirement: Plant Physiology, Botany, Zoology.[2]

Table 1. Frequency distributions, shown in percentages of total working time taken over whole year, of bench length used by *Scientific Officers* in each discipline.

Discipline	Total no. of obs.	Percentage of total working time during which bench length (0–18 ft.) was in use							
		None	1–3	4–6	7–9	10–12	13–15	16–18	>18
Chemistry	406	62·8	5·4	15·3	8·6	5·4	2·0	0·2	0·2
Physics	429	49·9	14·2	19·1	10·5	4·9	1·2	0·0	0·2
Biochemistry	429	38·9	9·6	20·3	12·6	10·3	5·4	1·9	1·2
Biophysics	170	81·8	1·2	7·6	6·5	2·4	0·6	0·0	0·0
Microbiology	439	43·5	10·5	23·0	11·6	8·0	3·0	0·4	0·0
Entomology	399	59·1	12·3	17·5	7·0	2·3	1·3	0·5	0·0
Animal Physiology	418	72·7	8·1	9·8	6·2	2·2	1·0	0·0	0·0
Plant Physiology	327	79·5	8·3	9·5	2·4	0·3	0·0	0·0	0·0
Botany	421	84·8	7·4	5·5	1·0	1·4	0·0	0·0	0·0
Zoology	344	72·4	6·1	12·5	7·3	1·2	0·3	0·0	0·0
Pathology	384	35·2	13·0	24·5	12·0	10·4	4·2	0·8	0·0

Table 2. Frequency distributions, shown in percentages of total working time taken over whole year, of bench length used by *Experimental Officers* in each discipline.

Discipline	Total no. of obs.	Percentage of total working time during which bench length (0–18 ft.) was in use							
		None	1–3	4–6	7–9	10–12	13–15	16–18	>18
Chemistry	428	22·7	17·3	25·5	18·5	12·6	2·8	0·2	0·5
Physics	239	49·8	9·6	12·1	12·1	12·6	2·5	1·3	0·0
Biochemistry	414	45·2	9·9	20·0	13·3	5·3	5·3	1·0	0·0
Microbiology	425	46·8	12·0	25·4	8·7	4·0	2·6	0·5	0·0
Entomology	321	59·2	10·3	17·1	8·4	2·2	2·8	0·0	0·0
Animal Physiology	304	36·2	10·2	27·3	16·8	5·9	3·3	0·0	0·3
Plant Physiology	106	75·5	7·5	14·2	0·0	2·8	0·0	0·0	0·0
Botany	441	53·3	12·2	17·0	13·6	2·7	0·9	0·2	0·0
Zoology	410	58·3	11·2	22·9	7·1	0·5	0·0	0·0	0·0
Pathology	131	19·8	5·3	23·7	28·2	6·1	9·2	3·8	3·8

[1] An account of the methods used in this survey, and in the analysis of the data is given in Part I, Chapter 3.

[2] These classifications are used to define disciplines in Tables 4, 5, 6, 7, 8, 9, 10.

Table 3. Frequency distributions, shown as percentages of total working time taken over whole year, of bench length used by *Assistants* in each discipline.

Discipline	Total no. of obs.	Percentage of total working time during which bench length (0–18 ft.) was in use							
		None	*1–3*	*4–6*	*7–9*	*10–12*	*13–15*	*16–18*	*>18*
Chemistry	334	38·9	15·9	29·3	11·7	3·6	0·6	0·0	0·0
Physics	284	54·2	17·6	18·3	5·6	3·9	0·4	0·0	0·0
Biochemistry	337	35·3	14·8	30·9	13·4	4·7	0·9	0·0	0·0
Biophysics	143	69·9	2·8	7·0	11·9	3·5	3·5	1·4	0·0
Microbiology	360	34·4	18·6	30·0	13·1	2·2	1·7	0·0	0·0
Entomology	327	44·0	17·4	26·3	8·9	2·8	0·6	0·0	0·0
Animal Physiology	363	56·2	9·6	18·5	9·9	3·3	1·9	0·3	0·3
Plant Physiology	221	82·8	8·6	5·4	3·2	0·0	0·0	0·0	0·0
Botany	260	50·0	8·8	19·6	14·2	5·4	1·2	0·8	0·0
Zoology	348	49·4	8·0	26·4	10·3	4·3	0·0	0·6	0·9
Pathology	285	26·0	16·1	38·6	9·5	6·3	2·8	0·4	0·4

Table 4. Frequency distributions, shown as percentages of total working time, of bench length used by *Scientists and Assistants* in high, medium, and low groups of disciplines.

Staff grade	Discipline class	Percentage of total working time during which bench length (0–18 ft.) was in use							
		None	*1–3*	*4–6*	*7–9*	*10–12*	*13–15*	*16–18*	*>18*
Scientists	High	42·0	9·7	20·2	12·9	7·8	5·4	1·4	0·6
	Medium	48·7	11·2	20·0	11·0	6·3	2·4	0·3	0·1
	Low	68·6	9·3	14·1	6·3	1·4	0·2	0·1	0·0
Assistants	High	35·3	14·8	30·9	13·4	4·7	0·9	0·0	0·0
	Medium	44·3	14·9	25·3	10·1	3·6	1·5	0·2	0·1
	Low	58·5	8·4	18·7	9·6	3·5	0·4	0·5	0·4

Table 5. Frequency distributions, shown as percentages of time during which some bench was in use, for *Scientists and Assistants* in high, medium, and low groups of disciplines.

Staff grade	Discipline class	Percentage of time during which some bench length (1–18 ft.) was in use						
		1–3	*4–6*	*7–9*	*10–12*	*13–15*	*16–18*	*>18*
Scientists	High	16·7	34·8	22·3	13·5	9·3	2·4	1·0
	Medium	21·8	39·0	21·4	12·3	4·7	0·6	0·2
	Low	29·6	44·9	20·1	4·5	0·6	0·3	0·0
Assistants	High	22·9	47·7	20·7	7·3	1·4	0·0	0·0
	Medium	26·7	45·4	18·1	6·5	2·7	0·4	0·2
	Low	20·2	45·1	23·1	8·4	1·0	1·2	1·0

It was also found that the variation between the Scientific Officer grade (Table 1) and the Experimental Officer grade (Table 2) was small. These two grades of staff are therefore grouped together as 'scientists' in the subsequent tables.

It will be seen from Tables 1 to 3 that a considerable time is spent by nearly all research workers away from the laboratory bench. It is also apparent that the essential problem in providing appropriate bench length is the wide variation in need from time to time.

Tables 4 and 5 present a picture of the fluctuating demand for bench length, and enable certain broad conclusions to be drawn. A fairly small amount of bench is in use by any one man, 10 or 12 ft. of bench run being sufficient to satisfy most individuals most of the time. However, there are occasions when scientists use considerably greater lengths and it is important that laboratory planning should be sufficiently

flexible to allow for this. Even if over 19 ft. of bench is provided for each worker, there will still be rare occasions when more length is needed by some individuals. Clearly, the very exceptional demand will have to be met by a measure of improvisation. Nevertheless, in planning laboratory rooms it is obvious that an effort should be made to provide for what might be called the normal peak demand, and Tables 6 and 7 have been produced from the data to show the bench lengths required to satisfy such a demand. Figures are given in 'percentage satisfaction', which is defined as *the proportion of the worker's time for which he has sufficient bench at his disposal to meet all his needs.* Table 6 shows the necessary lengths in terms of 'percentage satisfaction' based on total working time. Table 7 shows 'percentage satisfaction' in terms of the time during which some bench length was in use. The latter naturally results in somewhat higher bench requirements. Examination

Table 6. Bench lengths required to give various degrees of satisfaction, based on total working time, for *Scientists and Assistants* in high, medium, and low groups of disciplines.

Staff grade	Discipline class	Bench length in feet to give levels of satisfaction between 90 and 99 per cent.									
		90	91	92	93	94	95	96	97	98	99
Scientists	High	11·5	11·9	12·3	12·7	13·3	13·8	14·4	14·9	15·5	17·6
	Medium	9·3	9·5	10·0	10·5	11·0	11·5	11·9	12·4	13·5	14·8
	Low	6·1	6·3	6·5	7·0	7·5	7·9	8·4	8·9	9·4	11·0
Assistants	High	8·5	8·7	9·0	9·2	9·4	9·9	10·5	11·2	11·8	12·4
	Medium	8·1	8·4	8·7	9·0	9·3	9·8	10·7	11·5	12·3	14·1
	Low	7·9	8·2	8·5	8·8	9·1	9·4	10·2	11·0	11·9	14·8

Table 7. Bench lengths required to give various degrees of satisfaction based on the time during which some bench was in use, for *Scientists and Assistants* in high, medium, and low groups of disciplines.

Staff grade	Discipline class	Bench length in feet to give levels of satisfaction between 90 and 99 per cent.									
		90	91	92	93	94	95	96	97	98	99
Scientists	High	13·4	13·7	14·0	14·3	14·7	15·0	15·3	16·0	17·2	18·5
	Medium	11·4	11·6	11·9	12·1	12·4	12·8	13·5	14·1	14·7	15·4
	Low	8·8	9·0	9·1	9·3	9·4	9·8	10·4	11·1	11·8	12·4
Assistants	High	9·3	9·5	9·8	10·2	10·6	11·0	11·4	11·8	12·3	..
	Medium	9·5	9·9	10·3	10·8	11·3	11·7	12·2	12·8	13·9	15·1
	Low	10·1	10·4	10·8	11·1	11·5	11·9	12·2	13·1	16·0	18·5

Table 8. Bench lengths required to give 90 and 95 per cent. satisfaction, based on total working time, for groups of *Scientists and Assistants* in high, medium, and low groups of disciplines.

No. of Scientists	No. of Assistants	Bench length in feet to give 90 and 95 per cent. levels of satisfaction in high, medium, and low groups					
		High		Medium		Low	
		90%	95%	90%	95%	90%	95%
1	0	11·5	13·8	9·3	11·5	6·1	7·9
	1	16·9	19·7	14·5	17·3	11·0	13·7
	2	20·4	23·3	18·1	20·9	15·1	17·9
2	0	18·6	21·6	15·0	17·9	9·2	11·7
	1	22·2	25·3	18·7	21·4	13·8	16·4
	2	29·1	32·9	24·8	28·5	18·4	22·0
3	0	23·8	27·2	19·3	22·2	12·2	14·8

Table 9. Bench lengths required for 90 and 95 per cent. satisfaction, based on time during which bench was actually used, for groups of *Scientists and Assistants* in high, medium, and low groups of disciplines.

No. of Scientists	No. of Assistants	Bench length in feet to give 90 and 95 per cent. levels of satisfaction in high, medium, and low groups					
		High		Medium		Low	
		90%	95%	90%	95%	90%	95%
1	0	13·4	15·0	11·4	12·8	8·8	9·8
	1	17·6	20·3	15·3	18·0	12·8	15·5
	2	20·7	23·5	18·4	21·2	16·3	18·9
2	0	19·6	22·6	16·2	18·9	11·5	13·8
	1	22·5	25·6	19·2	21·9	15·0	17·5
	2	29·3	33·0	25·1	28·7	19·5	22·9
3	0	24·2	27·5	19·9	22·8	13·8	15·9

of Table 6 shows that the provision of 15 ft. of bench length will give 99 per cent. or more satisfaction of demand for all workers other than biochemists, for whom it will afford a 97 per cent. satisfaction level. It would therefore seem that the facility to use, on occasion, up to 15-ft. run of benching would provide for all but very rare circumstances in laboratory use. A more conservative estimation, derived from Table 7, gives a figure of 15 ft. 3 in. for similar satisfaction. As there is evidence that a continuous straight run of benching is very much more convenient than bench runs going round the corner, it should be an objective in the design of research laboratories to provide for uninterrupted runs of up to 15 ft. in length. Rooms which do not lend themselves to this length of benching are open to criticism.

Examination of the survey data suggests that while the facility to use bench length of up to 15 ft. should be available, most of the time individual workers will be using a good deal less. Further, the data show that the use of a large bench length by an individual generally goes on for a considerable length of time. The nature of a man's current piece of work controls his bench requirement, and he may use a large amount of bench or a small amount for some weeks or months on end. In a unit housing a number of workers, while one or two may be using a large bench length, others will be using much less, and the occupation of laboratory rooms should adjust itself accordingly. It is useful therefore to turn from consideration of the maximum bench length which an individual may use on occasion to consider the overall amount of bench length for a number of workers.

Tables 8 and 9 show the bench lengths needed to give various groups of workers satisfaction of need for 90 per cent. and 95 per cent. of their time.

Table 8 gives the figures as percentages of total working time and Table 9 as the percentage of time that some bench length was actually in use. The tables were obtained by compounding data for individuals and do not assume any deliberate organization by the workers to share space. It will be seen that where two men work together their bench length requirement is noticeably less than they would need if they were in separate rooms. While it is reasonable to suppose that where two or three men work together they can share facilities to some extent, groups above three can hardly be expected to do so. It is therefore suggested that where a room is designed to house a large group of workers no sharing beyond groups of two or three should be envisaged. It is suggested elsewhere in this report that bench runs should be made up of small movable units. A length of about 5 ft. is a convenient one for such units. As a guide to planning Table 10 has been prepared to show in multiples of 5 ft. bench lengths for various groups of workers. The figures have been rounded *upwards* to the nearest multiple of 5 ft. from those given in Table 9. It appears that a unit of space providing 25 ft. of serviced bench would serve a wide range of purposes, particularly in the medium class which includes the great majority of scientific disciplines.

Table 10. Bench lengths required to give 95 per cent. or more satisfaction, based on time during which bench was actually in use, for groups of *Scientists and Assistants* in high, medium, and low groups of disciplines.

No. of Scientists	No. of Assistants	Bench length in feet required to give 95 per cent. or more satisfaction in high, medium, and low groups		
		High	Medium	Low
1	0	15	15	10
	1	20	20	20
	2	25	25	20
2	0	25	20	15
	1	30	25	20
	2	35	25	25
3	0	30	25	20

It would also meet the needs of slightly smaller groups in the high class, and larger groups in the low class.

The definition of bench length for the purpose of the survey excluded fume cupboards, sinks, storage space, and space used for reading or writing. In considering the total length required by an individual worker, however, provision must be made for these items as well as for his working-bench. Both sinks and fume cupboards require services and drainage and are normally placed in line with serviced benching. It is now necessary to consider, therefore, what extra serviced length must be added to that derived from the tables of bench length given above.

Sinks and draining boards

Two kinds of sink are provided in laboratories—large sinks, with draining boards, for washing-up, and drainaways or cupsinks intended to receive the effluent from experiments. The provision of drainaways is an integral part of the servicing arrangements for the working bench. The number needed is discussed elsewhere in this report and does not affect the bench length required by each man.

Sinks for washing-up and their draining boards are additional to normal benching. Data on the use of washing-up sinks and on the lengths of draining board required were collected in the laboratory survey. Tables 11, 12, 13 present the results. This takes no account of drainaway sinks used for purposes other than washing-up. These are dealt with separately in Chapter 3, below.

In these tables 'sink length' refers to the *combined length of sink and draining board in use*. An overall length for sinks and draining boards of about 5 ft. is likely to meet most of the demand. On the basis of limited sharing the conclusion may be reached that one sink and draining board will meet the needs of the laboratory group of two or three workers discussed above. One sink would meet the needs of a considerably larger number of workers, but beyond

Table 11. Frequency distributions, shown as percentages of total working time taken over the whole year, of sink length used by *Scientists and Assistants* (averaged over all disciplines).

Staff grade	Total no. of obs.	Percentage of total working time during which sink length (0–7 ft.) was in use								
		None	1	2	3	4	5	6	7	> 7
Scientists . . .	6,989	94·6	0·7	2·6	1·2	0·6	0·2	0·1	0·0	0·0
Assistants . . .	2,930	89·9	0·6	3·7	1·9	1·7	1·2	0·6	0·3	0·1

Table 12. Frequency distributions of sink length shown as percentages of time during which some sink length was in use by *Scientists and Assistants* (averaged over all disciplines).

Staff grade	Total no. of obs.	Percentage of time during which some sink length (1–7 ft.) was in use							
		1	2	3	4	5	6	7	>7
Scientists	396	14	48	21	10	4	1	1	1
Assistants	328	6	36	19	17	12	6	2	2

Table 13. Sink lengths required to give 90 and 95 per cent. satisfactions, in groups of *Scientists and Assistants*, based on the time during which some sink length was in use (averaged over all disciplines).

No. of Scientists and Assistants	Sink length in feet required to give 90 and 95 per cent. satisfaction	
	90	95
1 Scientist	4·2	4·9
1 Scientist + 1 Assistant .	5·4	6·3
1 Scientist + 2 Assistants .	5·9	6·9
2 Scientists + 2 Assistants .	5·9	7·0

a group of two or three inconvenience might be caused by having to carry items to the sink over longer walking distances. It should also be noted that in some disciplines, such as biochemistry, the use of chromic-acid baths may add to the sink length required. If a tray is provided for this purpose the wash-up area may be up to 10 ft. in length.

In many research establishments washing-up is now done centrally. When this is the case, valuable serviced wall is released for other purposes. Central wash-up facilities are discussed below in Chapter 2.

Fume cupboards

The length of serviced wall occupied by fume cupboards must also be added to the bench lengths derived from the survey. As fume cupboards may be standardized in size, the following discussion is in terms of the number of cupboards required. Length may be deduced from the size of cupboard chosen. Tables 14 and 15 present the basic data on the number of fume cupboards in use by Scientists and their Assistants. From these tables it appears that in most disciplines the use of fume cupboards is light. Disciplines which make considerable use of fume cupboards are chemistry and biochemistry, and the appropriate provision for these is discussed in some detail below.

In the other disciplines, where fume cupboards are rarely used, some provision must nevertheless be made. It can be argued that in most disciplines a fume cupboard is so valuable from the point of view of health and safety, there should be one available even if its use is very intermittent. The figures in Tables 14 and 15 suggest that in disciplines other than chemistry and biochemistry, one fume cupboard would meet the needs of a considerable number of workers. There is some evidence that the use of fume cupboards is increasing and in the interests of flexibility, as well as of health and safety, it may be wise to make provision for a fume cupboard in every general laboratory, even though in some cases the cupboard itself is not installed when the building is first occupied.

Chemists and biochemists will need more fume cupboards. Tables 16 and 17 present the needs of various groups of workers in these two specialities.

Table 14. Frequency distributions, shown as percentages of total working time taken over whole year, of number of fume cupboards required by *Scientists* in each discipline.

Discipline	Total no. of obs.	Percentage of total working time during which fume cupboards (0–3) were in use			
		None	1	2	3
Chemistry . .	834	86·0	11·6	1·5	0·9
Physics . . .	668	98·5	1·5	0·0	0·0
Biochemistry . .	843	91·9	7·8	0·2	0·0
Biophysics . .	170	100·0	0·0	0·0	0·0
Microbiology . .	846	100·0	0·0	0·0	0·0
Entomology . .	720	100·0	0·0	0·0	0·0
Animal Physiology .	722	98·5	1·5	0·0	0·0
Plant Physiology .	433	99·8	0·2	0·0	0·0
Botany . . .	862	99·7	0·2	0·0	0·0
Zoology . . .	754	99·5	0·5	0·0	0·0
Pathology . .	515	99·4	0·6	0·0	0·0

Table 15. Frequency distributions, shown as percentages of total working time taken over whole year, of number of fume cupboards required by *Assistants* in each discipline.

Discipline	Total no. of obs.	Percentage of total working time during which fume cupboards (0–3) were in use			
		None	1	2	3
Chemistry . .	331	76·1	20·2	3·6	0·0
Physics . . .	284	98·9	1·1	0·0	0·0
Biochemistry . .	337	94·4	5·6	0·0	0·0
Biophysics . .	143	96·5	3·5	0·0	0·0
Microbiology . .	359	99·7	0·3	0·0	0·0
Entomology . .	327	97·8	2·2	0·0	0·0
Animal physiology .	363	99·7	0·3	0·0	0·0
Plant physiology .	221	98·2	1·8	0·0	0·0
Botany . . .	260	85·0	14·2	0·4	0·4
Zoology . . .	348	99·7	0·3	0·0	0·0
Pathology . .	285	99·6	0·4	0·0	0·0

Table 16. Percentage satisfaction of demand for fume cupboards in groups of *Scientists and Assistants* in chemistry.

	Percentage satisfaction of demand for fume cupboards (1–4)			
	1	2	3	4
1 Scientist + 1 Assistant .	77·4	96·0	99·6	100·0
1 Scientist + 2 Assistants .	69·4	92·9	98·8	99·9
2 Scientists + 2 Assistants .	63·8	89·3	97·3	99·4

Table 17. Percentage satisfaction of demand for fume cupboards in groups of *Scientists and Assistants* in biochemistry.

	Percentage satisfaction of demand for fume cupboards (1–3)		
	1	2	3
1 Scientist + 1 Assistant . .	95·0	100·0	100·0
1 Scientist + 2 Assistants .	91·9	99·5	100·0
2 Scientists + 2 Assistants .	88·5	99·3	100·0

The tables show the relationship between the number of cupboards available and the percentage of demand met. It will be seen that two, three, or even four fume cupboards may be needed if it is held necessary to provide something close to 100 per cent. satisfaction of demand.

Table 18. Numbers of fume cupboards required to give, approximately, specified percentage satisfactions for *large groups of chemists.*

	Number of fume cupboards required to give levels of satisfaction between 90 and 99 per cent.		
	90%	95%	99%
4 Scientists + 4 Assistants .	3	4	5
8 Scientists + 8 Assistants .	5	6	7
16 Scientists + 16 Assistants .	8	10	12

Table 19. Numbers of fume cupboards required to give, approximately, specified percentage satisfactions for *large groups of biochemists.*

	Number of fume cupboards required to give levels of satisfaction between 90 and 99 per cent.		
	90%	95%	99%
4 Scientists + 4 Assistants .	2	2	3
8 Scientists + 8 Assistants .	2	3	4
16 Scientists + 16 Assistants .	3	4	5

Fume cupboards are usually shared, however, and if, as is common in chemistry laboratories, large laboratory rooms are used to house considerable numbers of workers, sharing results in greater economy of provision.

Tables 18 and 19 show the results where different numbers of fume cupboards are provided for large groups of chemists and biochemists. It can be seen that high levels of satisfaction can be achieved with fairly small numbers of cupboards.

The method employed in compiling these tables does not assume any deliberate effort by the scientists to adjust their work in the interests of sharing fume cupboards, and the satisfaction of need shown will be met even if each man makes use of a cupboard without any reference to the others. The levels of satisfaction of need will of course be still higher if there is some measure of co-operation, as will obviously occur in practice.

Bench width and bench spacing

The concept of a unit of laboratory space, appropriate to a small group of workers, has been developed above. The *length* of the unit is determined by the length of serviced bench-run or serviced wall, the *width* is determined by bench width and bench spacing.

Means of determining the length dimension for various types of work have already been dealt with; it remains to consider the width dimension. For reasons set out elsewhere in this report, the benching should be planned to run at right angles to the outside walls. Unit width will therefore tend to deter-

mine the position of structural columns and thus the structural grid of the building generally. From the point of view of economy in construction it is important that unit width should be no larger than is necessary. Equally, it must not be too small for efficient and safe working.

Current practice

In laboratories visited by the team the space between benching was between 1 ft. 6 in. and 7 ft., and bench and table widths[1] were between 1 ft. 9 in. and 3 ft. In recent buildings the bench spacing is often related to the structural grid, but it is rarely clear which of the two is the determining factor. In buildings of this kind, island and peninsular benches are spaced at anything from 8 ft. to 12 ft. from centre to centre. Most of the variation is in the clear distance between the benches, with only minor differences in bench or table width.[2]

The dimensions recommended by various authorities[3] also vary though less widely. C. Haines (2) arrived at a bench width of 2 ft. 1 in. He considers that bench spacing should be determined by safety and convenience and that the need to move quickly back from the bench, and the presence of mobile equipment on the floor, should not be forgotten. In a bay containing two occupants there should be enough room for them to work back to back. He concludes that the minimum space between benches should be 3 ft. 6 in., that more than 6 ft. wastes space, and that 4 ft. to 5 ft. is satisfactory in most cases.

In discussing the Johns-Manville Research Centre E. M. Jenkins (3) considers that 3 ft. 6 in. between benches is 'cramping' and 4 ft. 6 in. should be taken as a minimum. Aisles should allow two people to work back to back but are better if a third person can pass comfortably between them. 6 ft. 6 in. clearance is recommended for situations 'where bulky articles are involved'. In the Johns-Manville building a 10 ft. 6 in. module is used, of which 4 ft. is taken up by the benches themselves.

F. Lassen (1) recommends 2 ft. 5 in. (0·75 m.) for bench width and 5 ft. 11 in. to 6 ft. 7 in. (1·8 to 2·0 m.) clearance between them. Werner Schramm (4) suggests a bench width of 2 ft. 7 in. (0·80 m.)

---

[1] Throughout the report 'bench width' means *clear* width, free of service points, upstands, &c.

[2] The figures given here are for laboratories in the British Isles, but it is interesting to note that Fritz Lassen (1) in comparing 22 laboratories in Germany, France, Sweden, Switzerland, and U.S.A. gives bay widths between 9 ft. 2 in. (2·8 m.) and 13 ft. 1 in. (4 m.). The range is very similar to that found in this country.

[3] The recent British Standards Institution publication, B.S. 3202, *Recommendations on laboratory furniture and fittings*, suggests that a clear width of 2 ft. is sufficient for most purposes. Bench spacing for back-to-back working is given as 4 ft. 6 in. when there is no circulation between the benches and 6 ft. when the space is also to be used as a communal passage. For single-line working, a clear space of 3 ft. 6 in. should be allowed with an increase to not less than 4 ft. if the space is also used as a passage way.

and gives the following figures for bench spacing for a number of conditions of use:

	Conditions of use	Clear space
a.	Two workers back to back no through traffic	4 ft. 7 in. (1·4 m.)
b.	Two workers back to back, just room for a third to pass between	5 ft. 5 in. (1·65 m.)
c.	Two workers back to back, room for a third to pass comfortably	6 ft. 3 in. (1·9 m.)
d.	Gangway only, no working spaces on either side	2 ft. 7 in. (0·80 m.)
e.	Gangway with a fume cupboard, or a table at which a worker may sit to write or read on one side only	3 ft. 3 in. to 4 ft. 1 in. (1·0 to 1·25 m.)

It is interesting to compare recommended gangway widths for kitchen planning. The Ministry of Education recommendations (5) are as follows, and come very close to the dimensions given by Schramm (above):

	Conditions of use	Clear space
a.	One worker at a bench	2 ft. 6 in.
b.	Two people back to back	4 ft. 6 in.
c.	One worker, intermittent trolley traffic	3 ft. 6 in.
d.	One worker, frequent trolley traffic	4 ft. 6 in.
e.	Two workers, intermittent trolley traffic (between them)	5 ft. 6 in.
f.	Two workers, frequent trolley traffic (between them)	6 ft. 6 in.

Anthropometric data

In view of the variation in current practice it is useful to consider such objective evidence as can be found bearing on the questions of bench width and bench spacing. Bench width turns largely on considerations of arm-reach, and bench spacing is affected by body size, hence anthropometric data for the population likely to be found in laboratories are relevant.

With the advice and assistance of Dr. D. F. Roberts of the Medical Research Council Unit of Climate and Working Efficiency, Oxford, the team was able to compile certain material related to the laboratory staffs of the Medical Research Council and the Agricultural Research Council. In addition certain original measurements were made on a small number of subjects.

Average body measurements vary with age and sex, and in order to find the relevant range, the team consulted the 1956 staff records of the Agricultural Research Council and the Medical Research Council. These were analysed as shown in Table 20.

The distribution of population within the age-groups is similar for both samples, and it is reasonable to assume that other laboratory populations (e.g. industrial) would not be very different to those shown in the table. The populations in Table 20 are concentrated around the ages where men are at their greatest size and women nearly so. Body dimensions given below are all relevant to these age-groups.

Table 20. Agricultural Research Council and Medical Research Council staffs by age and sex: percentages of total numbers of workers within each of six 10-year age-groups.

		Percentage of total number of workers within six 10-year age-groups						
		16–25	26–35	36–45	46–55	56–65	over 65	Total numbers
MEN	A.R.C.	17·2	48·1	20·4	9·6	4·3	0·4	1,388
	M.R.C.	16·0	36·7	30·0	11·3	5·7	0·2	755
WOMEN	A.R.C.	58·9	27·1	7·4	4·6	2·2	0·1	513
	M.R.C.	49·8	30·1	11·8	5·6	2·4	0·3	348

Table 21. Arm-reach dimensions for the relevant sample of women, standing and sitting.

	Measurement		Mean	Standard deviation
(1) *Standing*, with arm extended forward, 45° down from horizontal	Height (without shoes)		65 in. (slightly over the mean for the whole population)	Not given
	Finger tips to abdomen		15·9 in.	1·17 in.
(2) *Sitting*, on a chair (10 in. lower than table-top) with arm extended forward, and palm on table-top	Height		64·7 in.	Not given
	Finger tips to abdomen		19·4 in.	1·41 in.

BENCH WIDTH

Arm-reach from standing or sitting positions controls the width of bench on which manual operations can be carried out without leaning the body forward over the bench. The commonest way of reaching forward is with one arm only and the dimensions relevant to bench width are those reaching down as A in Fig. 38, and reaching forward as B in Fig. 38. The nearer the arm-reach is to the horizontal position, the greater it becomes, so that, so far as controls above bench level are concerned, the nearer they are to shoulder height the more possible it is to reach them without leaning.

When dealing with limits imposed by arm-reach, mean dimensions which apply to that part of the population with the *shortest* reach must be considered. Consequently the dimensions[1] given in Table 21 are for women.

For comparison with the mean values in the table the data were also analysed to find the arm-reaches of the smallest women in the sample. All but the very shortest (0·3 per cent.) of the women were able to reach 12 in., 45° (downward from standing position) and 15 in. (forward from sitting position), without leaning or twisting. This can be compared with figures given by Murrell (6). He gives normal forward reach for women as 11 in. (measured from the front edge of the bench).

Instruments of many kinds have their manual controls at the front only, and only that part of the apparatus which the scientist manipulates frequently

---

[1] Data supplied by the Medical Research Council Unit of Climate and Working Efficiency.

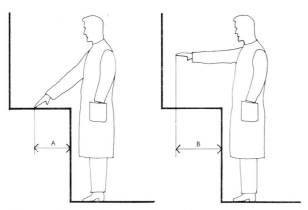

Fig. 38. Forward arm-reach position.

needs to be within normal reach as defined above. The team observed that workers almost invariably leaned forward to some extent to increase normal arm-reach, even in quite hazardous situations. In the laboratory, therefore, where safety is of major importance, the criterion should be to provide a bench width which allows the scientist to work in comfort, but which does not encourage him to lean so far over the bench that quick recovery and retreat become impossible.[1]

With this in mind, measurements were made in order to assess what useful and safe increments of width might be added to the normal 12 in. to 15 in., bearing in mind that some leaning is normal practice, and under most conditions allowable. Within the time and facilities at its disposal the team made a limited scale study on these lines, making measurements on only a small sample of subjects, all women.

A 2 ft. 10 in. high table was used in these measurements. The women (mean height 66 in.: standard deviation $1\frac{1}{2}$ in.) were asked to stand at the table and extend one arm forward and to place their finger tips on the surface without consciously leaning, but comfortably. The average reach (abdomen to finger-tips) was $17\frac{1}{2}$ in. When asked to place a 4-in.-diameter bottle on the table at a comfortable arm's length, again without consciously leaning, the average distance of the *back* of the bottle from the front of the bench was $21\frac{1}{2}$ in. Under similar instructions but from a sitting position (chair 10 in. below table top), average reach was 23 in. and average distance to back of bottle was $23\frac{1}{2}$ in. When leaning was specifically allowed, but only to a comfortable degree and so that quick and easy recovery would be possible, all subjects could reach with fingertips to just over 27 in., both when sitting and standing at a 2 ft. 10 in. high table.

Morant (7) has said that before any general interpretations can be made from static body measurements, other definitions are needed 'in terms of measurements, of allowances to be made for body movements and for various conditions regarding ease in operation, vision, and safety, and any other special conditions which may apply in a particular case'. It has not been the team's aim to make such general interpretations from the data, and it agrees with Morant that 'a theoretical treatment would probably be found to be intractable owing to the complexity dependent on interrelationships between concurrent and variable factors'. Nevertheless, guidance can be given to the designer with some degree of confidence.

Whilst it will be easier for the scientist to handle controls and manipulate apparatus on the front 15 in. or so of his bench, in practice it seems that he can use fully a bench width of about 24 in. This allows also some margin of safety against leaning forward to an unsafe degree. Except in special circumstances, for example, where bulky apparatus is in use which does not require manipulation at the back of the bench, it would be difficult to justify widths greater than 27 in.

The team did not collect measurements for normal forward reach (B, Fig. 38) but Murrell (6) gives 18 in. and 14 in. ('maximum forward reach', measured from the centre-line of the body), for men and women respectively. If an allowance is made for leaning, a bench width of 24 in. would allow comparatively easy manipulation of service taps and outlets. The nearer these are to shoulder height, the easier they will be to operate.

SPACE BETWEEN BENCHES

In considering the space to be allowed between parallel runs of laboratory benching, there are three relevant factors to which anthropometric data may be applied:

(1) Space taken up by the worker when actually engaged in working at the bench. This was taken to be equivalent to having the upper arms vertical and lower arms horizontal, hands on the front of the bench.[2] (Working at benches without kneeholes for the sitting position is not allowed for.)

(2) Space taken up when walking parallel with and close to the bench.

(3) Space needed for bending down in front of the bench, for example, to take something from a cupboard under the bench. Cupboard doors or drawers would not normally take up more space than a person in the bending position.

It is also essential in considering bench spacing to take account of the possible need to move back from the bench quickly in an emergency. This cannot be assessed anthropometrically and is discussed separately below.

The team has used data[3] supplied by the Medical

---

[1] Bench width which cannot easily be reached for normal use is used for storage space, and becomes 'dead area' so far as day to day bench processes are concerned.

[2] For getting up from a sitting to a standing position, an allowance should probably be made for pushing the seat directly back, leaving distance between bench and seat equal to the normal working space.

[3] The available data in this case are for men, and originate in the United States. Body measurements have been reduced in ratio of average American to British body heights.

Research Council Unit of Climate and Working Efficiency to prepare Table 22 on the basis of the three factors listed above.

The sizes for the bending position in Table 22 were composite and seemed unduly large. The team, therefore, carried out tests on a small number of subjects, men and women (average height $68\frac{1}{2}$ in.), by measuring the space used in bending down to take objects from the fronts and backs of 14 in. deep shelves placed 1 in., $11\frac{1}{2}$ in., and $22\frac{1}{2}$ in. above the floor. They approached the shelves from immediately in front of them, and the width occupied when bending was measured at right angles to the shelves. The *average* of their most space-consuming positions was 35·2 in.

Table 23 shows gangway widths for four types of use, worked out from the body measurements given above. In each column of the table subjective judgements on the dimensions are given. These have been summarized, from the judgements made on the spacing, by three experienced members of the laboratory team, chosen to cover the greatest range of body height ($66\frac{1}{2}$ in. to $80\frac{1}{2}$ in.). The judgements on the dimensions for average men bear out the experience gained in other fields that rooms based rigidly on anthropometric data tend to seem slightly cramped. It may be necessary therefore to allow rather larger clearances than the 3 in. allowed here.

Emergency movement away from the benches seems to the team to be adequately catered for in the dimensions in the table, but specially hazardous circumstances might arise where this was not so and each case of this kind would require consideration on its merits.

There are other factors which may affect the designer's decision on bench spacing. For example, the frequent use of trolleys for carrying supplies or equipment such as portable pumps or compressors may necessitate a greater allowance for passing between workers. If the gangway is used as an access route to other working areas or special rooms, additional width may be required if undue disturbance is to be avoided.

Flexibility of room or equipment use may be deemed of greater importance than rigid economy in floor area in some cases. Where benches are themselves movable, or where under-bench units are used at right angles to the normal runs of benching, considerations other than anthropometric ones may be critical.

HEIGHT OF BENCHES

No special studies of bench height were made by the team but a table has recently been prepared by members of the British Standards Institution's Advisory Committee on Anthopometric Evidence for Equipment Dimensions (8). This table is reproduced as Table 24 below. The two recommendations for standing and sitting heights, 2 ft. 10 in. and 3 ft.

Table 22. Body measurements relevant to bench spacing.

Activity	Average	To allow for 97 per cent. of population
(1) Working position . . .	18·7 in.	21·1 in.
(2) Walking between benches .	18·5 in.	21·0 in.
(3) Bending (derived from arm length correlated with trunk length)	48·8 in.	52·8 in.

Table 23. Gangway widths based on anthropometric data for average and large men.

Activities in gangway carried out opposite each other	Dimensions*			
	Average men		Large men	
(1) 1 working and 1 passing (sitting or standing)	43·2 in.	Adequate for normal sized people only	48·1 in.	Adequate for all subjects
(2) 1 working and 1 getting up from sitting to standing position (18 in. allowed for chair)	57·4 in.	Not quite adequate	63·2 in.	60 in. considered adequate
(3) 1 working and 1 bending (allowing 36 in. as average bending, *not* 48 in.)	as in (1) above		as in (1) above	
(4) 2 working and 1 passing	61·9 in.	60 in. not enough	69·2 in.	66 in. considered adequate

* 3 in. has been allowed between stationary people and on either side of those passing.

respectively, coincide with those recommended in B.S. 3202, *Recommendations on laboratory furniture and fittings*, for adult workers generally (3 ft.). and for use mainly by females (2 ft. 10 in.). The height given in Table 24 for sitting only (2 ft. 4 in.) is 2 in. lower than that recommended in B.S. 3202 but is the same as that recommended for desks and tables in B.S. 3079: 1959, *Anthropometric recommendations for dimensions of non-adjustable office chairs, desks and tables*. The latter publication also gives definitions of vertical clearance, horizontal clearance, and kneehole width.

It should be noted that in the recommendations for seat heights for the 2 ft. 10 in. and 3 ft. bench heights, i.e. 2 ft. 1 in. and 2 ft. 3 in., it is assumed that foot rests will be provided at heights of 8 in. and 10 in. respectively from the floor.

A unit of laboratory space

The limiting dimensions of a basic unit for the planning of laboratory rooms can now be considered. As described earlier, length is determined by the necessary run of serviced wall or bench, and width by the optimum width of bench, and the amount of clear space between runs of benching or equipment. It has also been established earlier in this chapter that the most useful general purpose unit is one which will house a small group of scientific workers, perhaps two or three in number.

Table 24. Recommended heights and clearances for laboratory furniture (8).

| Type of bench | Bench height | Seat height | Minimum vertical clearance from ground to under-side of bench | Minimum horizontal clearances under bench | | Minimum knee-hole width | Remarks |
				At bench level	At ground level		
Sitting only	2 ft. 4 in. (28 in.)	1 ft. 5 in. (17 in.)	2 ft. 2 in. (26 in.)	1 ft. 6 in. (18 in.)	2 ft. 0 in. (24 in.)	1 ft. 11 in. (23 in.)	The whole of the space under-neath the bench, within the limits defined should be clear of obstructions, fittings, apparatus, &c.
Standing and sitting	2 ft. 10 in. (34 in.)	2 ft. 1 in. (25 in.)	2 ft. 8 in. (32 in.)★	1 ft. 6 in. (18 in.)	2 ft. 0 in. (24 in.)	1 ft. 11 in. (23 in.)	
Standing and sitting	3 ft. 0 in. (36 in.)	2 ft. 3 in. (27 in.)	2 ft. 10 in. (34 in.)★	1 ft. 6 in. (18 in.)	2 ft. 0 in. (24 in.)	1 ft. 11 in. (23 in.)	

★ These dimensions may be reduced by not more than ½ in. if constructional requirements make it necessary but the figures given in the tables are to be preferred.

The unit under consideration is shown diagrammatically in Fig. 39A. Before proceeding to discuss the dimensions involved the shape of the space must be considered. In Fig. 39A the unit is shown with benching or laboratory rigs planned to run along the long sides of the unit only. It is of course also possible to plan a square unit with benching running on three sides, as in Fig. 39B. But it can easily be shown that this arrangement is much less satisfactory. First, it is inconvenient, in not providing the long, straight runs which have been shown to be necessary to meet peak demands for bench length (see p. 44). Second, it is more expensive to run services to benches arranged around three sides of a unit (see p. 82). Third, it is wasteful of floor space: to give 40 ft. of bench run (measured along inner edge of benching) a square room needs an area of 255 sq. ft. as against 200 sq. ft. for a room planned as in Fig. 39A. Finally, a building composed of units planned as in Fig. 39A will require less corridor space, and be more compact and economical than one composed of square units. The dimensions of the unit shown in Fig. 39A may therefore be considered.

Earlier in this chapter it was shown that a total length of 25 ft. bench-run gives the basis for a useful unit, housing comfortably groups of two, three, or four workers, depending on the work going on. Further it was shown that the peak needs of individuals were met so long as a 15-ft. run of bench could be made available. The data for the use of sinks and fume cupboards indicates that one of each will generally be needed, with occasional demands for an extra sink or cupboard by some disciplines. Sinks and fume cupboards require connexions to services and must be added in line with the bench-run to maintain services economy. Taking a 5-ft. unit as the basis for planning, and assuming that the sink unit and fume cupboard each are 5 ft. in length, we arrive at 35 ft. as the necessary length of bench-run. But it will be wise to make some allowance for bench space over and above this figure. In some disciplines two fume cupboards may be needed, in others an extra length of sink. Often a special piece of apparatus has to be housed, and sometimes there is good reason to keep some built-up experimental equipment in the laboratory, even though it is not in

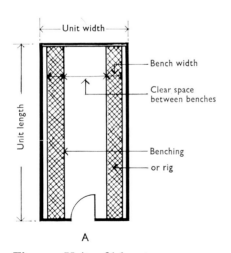

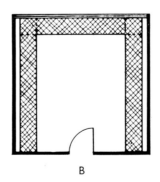

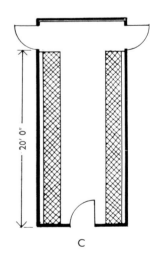

Fig. 39. Units of laboratory space.

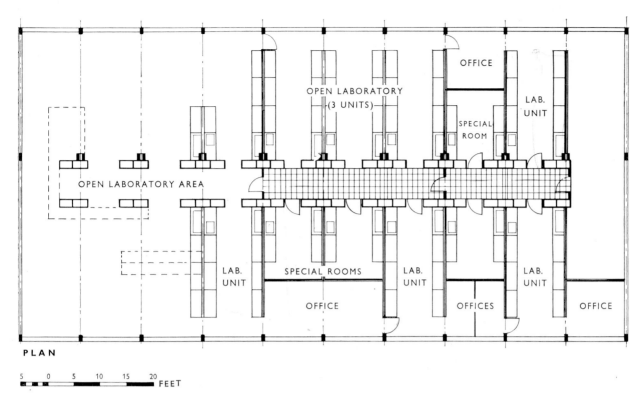

OFFICE

OPEN LABORATORY
(3 UNITS)

LAB.
UNIT

SPECIAL
ROOM

OPEN LABORATORY AREA

LAB.
UNIT

SPECIAL ROOMS

LAB.
UNIT

LAB.
UNIT

OFFICE

OFFICES

OFFICE

PLAN

5   0   5   10   15   20
FEET

Fig. 40. Alternative arrangements of laboratory units.

active use. All these uses, if they arise, tend to occupy bench area for long periods. Therefore, to maintain the provision of bench length at its proper level some allowance is necessary. The team's observations suggest that one extra 5-ft. length will be appropriate for this purpose. Thus we reach a total bench length of 40 ft., Fig. 39C.

The simplest and most obvious way of providing this length is in the form of two parallel 20-ft. runs, with working and circulation space between. In considering the length of a laboratory unit on this basis it is advisable to allow a clear space between the end of the run and the outside wall of the building in order to provide for a doorway between rooms or an open circulation gangway in the case of open laboratory areas. This is highly desirable from the point of view of safety, as it gives an alternative direction of escape in the event of fire or explosion. It is also useful to give access from one room to another, where part of the space is subdivided to give special rooms (see Part II, Chapter 2). The other end of the bench run can abut the partition which divides the laboratory from a centre corridor. Sometimes a clearance space for communicating doors is also provided at this end, but this seems unnecessary in view of the presence of the main corridor immediately adjoining. Where a number of units are used to form a large open laboratory, the centre circulation area will take the place of the normal corridor, Fig. 40.

The unit derived from the survey data gives an overall depth of room, from corridor to outside wall, of 24 to 25 ft. Rooms much shallower than this will not provide the essential 15-ft. run of available

bench space. Rooms deeper than this can be planned, and some have been built, generally with the aim of providing a writing-desk in line with the working-bench. However, rooms of 30 ft. or more are very long and narrow and the presence of additional workers in them raises problems of circulation between the rows of benching. On balance, therefore, it seems that a depth of 24 or 25 ft. has much to recommend it, particularly if some additional accommodation for reading and writing can be made available in one of the ways discussed later.

The centre to centre dimension between two parallel runs of benching of the sort described above must now be considered. It has been shown earlier that bench width should be about 2 ft. (see p. 46). When two rows of benching run back to back, services run between them attached either to a partition wall or to a low service spine. There are strong arguments for attaching all services including drainage to the partition or spine, so that benches and rigs are freely removable. This means in most cases that a narrow shelf carrying drip sinks, taps, &c., must run along the partition wall at or above bench level. Depending on the construction of the wall and the width of the service spine, the total space required between two rows of benching arranged back to back may be from 1 ft. to 1 ft. 6 in. Finally, there must be clearance and circulation space between benches. From the earlier discussion it will have been seen that as many as four people may on occasion be working in a unit bay and for such occupancy the clear space between benches should not be less than 5 ft. 6 in., that 6 ft. is desirable, and that up to 7 ft. may be needed in very deep rooms. Putting these considerations together leads to the conclusion that the centre-to-centre dimension between runs of benching may be between 10 ft. 6 in. and 12 ft., the larger dimension being only appropriate in the case of rooms approaching 30 ft. in length. Rooms 24 ft. to 30 ft. long and from 10 ft. 6 in. to 12 ft. in width have floor areas between 252 and 360 sq. ft. Units of this size provide efficient accommodation for a team of three workers in most scientific disciplines; they will also serve for two workers in disciplines with a high space requirement, such as biochemistry, or perhaps for four where the needs are less, as in botany and plant physiology. When used by three men the floor area per worker in the unit is between 84 and 120 sq. ft. The unit is shown in Fig. 39C.

Scientists' opinions on laboratory space

The conclusions set out above have been reached on the basis of objective data: observations of the space actually used by scientists in the survey described in Part I, Chapter 3, and anthropometric material. Another approach to this problem is, however, possible—that of consulting the opinion of the scientific workers themselves. An attempt was made to approach the question from this point of view and to compare the results of those arrived at by objective means.

A series of 189 laboratory rooms was chosen for the investigation, most of them in Agricultural Research Council Stations included in the main field study (see Part I, Chapter 3). Each individual working in these rooms was invited to comment on the adequacy of his working space,[1] and to express his judgement in terms of a 5-point scale as follows:

Five-point scale, on which scientists were asked to place their own laboratory accommodation.

Judgement	Category
0	Crowded
1	Medium to Crowded
2	Medium
3	Medium to Roomy
4	Roomy

The following characteristics of the rooms were measured or recorded:

1. Free floor area per man (sq. ft.).
2. Built-up floor area per man (sq. ft.). (Area occupied by furniture and fixed equipment.)
3. Length of benching and sinks per man (ft.).

4. Number of people in room.
5. Number of re-entrant corners in room (the number of corners making a projection of about 3 ft. or more into the room. This was used as a measure of room shape. For example, a high value would result where there were many awkward recesses or bays in the room).
6. Number of island benches.
7. Room height from floor to ceiling.

The general character of the work (whether predominantly chemical, physical, biological, &c.) was also noted, but as no appreciable differences could be detected between these disciplines as found in the sample, the examination of the data was based on the group as a whole.

A multiple regression analysis was used to investigate the relationships between subjective judgements and the factual data on room characteristics. Standard significance tests showed a correlation between subjective judgement and free floor area per man (1 above). No correlation was found with any of the other six room characteristics (2 to 7 above).

The relationship of judgements to free floor area[2] is roughly linear for areas between 10 sq. ft. and 120 sq. ft. per man (Fig. 41). An increase of about 30 sq. ft. of free floor area per man is needed to give a rise of one unit on the scale of subjective judgements. The average judgement value was 1·7, very near to 'medium' on the scale.

The data can be readily applied in the form of a table to predict the reactions of scientists to given values of free floor area (Table 25).

Table 25. Distribution of response shown as percentages for different values of free floor area per worker.

Free floor area per worker (nearest 10 sq. ft.)	Subjective response (per cent.)			No. of observations
	Crowded	Medium	Roomy	
20–30 sq. ft..	70	30	0	23
40–50 sq. ft..	46	48	6	53
60–70 sq. ft..	30	52	18	47
80–90 sq. ft..	17	47	36	30
100–110 sq. ft.	2	36	62	20

Intermediate judgement, categories 1 and 3,[3] were poorly represented in the collected data, and have been eliminated from Table 25 by distributing the responses in these classes equally between the two adjacent ones. The area values have been grouped to avoid the influence of sampling variations which occur when the total number of observations is small.

Although there is a wide variation in the subjective responses to given amounts of free floor area, the

---

[1] Where there were several workers in the same room, their judgements were found to correspond very closely. The average of their judgement was treated as a single value for that room.

[2] The values observed, though significant, were small.

[3] Most of the subjects gave answers in the 0, 2, and 4 categories. This commonly occurs in studies of this kind and is usually dealt with as described.

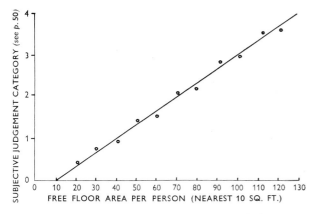

Fig. 41. Relationship between subjective judgements and free floor area.

(*There are only a few observations of area above 120 sq. ft. per person at which point the opinions tend towards the high limit. The line has been calculated as the best fit to the points.*)

reactions of laboratory workers to a range of values of free floor area can be approximately gauged from the table. For example, about 30 per cent. of workers would feel crowded with 60–70 sq. ft. of free floor area per person: with 80–90 sq. ft. the proportion of workers feeling crowded would fall to 17 per cent., the remainder being almost equally divided between 'medium' and 'roomy'.

Bearing in mind the size of the sample and the types of buildings covered in the study, some general conclusions may be drawn from the results. For all practical purposes the scientists' subjective impression of the spaciousness of his working environment is quite unrelated to 'built-up' floor area, ceiling height, the length of bench available, the general shape and layout of the room, or the number of people working in it. His impression is, however, to some extent, related to the average area of free floor per person. This allows rough predictions to be made about his subjective response to given room designs, though there is considerable variation between individuals. It is easier, therefore, to predict the pattern of responses from a group than the reaction of any one scientist.

For example, these results may be applied to forecast scientists' reactions to the unit of space developed from other considerations earlier in this chapter.

If the dimensions of the unit are taken as 25 ft. by 12 ft., the total area of the room is 300 sq. ft. Free floor area will be 200 sq. ft., allowing for benching 2 ft. wide and a 6-in. shelf behind benching.

Table 26. Free floor area per worker in a laboratory unit 25 ft. long and 12 ft. wide.

Occupation of room	Free floor area per worker (sq. ft.)
2 men	100
3 men	66
4 men	50

Table 26 shows the free floor area per man, with various numbers using the room. Reference to Table 25 shows that under the most usual conditions, occupation by a team of 3 men, over half the judgements are likely to class the room as 'medium'. When used by two men the majority will class the space as 'roomy', and when used by four, over one-third of the judgements will put the room in the 'crowded' category. Thus, broadly, the subjective approach appears to present a similar conclusion to the objective study previously described.

Room height

The foregoing discussion has been concerned with the dimensions of laboratory rooms in plan. We have still to consider room height, which will affect lighting and ventilation, working convenience, and building cost.

It is necessary to consider the question of height from several points of view. First of all, as shown later in this report, ceiling height is an important factor in building cost. Therefore, from the cost point of view, the aim must be to keep ceiling heights as low as will be otherwise acceptable. It must further be remembered that high rooms not only cost more to build, they also cost more to heat and to maintain. The requirements for lighting and for ventilation have sometimes been put forward to justify the very high laboratory rooms frequently built in the past. The studies in lighting reported in Part II, Chapter 4, demonstrate that increased ceiling height is not a very useful way of solving the problem of lighting in laboratories. It is shown that laboratory rooms, of the dimensions considered above, cannot be effectively lit from windows on one side only, even if the ceiling height is as great as 12 ft. It is argued, therefore, that the solution to laboratory lighting must be sought by other means: top lighting in single-story buildings and supplementary artificial lighting in multi-story buildings. In sum, lighting studies point to the conclusion that ceiling height should not be increased on grounds of lighting, but determined for other reasons. Similarly the discussion on laboratory ventilation in Part II, Chapter 3, concludes that there is no argument on grounds of ventilation for ceiling heights greater than 9 ft. Ceiling heights greater than 9 ft. are therefore only justifiable when dictated by the requirements of the work. Observations also lead to the conclusion that there is no general demand for a working height exceeding 9 ft. in the majority of laboratories. There are, however, some laboratories in physics and chemistry where the requirement is 10 ft., and in many laboratories occasional requirements for ceiling heights considerably in excess of what is generally provided, for example, where long distillation columns are used. It is necessary, therefore, in many laboratories, to provide for the use of double-story height at some convenient point in the building. This has

Extension to the Agricultural Research Council's Animal Research Station, Cambridge; an experimental building designed by the Nuffield Foundation's Division for Architectural Studies. Interior of one of the laboratory units.

been done by providing removable panels in the floor, enabling tall constructions to pass through the ceiling into a laboratory space above. If there is likely to be a regular demand for very tall constructions, however, it may be necessary to plan one laboratory room of double height for this purpose.

On general grounds of architectural proportion and harmony, ceiling height should be broadly related to the size of the room. Very large laboratories housing many workers in big rooms can appropriately have rather higher ceilings than are satisfactory where the building is subdivided into comparatively small rooms. The unit room, discussed earlier in this chapter, which is about 12 ft. wide, will be satisfactory if the ceiling is 9 ft. to 10 ft. high. From the results of the subjective study discussed earlier, we may conclude that within fairly broad limits room height makes no difference to the working scientist's assessment of his accommodation.

Application of research data to practical design problems

The principles outlined in this chapter have now been used in the design of several research laboratories, notably the extension to the Animal Research Station at Cambridge for the Agricultural Research Council, designed as an experimental building by the team, the Agricultural Research Council's new laboratories at Letcombe Regis, and in the new laboratories for the Imperial Cancer Research Fund in London. These buildings house a large range of scientific disciplines, and whilst they vary greatly in their detailed design, the concept of deep rooms with benches at right angles to the window wall only is common to all three. Simple and direct servicing from the central corridor has not been found unduly restrictive and considerable variations in the method of use of the deep bays have been found possible.

For the extension to the **Animal Research Station at Cambridge** the accommodation required was specified as follows:

1. Four laboratory units, each to house a team of three workers. These units to provide adequate serviced bench space, floor space, space for reading and writing, and local storage.

2. Special rooms for use by all members of the team or in conjunction with current work:
   (a) Chromatography room.
   (b) Tissue-culture room.
   (c) Room for handling and storage of radio-active materials.
   (d) Instruments room (balances and other instruments for communal use).
   (e) Cold room (temperatures above 0° C.).
   (f) Centrifuge room.

3. Common room to be used for meetings, conferences, exhibitions, and other communal activities.

4. Ancillary rooms:
   (a) Storage space.
   (b) Lavatories.
   (c) Cleaner's store.

5. Enclosed corridor to link new building to existing laboratory.

A plan and section of the building which is now completed and in use are shown in Fig. 42. There are four laboratory units, each of which will normally provide space for three workers, although sometimes there may be only two people in each room and occasionally four. The total maximum population is therefore sixteen and the probable population between twelve and fourteen workers.

The width of the laboratory bays was assessed on the principles outlined earlier in this chapter, the bench width being 2 ft. and each service spine which serves two adjacent rooms being $13\frac{1}{2}$ in. wide. The clearance between benches in the laboratory units themselves had to be generous because of the frequent use of trolleys. A bay size of 11 ft. 6 in. was therefore adopted, leaving a clearance of 6 ft. $4\frac{1}{2}$ in. between the benches. This bay size was found to be just adequate for further subdivision into offices opening directly off the laboratory units. Room depth was arrived at by assessing the bench length required to meet the normal demands of the stipulated number of users. On the rare occasions when four workers use one laboratory unit, it is unlikely that more than two of them will be in the Scientists' grade. The maximum bench requirement will therefore be for two Scientists and two Assistants in a high use discipline (biochemistry). From Table 9 it will be seen that the length needed to give 95 per cent. satisfaction is 33 ft. Normal occupancy of the units, however, would be two Scientists and one Assistant or one Scientist and two Assistants. Clear bench space in the units is 25 ft. made up of five 5 ft. units. In addition to this, space is provided in each unit for a fume cupboard and a wash-up sink, both of which are also 5 ft. in length, and 5 ft. of serviced wall space is left clear. There is therefore the possibility of increasing normal bench length to 30 ft. and, if the occasion arises when further bench length is needed, it can be provided between the last bench unit and the window in laboratory units nos. 1 and 4. Thus the maximum requirement (four workers) is obtainable, and with normal occupancy (three workers) clear wall space is available for housing standing equipment. High-level cupboards above the laboratory benches and normal under bench units provide storage space in the laboratory. The bench units are entirely free of services and can be used either parallel with or at right angles to the serviced walls.

The overall depth of the laboratory units is 24 ft., there being 4 ft. between the bench and the window wall for access to offices or intercommunication between laboratories where required. The natural lighting problems involved in rooms of this kind were

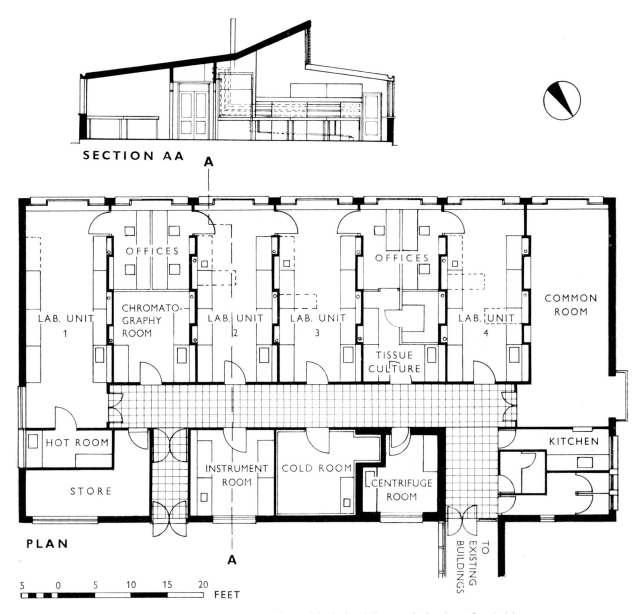

SECTION AA

PLAN

5 0 5 10 15 20 FEET

Fig. 42. Extension to the Agricultural Research Council's Animal Research Station, Cambridge.

studied at the Building Research Station with special reference to this building and are fully described in Part II, Chapter 4: the design of the service spine is illustrated and described in Chapter 3.

It will be seen from Fig. 42 that deep rooms are placed on one side of the corridor, and that rooms 12 ft. only in depth are placed opposite them. This arrangement is due only to the small size of the building and the necessity of linking it with existing buildings of similar size. It should be noted that the design of the laboratory units is such that they could be placed on either side of the corridor giving a building of much greater depth, as in the **Agricultural Research Council's Laboratories at Letcombe Regis,** a plan and section of which are shown in Fig. 43. In this building advantage has been taken of the space formed between the roof lights to house

plant required for the special ventilation needed in connexion with the use of radioactive materials in the building. A number of variations in the method of planning within the laboratory units can be seen in the plan.

Fig. 44 shows a plan of one floor in the new laboratories at present under construction for the **Imperial Cancer Research Fund in London.** This building houses a number of disciplines (physiology, pathology, biochemistry, &c.) in a multi-story building, all the floors of which are planned with deep rooms serviced directly from vertical service ducts. Here again, owing to site restrictions it was not possible to plan deep rooms on both sides of the central corridor, but it will be seen that shallower rooms are placed opposite the laboratory units in one wing of the building and these rooms are sufficient to pro-

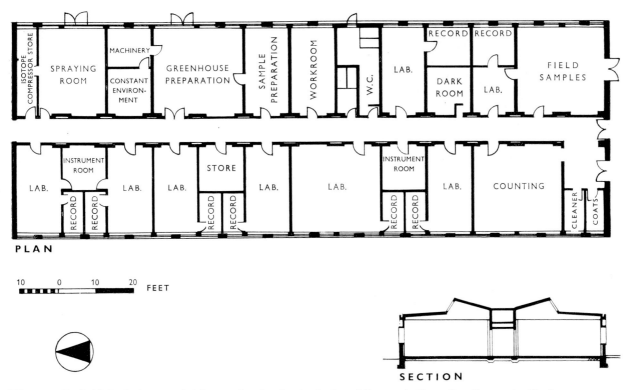

Fig. 43. Radiobiological research laboratories for the Agricultural Research Council at Letcombe Regis.

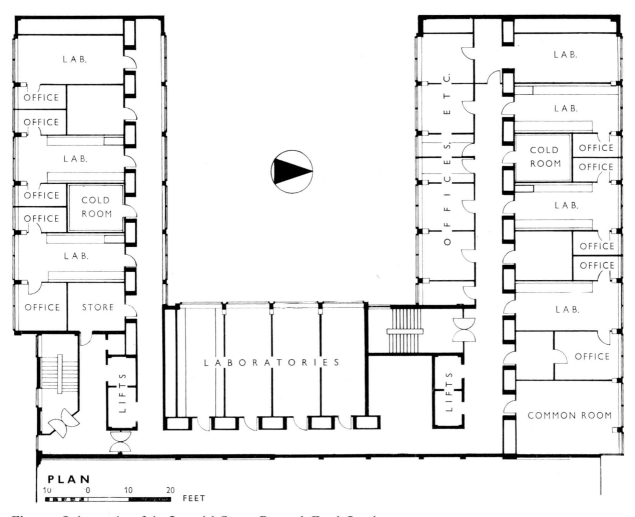

Fig. 44. Laboratories of the Imperial Cancer Research Fund, London.

vide the unserviced and partially serviced space required in a large research establishment. The rooms are used as offices, staff rooms, &c., and in some cases as balance rooms and instrument rooms.

The rapidly developing character of the work which this building houses makes it necessary to provide removable partitions. These have been designed in conjunction with the bench units so that the latter can be easily taken down and stored. Vertical metal channels are placed at bench unit centres to carry service lines, overbench cupboards, and shelves. The spaces between the verticals are filled with removable panels or left open to form multi-unit laboratories. Service lines, overbench cupboards, and infill panels can all be removed from one side of the partition only without disturbing work in progress in an adjacent room. The system is illustrated and discussed more fully in Part II, Chapter 3, in connexion with servicing.

REFERENCES

(1) LASSEN, F. *Laboratorien. Planung Bau Einrichtung.* Darmstadt, 1957, p. 49.

(2) HAINES, C. 'Planning the scientific laboratory.' *Archit. Rec.* **108,** 1950, pp. 110–11, 113.

(3) COLEMAN, H. S. *Laboratory design.* New York, 1951, p. 345.

(4) SCHRAMM, W. *Chemische und biologische Laboratorien-Planung, Bau und Einrichtung.* Leipzig, 1957, pp. 123–4.

(5) MINISTRY OF EDUCATION. *The design of school kitchens.* London, 1955, pp. 29–30. *Building bulletin,* no. 11.

(6) MURRELL, K. F. H. 'Data on human performance for engineering designers.' *Engineering, Lond.* **184,** 1957, pp. 247–9.

(7) FLOYD, W. F., and WELFORD, A. T. 'Symposium on human factors in equipment design.' THE ERGONOMICS RESEARCH SOCIETY. *Proceedings II*, London, 1954, p. 21.

(8) NORMAN, A. S. (Secretary to the British Standards Institution's Advisory Committee on Anthropometric Evidence for Equipment Dimensions). Personal communication.

Chapter 2

ROOMS ASSOCIATED WITH LABORATORY SPACE

THE general laboratory, as discussed in the preceding chapter, is the scientist's working base, where most of his time is usually spent. From time to time, however, scientists need to use other rooms. Some of these are used so often or in such close connexion with current work, that they must be very near to the general laboratory. The function and design of these rooms, which have to be planned in close association with general laboratory space, are discussed in this chapter. (Rooms not so closely connected with the laboratory space, e.g. staff common rooms, canteens, and central stores, are not dealt with.)

Rooms associated with laboratory space fall into three principal groups:

(1) offices for scientific staff;

(2) rooms for special purposes;

(3) animal houses.

Offices for scientific staff

It is common knowledge that a good deal of the scientist's time is spent in reading and writing, and there has been considerable discussion on the best means of providing space for this purpose in laboratory design. Some of the solutions adopted are discussed in Part I (Chapter 2, Current Practice in Laboratory Design). The alternatives include the provision of desks in the laboratory itself, the provision of separate offices adjoining the laboratory, and the provision of offices more or less remote from the laboratory.

In the laboratory survey made by the team, a study of office needs was included. The survey covered laboratory staff of all grades below that of Principal Scientific Officer. The time they spent in reading and writing was recorded. (The making of notes during an actual experiment was not included.) Tables 27, 28, and 29 give the results, classified by discipline and by grade of worker. Table 30 gives the percentage of total working time spent in reading and writing by Scientists and Assistants, averaged over all disciplines. The broad conclusion from the survey is that Scientists spend between a quarter and a half of their working time in reading or writing, most of them spending about a third of their time in this way. Time spent in these activities by Assistants is much less, but still considerable.

These results suggest that the scientific worker should have a permanent place in which he can read and write. Observations in laboratories and discussions with scientists led to the further conclusion that this space should preferably have a measure of quiet and privacy. But there are strong arguments

Table 27. Percentage of total working time taken over whole year spent in reading and writing by *Scientific Officers*.

Discipline	Total no. of observations	Percentage of total working time spent in reading and writing
Chemistry	406	41·4
Physics	429	30·3
Biochemistry . . .	429	30·3
Biophysics. . . .	170	31·2
Microbiology . . .	439	26·9
Entomology . . .	399	29·6
Animal Physiology . .	418	39·5
Plant Physiology . .	327	44·0
Botany	421	35·1
Zoology	344	50·0
Pathology . . .	384	25·5

Table 28. Percentage of total working time taken over whole year spent in reading and writing by *Experimental Officers*.

Discipline	Total no. of observations	Percentage of total working time spent in reading and writing
Chemistry	428	13·1
Physics	239	20·9
Biochemistry . . .	414	24·6
Biophysics. . . .	nil	..
Microbiology . . .	425	17.4
Entomology . . .	321	11·2
Animal Physiology . .	304	8·9
Plant Physiology . .	106	26·4
Botany	441	22·9
Zoology	410	29·0
Pathology . . .	131	6·1

Table 29. Percentage of total working time taken over whole year spent in reading and writing by *Assistants*.

Discipline	Total no. of observations	Percentage of total working time spent in reading and writing
Chemistry . . .	331	14·2
Physics . . .	284	25·0
Biochemistry . .	337	8·6
Biophysics. . .	143	2·8
Microbiology . .	359	6·4
Entomology . . .	327	13·5
Animal Physiology . .	363	3·9
Plant Physiology . .	221	27·1
Botany . . .	260	14·2
Zoology . . .	348	13·8
Pathology . . .	285	8·8

Table 30. Percentage of total working time taken over whole year spent in reading and writing by *Scientific Officers, Experimental Officers, and Assistants* (averaged over all disciplines).

Staff grade	Total no. of observations	Percentage of total working time spent in reading and writing
Scientific Officers . .	4,166	33·92
Experimental Officers . .	3,219	18·67
Assistants . . .	3,258	12·34

against providing offices in any position except opening directly from their laboratories. It is urged that separating the office, even by placing it directly across the corridor from the laboratory, is undesirable owing to the need to keep in continuous and close contact with work in progress in the laboratory. Against this it has been pointed out by Haines (1) and others that floor space in the laboratory area is very expensive, costing perhaps twice as much as floor space in a wing devoted entirely to offices. A compromise solution to this conflict may be found by planning very small offices, no larger than cubicles, directly adjoining the laboratory. These are especially useful to medium grade scientific staff. They should be large enough to contain the scientist's desk, his books, and to allow him to interview one or two people in privacy. Such functions require only a small area, perhaps as little as 50 sq. ft., and the fact that the office is in direct contact with the laboratory helps to ensure that its uses are limited to those for which it is specifically designed. The number of office cubicles which will be needed in relation to laboratory space depends on the ratio of senior workers to assistants. This will vary from time to time and it is convenient if the laboratory is planned on a dimensional grid, such that office space can be freely formed in a laboratory area by partitioning and subsequently revert to use as a laboratory where necessary. Some examples of laboratory plans providing this facility are illustrated in Chapter 1 above.

An alternative solution is to provide desk space in the laboratory itself. This gives no privacy for reading and writing and results in an increase in the size of the laboratory unit. If the desk is placed in the centre of the room, an increase in width is necessary, and this is extremely uneconomical: if it is added to the run of bench, the length of the unit will be increased by about 5 ft.

Apart from the provision for the working scientist there will, of course, be a need for office accommodation for more senior staff whose time is spent mainly or wholly in administration. Here the need for very close association of office and laboratory is less. If a man spends a substantial part of his working day in an office, it will need to be considerably larger and may be planned as one of a number of separate rooms opening off a corridor, or in a separate wing.

Rooms for special purposes

Apart from office space certain special rooms are found in close association with laboratories. These include instrument rooms, dark rooms, controlled environment rooms, and rooms for housing special techniques such as chromatography and tissue culture which cannot be carried out conveniently or efficiently in the open laboratory. Whilst some of these rooms are more or less permanent, particularly those designed to provide controlled environment, such as cold rooms and constant temperature rooms, others may be needed temporarily and become redundant after the conclusion of a project or a particular line of work. As a rule these rooms are small, housing one or two workers and the necessary equipment. Their use may be intermittent, but it is often closely connected with work in the general laboratory, and they must be conveniently placed in relation to it. They are usually equipped with the normal laboratory services, electricity, water, and drainage, and often require extract ducts for fume cupboards or special ventilation as well as accommodation for special plant such as compressors in the case of cold rooms. The best method of providing these rooms is to ensure that the general laboratory space lends itself to subdivision, in such a way to enable rooms of appropriate size, generally from 50 to 120 sq. ft., to be formed by temporary partitions. Thus, such rooms became partitioned off areas of the laboratory space. When the rooms are no longer needed, the partitions can be removed and the area can revert to normal laboratory use.

In large establishments, where there is a widespread demand for special facilities, it may be uneconomical to provide large numbers of expensive special rooms scattered throughout the building. In such cases, it may be necessary to centralize special rooms in one area, convenient for services and placed in a position which will cause as little inconvenience to the users as possible.

The scale on which special rooms are provided has a marked effect on building cost. As they must be regarded as a shared service, and do not enable additional scientific staff to be housed in the building, they are bound to increase the cost of the building per worker housed.

It is therefore advisable to consider the case for each special room carefully before deciding to provide it. Later in this chapter some guidance is given on the circumstances in which special rooms are essential. In some cases it is possible to avoid the provision of a special room by using apparatus or equipment designed to produce the necessary environmental conditions on a small scale. When special rooms are essential, however, every effort should be made to keep them as small in size as is compatible with efficient use. This will give economy of building space. It will also yield savings on the running cost and first cost if special plant is needed to maintain defined environmental conditions in the room.

Whilst carrying out the laboratory survey and in the course of visits to other laboratories, the team made notes on a number of special rooms. It is not claimed that these notes are comprehensive either in their coverage of types of special room or in the variations within each type.

Balance and instrument rooms

Balances are occasionally used in the laboratory but more frequently are housed in a separate room, centrally placed in relation to the laboratories they serve. Tables or benches must be of solid construction, giving a firm surface on which to place the instruments. Sensitive balances, used for weighing micro-quantities, may require protection against vibration. Modern instrument mountings have reduced the need for structural measures against vibration. Except under extremely difficult conditions, a bench which is itself rigid, combined with properly designed mountings on the instruments, will meet most needs. Slate slab or cast *in situ* concrete bench tops supported on brick or concrete dwarf walls at 3 ft. to 4 ft. centres are widely used and have proved satisfactory. The alternatives of structural protection and flexible mountings are discussed in Chapter 5 under Noise and Vibration. A useful method of preventing local vibration caused by the balance operator himself is shown in Fig. 45. The balance is supported on a small pad cantilevered from a wall; the table has an opening cut in its top of sufficient size to clear the cantilevered pad on all sides. This ensures that local disturbance caused by the worker's contact with the table is not transmitted to the surface supporting the balance.

Balances should not be placed near heat sources, such as ovens or furnaces, and naturally lit balance rooms should be equipped with adequate protection against solar heat gain. Fluorescent artificial lighting produces negligible radiant heat. If tungsten

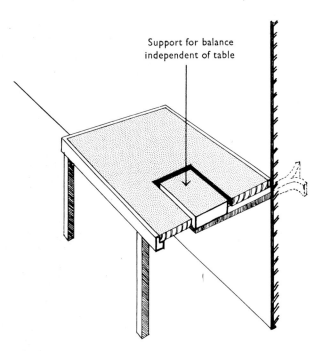

Fig. 45. Support for a sensitive instrument cantilevered from a wall.

light sources are used, they should be placed far enough from the instrument to avoid any appreciable effects of radiant heat. Balance rooms need moderately high general illumination levels (20 lumens/sq. ft.) with additional local lighting on the instruments themselves, depending on the fineness of the scales. Many modern balances have built-in lighting and only general lighting is then needed in the room.

The balance room should be as free as possible from contamination by corrosive fumes, excessive humidity, dust, &c. If directly communicating with the laboratory, the door should be close-fitting and provided with draught-strips. If the users regularly carry samples for weighing, the door handles should be elbow-operated, especially if dangerous substances are involved.

Air-conditioned balance rooms may be essential for micro-analytical work, and greater care must then be taken to ensure that conditions in the room are not upset by the laboratory atmosphere. The balance room should not adjoin the laboratory, and preferably have an air-lock at the entrance.

It is difficult to recommend a single satisfactory bench height for balance rooms, because of variation in the methods of operation of balances. The visual scales are mounted at varying heights above the bench and the user may have to vary his eye level when moving from one balance to another to avoid parallax effects. Scales vary in height from a few inches to as much as 1 ft. 6 in. above bench level. Where a number of different balances are in use, therefore, a bench (2 ft. 10 in. high) and chairs or stools which can be varied in height may be satisfactory (Fig. 46), but for some types of balance (e.g. those with scales at high level), normal table height

59

Fig. 46. Balance room at the Chemical Research Institute, Munich. Benches supported on concrete pins; adjustable height stools.

(2 ft. 4 in. to 2 ft. 6 in.) benches are needed. It may be necessary to provide benches of different heights in large balance rooms. In designing accommodation for work which includes exacting visual discrimination such as reading from balance scales, variations in body size (especially as between men and women) cannot be neglected (see Part II, Chapter 1, pp. 45–47). A very small difference in eye level may seriously reduce visual efficiency. These differences cannot always be met by body movement without some discomfort. It is reasonable, therefore, to recommend the use of adjustable chairs or stools for balance rooms, particularly where routine weighing necessitates long continuous periods of balance-room work.

Most of the above notes on balance rooms apply also to rooms housing other sensitive instruments. Consideration must be given to each type of instrument likely to be used. For example, some optical instruments need vibration-free conditions as much as micro-balances, and any disturbance to the instrument may involve lengthy recalibration.

Generally, instruments should be protected from excessive humidity, dust, and corrosive fumes. For example, manufacturers recommend controlled humidity (R.H. 35/40 per cent.) for infra-red spectrometers. Local lighting on scales and dials should be adequate for scale reading; reference may be made to Fig. 69, p. 100, for recommended levels. The services to run the instruments are usually specified in manufacturers' catalogues, but water and a sink for disposal of samples are normally required in all instrument rooms in addition to electricity. Special services may also be essential, for example, compressed air or steam for pressurizing, water jet pumps for cleaning routines associated with some techniques, &c. In rooms designed to house a number of small instruments, flexibility and interchangeability will depend upon the services being readily available in the room.

Rooms with controlled environment

The range of provision of controlled environment in research laboratories varies greatly. At one end of the scale small refrigerators, incubators, or ovens are placed in the laboratory, at the other, controlled temperature rooms are equipped for storage of large numbers of samples (e.g. storage of media in quantity), or to accommodate experimental work.

Often temperature only is controlled, but there are cases in which humidity is also of importance, for example, the accuracy of some instruments is impaired if humidity varies to a marked extent (see section on balance and instrument rooms).

To provide accurate temperature control—and control to $\pm\frac{1}{2}°$ may be required—is expensive. It involves not only the use of plant for heating and cooling, but insulated structure, specially constructed doors, and possibly air-locks. Equipment is usually designed to provide only one temperature within a given room, or at most only a small temperature range. Where a larger temperature range is required, for example, in the case of psychrometric chambers, the provision is usually regarded as specialized equipment rather than as a special room: equipment of this kind requires considerable plant space and is usually designed by the mechanical engineer in collaboration with the user.

Research techniques and processes develop and change rapidly and an expensive facility may be rapidly outgrown. The cost of environment control in volumes of room size (500 to 1,500 cubic feet) is high, and if requirements change, it is difficult and costly to modify the equipment. In addition, the larger the volume, the more difficult accurate control becomes. It is reasonable, therefore, that volumes should be kept as small as possible, and small units used in preference to large ones, both on grounds of economy and accuracy. For experimental purposes, as opposed to storage purposes, the tendency is to try to reduce the scale of provision for controlled environment. Much less expense is involved in providing a small volume at controlled temperature within the laboratory than in conditioning a complete room, and many pieces of equipment of this kind are available. The latter usually require only electrical servicing and are mobile in the sense that they can be moved from room to room as the need arises. A further advantage of local provision within the laboratory is that the equipment can be maintained by the laboratory maintenance staff, whereas the plant needed for conditioning a whole room may require specialist maintenance. Also plant failure may be extremely serious if reliance is placed on one controlled environment room, whereas the failure of a number of local units simultaneously is unlikely. An example of the way in which cabinet-scale control can take the place of controlled environment rooms is shown in the section on Chromatography below (p. 65).

Good thermal insulation is essential to controlled environment rooms, and is made easier and thus cheaper by removing the rooms from the effects of fluctuations in outside temperature. Natural light is not usually needed, and rooms can be planned away from external walls. Economic provision for special rooms can be made when laboratory buildings are given ample depth from window to corridor wall (see Part II, Chapters 1 and 6).

The detailed design of controlled environment rooms and the plant associated with them are matters for the specialist engineer. The method of use of the room must be specified, for example, whether the room is to be used mainly for storage or as a working area, and if the latter whether for long or short periods of time.

Controlled environment rooms in which scientists work must be ventilated, and naturally the size and cost of the plant required to maintain a level temperature increase as the required rate of ventilation increases. Rooms which are to be occupied by one or more workers for periods of two or three hours will not usually be run at very high or very low temperatures, but there are many examples of such rooms at working temperatures of $+2$ to $+4°$ C. (cold laboratories) and around $+22°$ C. (hot rooms).

When a number of controlled environment rooms are needed in a building, the question inevitably arises whether centralized or individual conditioning plant should be used. In some cases the decision will be made on functional grounds. For example, it may be impossible to supply rooms with widely varying requirements from the same source. It may also be uneconomic in running costs to use a large plant if some of the rooms are used spasmodically rather than continuously. On the other hand, in terms of structure, it is easier and thus more economical to centralize the equipment in one specially designed room, localizing the necessary precautions against noise and vibration (see Part II, Chapter 5, under Noise and Vibration). Against this, however, must be set the cost of trunking and piping to take the service to rooms which may be widely separated in the building. Local plant can be operated and controlled by the individual scientist, but may raise difficult noise and vibration problems if the rooms are near to working areas or other rooms housing sensitive instruments. Problems of this kind are common, especially in light framed buildings, and may be a limiting factor. Individual compressor units, fans, &c., are, however, available which can be successfully screened against noise and provided with vibration-proof mountings.

When the rooms are in continuous use, failure in a centralized plant can jeopardize months or even years of long-term research work; individually serviced rooms minimize such hazards. The latter are also more flexible, as the rooms can be converted back to normal laboratory use without alteration to the centralized plant and without disturbance to the work being carried out in laboratories or special rooms.

It is often necessary to provide small areas, usually for storage purposes at very high or very low temperatures, for example, deep-freeze storage at $-20°$ C. The cost of such provision is greatly reduced if these rooms open off rooms which are already temperature controlled to a lesser degree. Deep-freeze cabinets or cupboards can be placed in cold rooms, and incubators, &c., can be placed in rooms already controlled to higher than normal temperatures.

Dark rooms

Photographic and photometric techniques are used in almost all scientific disciplines. Dark rooms are required, therefore, in most laboratory buildings for photographic processing whilst rooms which are either permanently darkened or fitted with light-proof blinds are needed for specialized optical instruments.

Photographic dark rooms vary widely in size from the large complex photographic department which handles the bulk of the work in a major research establishment to the small dark cubicle, possibly used by only one man in conjunction with some specialized laboratory techniques. The large photographic section will contain a studio as well as processing rooms. The latter may include a chemical mixing room, developing room with a loading cubicle, printing and enlarging rooms, finishing room, and stores. The small cubicle houses all the processes and is usually of very modest size (75 to 150 sq. ft.). The service requirements for photographic dark rooms are the same irrespective of size—hot and cold water for use in preparing developing and printing solutions and for washing, electrical points for safe-lights, enlargers, driers, &c.

There are many specialized items of equipment available for use in photographic processing. These include safe-lights of various kinds, thermostatically controlled tanks, driers, &c., all of which are designed to speed up or improve the processes. The large photographic room, handling a continuous volume of work, would be equipped with some or all of these items of equipment, but the simpler processes can all be carried out in a room equipped with one or more large sinks, a bench, and the necessary electrical outlets. A translucent panel let into the bench top and illuminated from below is useful for inspecting negatives or slides. Where speed and efficiency of working are essential, it may be necessary to have special arrangements of electrical switches. For example, if two kinds of safe-light are used, it is advisable to keep the switches well apart and also to provide the switches with covers to prevent accidental operation. The outlets for enlargers may have foot switches. It is convenient to have inspection lamps with pull-cord switches over sinks or tanks.

It may be necessary to provide light-trapped entrance doors to some dark rooms where frequent traffic to and from the dark room by a number of workers is expected, but it is now common practice, especially for small dark rooms, merely to provide a warning light above the door, outside the room. Water and chemical solutions may be spilt in dark rooms and the floor surface should be impervious. In larger units floor drainage may be necessary in the processing area. Light colours rather than dark ones should be used on walls and ceilings.

In common with other special rooms which may have no natural ventilation owing to the absence of windows, dark rooms should be artificially ventilated. For small dark rooms it is usually sufficient to provide an extract vent and a light-trapped inlet grille, but for larger units or where the worker may spend long periods on exacting photographic work it may be necessary to provide warmed input air as well as extraction. Air temperatures should preferably be between 65° F. and 70° F. Dark rooms should be protected against chemical fumes and against radiation, for example, from X-ray apparatus.

The special provisions outlined above also apply to dark rooms or laboratories designed for special instruments or scientific techniques. Such rooms may also require normal bench services, such as gas and compressed air, in addition to those given above for photographic dark rooms.

Centrifuge rooms

Noisy or potentially dangerous apparatus, and vibration-producing equipment, are often separately accommodated, especially where a number of such items can be brought together in a convenient position for use in conjunction with the laboratory. Centrifuge rooms are a typical case.

Centrifuges range in size from small models which stand on a bench to large high-speed models standing on the floor. They are usually very noisy and set up considerable vibration. If the machines are not equipped with vibration mountings by the manufacturer, frequency measurements can be made and appropriate mountings fitted (see Chapter 5 under Noise and Vibration).

Centrifuges are usually placed as far as conveniently possible from laboratory areas, because of noise, and should be well removed from instrument, balance rooms, &c., on account of vibration. In laboratories where several are in use, a good case can be made for housing them in a separate room within easy reach of laboratory areas, but with adequate insulation against high-frequency noise. This has been done in the experimental laboratory designed by the team as an extension to the Animal Research Unit at Cambridge (Fig. 42). There is an element of danger from high-speed centrifuges, and this is a further important reason for removing them from the general laboratory.

Some bench-mounted centrifuges are quite small (about 1 ft. in diameter, 1 ft. 6 in. high) and can be used on normal power supply. Large ultracentrifuges may be 7 ft. to 8 ft. long and 3 ft. wide, and some of these require 3-phase electrical supply. Hot and cold water and a large sink and draining board are usually required for use in conjunction with centrifuging. Glassware, centrifuge heads, &c., must be washed and stored near to the equipment. Some modern machines are water cooled and therefore require connexion to the water service and must be provided with a drainage point. Visible inspection of this drainage point is necessary unless a water-flow meter is installed and placed in a conspicuous position. It should also be noted that most of the large centrifuges require near access and it may be necessary to allow as much as 1 ft. 6 in. clear all round the machine.

Chromatography rooms

Chromatography is one of the specialized laboratory techniques which has developed rapidly over the last few years. It is dealt with in some detail as an example of how a technique of growing popularity may necessitate special provision either in the laboratory itself or of a special room devoted entirely to one purpose. This technique is also a good example of the way in which the demand for a closely controlled environment may be made on a small scale in an enclosed cabinet to eliminate the cost of temperature control over the whole volume of a special room.

There are two main kinds of chromatography, requiring different provisions in the design of the laboratory intended to accommodate them: they are column chromatography (of gases and liquids) and paper chromatography.

COLUMN CHROMATOGRAPHY

Liquids

Liquid mixtures are separated by passing them through a vertical column packed with absorbent. This operation is normally carried out in the laboratory rather than in a special room. The illustration (Fig. 47) shows a Moore–Stein column. The Moore–Stein column is built up from the floor on a frame, and requires clear serviced wall and floor space rather than benching. Normally column length does not exceed 150 c.m. (about 5 ft.) but in special cases columns 10 ft. to 15 ft. in height are used.

The column and collector in Fig. 47 are 7 ft. high, and above this there is a reservoir which requires a head of pressure. The pressure head may be obtained simply by height or by artificial means. Height is usually preferred, but economy in room height may require the use of other methods. For example, the column illustrated would normally require 4 ft. above the frame to obtain an adequate head of pressure. In this building the room is only 8 ft. 6 in. high and it was necessary to use mercury to obtain the head. Ideally, in this case, a part of the laboratory, although not necessarily the whole room, should be at least 12 ft. 6 in. high. It is sometimes possible to fold back the columns if a very long column is needed, or shorter columns may be run in series. In biochemical laboratories in particular it may be useful to have an area with sufficient height to accommodate a very long column, possibly by omitting part of the floor above and allowing double-story height.

Precautions must be taken to protect columns from extreme changes of temperature. For example, solar radiation may upset the controls. The apparatus

Fig. 47. Moore–Stein chromatography column at the D.S.I.R. Low Temperature Research Station, Cambridge.

should also be protected from excessive structural vibration.

Gases

Similar considerations apply to gas or vapour-phase chromatography except that very long columns may often be folded or coiled.

Space should be provided for storing the cylinders of carrier gas used in the process and for housing them near the apparatus. Proprietary apparatus for gas chromatography is available and is more compact and more enclosed than the laboratory-built columns. One example of these units is about 5 ft. high, 2 ft. deep and 3 ft. wide, and is less sensitive to draughts and vibration than an open column. Such apparatus is, however, expensive and may not be suitable for all types of work. It should be noted that at least one proprietary unit must be fed with a glass tube some 4 ft. to 5 ft. long, vertically from above, and a room height of at least 10 ft. may therefore be required. The proprietary chromatography equipment may also include a separate recorder which must be carried on a bench or table, well mounted, or provided with a special supporting frame.

PAPER CHROMATOGRAPHY

This technique is increasingly used in all branches of analytical work. A small drop of the solution containing the substances to be separated is applied to a strip or sheet of filter paper and allowed to dry. The paper is then placed in the developing solution—usually a water-containing organic solvent—so that the solvent is drawn through the spot by capillary action to the other end of the paper, carrying with it the various constituents of the mixture at different speeds, leaving on the paper individual local concentrations or 'spots'. This process is known as running the paper. The paper is then dried and the spots are developed for identification and evaluation.

The papers are normally run in enclosed glass tanks which vary in size according to the size of the paper. Standard size sheets are 23 in. by 27 in. and $18\frac{1}{4}$ in. by $22\frac{1}{2}$ in. Sheets 36 in. by 36 in. are available but rarely used. Very small papers are also used. Some of these are small enough to be run in a test-tube and others for micro-scale work are even smaller. Provision should be made for storing the papers in the laboratory, preferably laid flat in drawers.

Many of the solvents used are volatile organic liquids, e.g. alcohols, light petroleum, benzene, &c. Although the papers are run in enclosed tanks some of the solvent-saturated atmosphere of the tank, or the gases (such as hydrogen cyanide) which are sometimes used in the process, will always escape into the room.

Accident and fire hazards are high in chromatography rooms. There is a risk of fire while solvent fumes are being removed during the drying process, and many of the organic compounds have a narcotic action. Regular exposure to them constitutes a positive danger to health.

Constant temperature is essential while running the papers. There should be no draughts across the tank. Adequate ventilation must be provided without excessive air movement. Natural lighting is not essential and solar radiation may upset temperature controls.

The papers are dried by passing a current of air (sometimes heated) over them and exhausting it to the outside air. This can be done under a hood, or, if warming is necessary, in an oven with an extract system.[1]

The papers may be developed in various ways, for example:

(a) Spraying with an indicator. The indicator itself may be a toxic liquid, e.g. ninhydrin or benzidine. In such cases it is essential to spray under a good hood. Good artificial lighting is necessary.

(b) Exposure to ultraviolet light. It must be possible to black-out the room for this process.

(c) Autoradiography. When mixtures of substances containing radioactive tracers have been separated, developing may be done by

[1] Drying cabinets are available with temperature control up to 150° C. and can be fitted with exhaust fans.
A description of the construction of chromatographic ovens is given in *Lab. Pract.* **8**, 1959, pp. 168–70.

contact with a photographic plate. This method is becoming more common and dark room facilities are essential.

Temperature Control

Most published work in chromatography concerns experiments in which the papers are run at temperatures between 18° and 25° C., the more common temperature range being between 20° and 22° C. There should be as little temperature fluctuation as possible whilst the paper is being run, although this may take up to 24 hours or more.

The degree of control needed is related to the degree of accuracy required. In some cases the papers run only for short periods, and so a slight change in temperature may be permissible, e.g. $\pm 1°$ or $\pm 2°$ C. Usually, however, control to $\pm\frac{1}{2}°$ C. is desirable. Such conditions are expensive to achieve over a whole room, and the cost may be out of all proportion to the amount of chromatographic work done in the room. Accurate control of temperature is easier and cheaper to provide within a small volume of space, and it is suggested (see below) that wherever possible cabinets should be used for running and drying the papers, thus avoiding the necessity for accurate control over the temperature of a room. Humidity is not normally critical except in microscale work when humidity control may also be needed to keep the water content of the papers within given limits.

Ventilation

If the papers are run in tanks in a temperature controlled room, 8–10 air changes per hour are necessary to prevent the room air from becoming stale or presenting a danger to the health of those using it. An unregulated system of ventilation in such a room makes temperature control difficult, and although an occasional thorough airing when the room is not in use may be sufficient to deal with the fumes, accurate equilibration of temperature afterwards will take several hours. If, on the other hand, a controlled cabinet with a hood is used, ventilation is less critical and may be needed only when papers are being handled.

When no heat is required during the drying process, it can be done under a normal fume hood. If drying is done in an oven or drying cabinet, an efficient exhaust system is essential to safety.

Spraying can be done in an ordinary fume cupboard, with washable surfaces which are unaffected by solvents (see Appendix II).

SCALE OF PROVISION

The comparative efficiency and economy of providing special rooms or special facilities within the laboratory have been discussed above. Chromatography is one of the techniques in which a decision between the two methods of provision must be

Fig. 48. Cabinet and hood apparatus for paper chromatography at the D.S.I.R. Low Temperature Research Station, Cambridge. Curtains are drawn back to show papers hung up to dry and a section of the top of the cabinet has been lifted to show one of the glass tanks.

Fig. 49. Sterile cubicle at the research laboratories of the Imperial Chemical Industries' Pharmaceuticals Division, Alderley Park.

made. In the past special rooms were often provided or adapted for the purpose and equipped with temperature control. All workers do not favour special rooms, and the cabinet shown in Fig. 48, developed at the Department of Scientific and Industrial Research Low Temperature Station at Cambridge, is an example of the way in which the running and drying of papers may be carried out under accurately controlled conditions in the laboratory. A more fully developed version of the chromatography cabinet is in use at Fison's Research Laboratory, Levington, and has given good service.

The team has found that chromatography rooms are used mainly for running the papers, although in large establishments such as the French National Zoological Research Centre at Jouy en Josas there may be a suite of rooms, each room used for one stage of the process.

The high rate of ventilation required to maintain a healthy and safe atmosphere in chromatography rooms complicates the temperature control problem. Therefore, if the degree of control within the room can be made less stringent by the use of boxes for running and drying the papers, overall building cost

will be reduced. In the experimental laboratory at Cambridge (Fig. 42, p. 54), the chromatography room has been equipped with boxes giving temperature control to $\pm\frac{1}{2}°$ C. and the room itself is provided with a rougher form of control on the heating system only, with no provision for cooling. The boxes can be made any convenient length to house the number of tanks needed, and have a further advantage over the temperature-controlled room in that a number of boxes can be run at different temperatures to meet the needs of a number of workers simultaneously. In common with other facilities of a similar kind, therefore, chromatography can be accommodated in the building more cheaply and more efficiently at process level than at structural level, while maintaining a greater degree of flexibility of room use.

Inoculation rooms

For the cultivation of micro-organisms suitable culture media are inoculated with the organism. According to the degree of precaution required against contamination, inoculation can be done under one of the following conditions:

(i) If the inoculation involves only one culture and the time taken is reasonably short, it is sufficient to spray the area of laboratory bench in use and the surrounding air with alcohol, immediately prior to inoculation. Irradiation of the working area with ultra-violet light may also be used.

(ii) When a few inoculations are done at a time, a glove box of simple design can be used.

(iii) An inoculation room may be needed if the technique is used on a large scale. This may simply be a small separate room with no special provision or, if rigorous air hygiene is essential, a fully air-conditioned room. Input air is filtered where risk of contamination is very great. Surfaces and finishes must be easy to clean and disinfect, and an air-lock entrance is desirable. Gas, electricity, and water are needed in these rooms, and balanced air extraction over the working area may be essential. When full aseptic techniques are practised, handwashing and changing facilities are essential.

Similar conditions to those described in (iii) above are required for tissue culture and a small room for this purpose has been provided in the experimental building at Cambridge. Warmed filtered air is supplied to the room and extracted over the work bench. The equipment associated with the culture room is in the area immediately surrounding it. This includes an autoclave, incubator, and washing facilities. Completely aseptic techniques are not essential in this case, but dust must be excluded from the room when it is in use. The input air maintains a slight positive pressure in the room. Benches are finished in laminated plastic, and culturing is done on stainless-steel trays which can be sterilized after use. Similar rooms visited by the team were equipped with stainless-steel benches and fittings, and walls were lined with plastics with stainless-steel trim. Fig. 49 shows a tissue-culture cubicle at the Imperial Chemical Industries' Pharmaceuticals Division Laboratories at Alderley Park.

Sterilization

In microbiological, biological, biochemical, and pathological disciplines, glassware, apparatus, and media must be sterilized; soil samples, animal cages and bedding may also require sterilization. Facilities for several methods may have to be planned in conjunction with washing-up and, possibly, media preparation. Three methods of sterilization most commonly used are: steam (100° C.), steam under pressure, and dry heat.[1]

---

[1] Laboratory methods of sterilization are described in J. J. PERKINS, *Principles and methods of sterilization*. Illinois, U.S.A., 1956.

(i) *Steam* (100° C.). Steam sterilizers are used when a higher temperature would be detrimental, e.g. to media culture. Models at present marketed give off steam while in use. Hoods with a good system of extraction are therefore essential.

(ii) *Steam under pressure.* Autoclaves are commonly used for sterilizing glassware. The steam pressure at which an autoclave is operated determines the length of time needed for killing vegetative micro-organisms.

Autoclaves will usually require hoods, though this will depend to some extent on the system of ventilation used in the sterilizing rooms. If the autoclaves are built in, the rear access compartments must be very efficiently ventilated. Bad installation of autoclaves may lead to inefficient sterilization (2).

Potentially the weakest point on a pressure steam sterilizer is the door. The majority of modern autoclaves are now fitted with pressure-locked safety doors to prevent explosive or premature opening while the chamber is under pressure. The locking mechanism of a truly pressure-locked door should be automatic when chamber pressure is applied and unlocked only by exhaust of pressure (see also Part II, Chapter 5, Safety Precautions).

(iii) *Dry heat.* Ovens may be used for dry-heat sterilizing at high temperature. It is difficult to achieve an even temperature over the whole volume of a dry heat sterilizer. In all but the smallest models, an air-mixing device is necessary. This usually takes the form of a fan with baffles, built into the back of the sterilizer. Thermometers should register the temperature at the lowest point in the sterilizing chamber. Sizes of oven vary but the external dimensions 33 in. × 25 in. × 24 in. are common.

Where dangerous organisms are present, glassware, &c., may be sterilized before wash-up. The following process is common though it may be varied in detail in different laboratories. Dirty glassware, brought from the laboratories, is taken to a collecting area and sterilized in autoclaves which connect the dirty area with an adjoining wash-up room. After sterilization the autoclaves are opened in the wash-up room and the residues of chemicals are emptied into bins. The glassware is then placed in stainless-steel tubs holding hot soda water. Following this, it is put into a steam sterilizer and finally rinsed at the sink, sometimes in distilled water (adequate draining-board provision is important), and placed in a drying cabinet. It may then be taken to a sterile glass store or reissued direct to the laboratories.

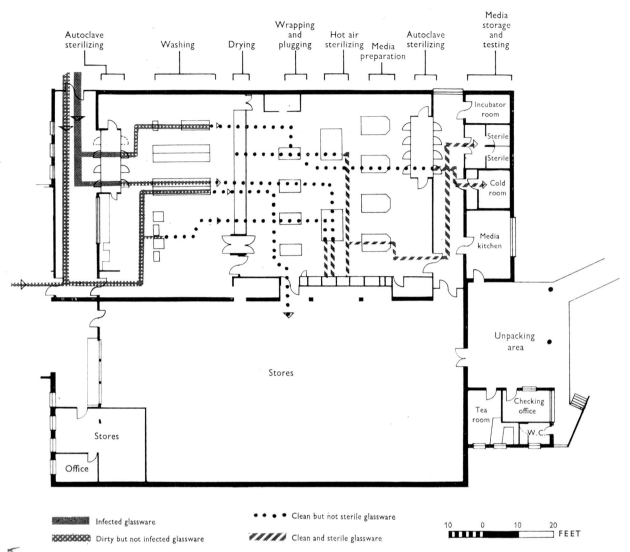

Fig. 50. Central wash-up, sterilization, media preparation, and glassware store, Imperial Chemical Industries' Pharmaceuticals Division, Alderley Park.

A separate adjoining room is often provided for sterilization of media and the glassware used in its preparation (see below). At the Imperial Chemical Industries' Pharmaceuticals Laboratories at Alderley Park, benches for preparation of media and autoclaves for sterilization are provided in the same room (Fig. 50).

Good ventilation is extremely important in sterilizing and wash-up rooms. Precautions should be taken against condensation by providing adequate extract ventilation in addition to hoods. Dilute hydrochloric acid, sometimes used in the processing of glassware, has a corrosive effect on steam sterilizers, metal hoods, &c., and materials must be chosen accordingly (see Appendix II, Material and Finishes).

Preparation of media

In microbiology much of the experimental work involves growing cultures, and artificial media are prepared on which to grow them. Both glassware and media must be sterile. Thus washing-up and sterilization are closely linked to media preparation

and, where the demand warrants it, special rooms may be provided for this purpose. All three parts of the procedure may be done in one room or each may be kept separate; washing-up and sterilization are most frequently combined.

Media preparation is a cooking process and the requirements are simple—serviced bench (water, gas, and electricity), scales and a balance, filters, and general cooking utensils. A supply of distilled water is necessary and adequate local storage for the ingredients, chemicals, and glassware.

Incubators may be used for drying the media and autoclaves for sterilizing. If the media is liquid and is to be put into tubes, space may be needed for an automatic filler.

Ample storage space for tubes, flasks, dishes, or bottles, both before and after filling with media, is essential. Screw-cap bottles, now in general use, enable media to be stored over long periods. Some media must be stored at constant temperature and provision for this should be made in a position near to the media-preparation area.

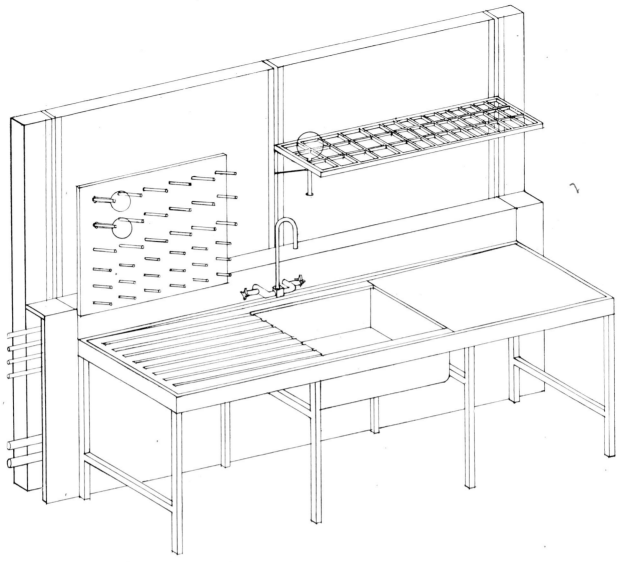

Fig. 51. Rack and peg board for drying glassware.

Washing-up

A large sink and draining board may be provided in each laboratory or the service may be centralized for a number of laboratories. Apart from sinks, draining boards, and racks, space must be provided for stacking dirty apparatus, for drying, and for storing the clean articles. Drying may be done on racks, pegs, or in a drying oven or cabinet (Fig. 51). Mechanical aids to cleaning (e.g. rotating brushes for test-tube washing) may also be used: electrical servicing is then needed. Wire trays, specially designed for safe handling of glassware, can be used for collection of dirty articles, and also for drying and storage.

Sink depths vary and it is difficult to arrive at a satisfactory bench height which allows easy handling of glassware on the bench and at the same time comfortable sink height for washing-up. With benches at 3 ft., it has often been necessary to provide walking boards, which become wet and dangerous. The 2 ft. 10 in. bench height suggested elsewhere in this report is probably better, particularly where the work is done mainly by women. Stainless-steel sinks have been tried in various laboratory buildings, but they have not always proved satisfactory. Taps are usually running continuously; elbow or leg control is therefore unnecessary. Taps should be placed well clear of the sink to avoid accidental breakage of glassware. Spray taps are useful for rinsing. Pipettes are easier to wash when held lengthways out in front of the worker. For washing long articles of this kind, one sink may be needed with its longer axis in the width of the bench.

Glassware may be sterilized both before and after washing-up. Where this is so, access between the two sites must be easy and convenient, or special wash-up areas may be provided in conjunction with the sterilizing equipment (see Sterilization, above, p. 66).

In many cases distilled water is required for rinsing, and whether the supply is piped from a central still or supplied locally, it should be easily available in the wash-up area.

At least two sinks are needed, for washing and rinsing, and where distilled water or other rinsing medium is used a third small sink is useful.

Speedy drying of glassware is important in order to avoid difficult storage problems. Ventilated drying cupboards are often used where washing-up is done centrally. One example seen by the team (at the Medical Research Council's Radiobiological Research Laboratories at Harwell) makes use of heated plenum air. The air is passed through the cupboard before being fed into the room.

Where washing-up is continually in progress, condensation may occur on room surfaces. Extract ventilation should be considered, and extract hoods may be essential over sinks.

In chemical disciplines the speedy and efficient washing and drying of glassware is an important feature of laboratory economy. It is important therefore that the equipment for washing-up is designed with this in mind. Where each laboratory room is equipped to carry out its own washing-up, a great deal of valuable serviced bench length may be taken up with sinks, draining boards, and drying racks or cupboards. In a central washing-up room it becomes economic to provide more expensive specialized equipment. It will be found, however, that for some kinds of work in the chemical, biochemical and biological disciplines, special care is needed in the cleaning and preparation of dirty glassware for re-use. For this reason many workers prefer either to carry out the process themselves or to supervise it closely in their own working area rather than rely on comparatively unskilled labour in a central wash-up room. Nevertheless, in many large establishments, even where extra care is called for, centralized washing of glassware has worked successfully once the initial organizational problems have been overcome.

Glass-blowing

A certain amount of glass-blowing is done in most chemical laboratories and a special bench is often provided in the general laboratory for this purpose. The bench should be placed in good light and, as a precaution against accidents, there should be ample space behind the worker. It is usual to screen the bench from other work with a fire-resistant screen. The bench should be of standing height (2 ft. 10 in.) and covered with a fire-proof top (see Appendix II, Materials and Finishes). Raised edges are necessary on the bench to prevent rolling of tubes, &c.

Town gas and compressed air are normally used in glass-blowing but may be supplemented with oxygen when high temperatures are needed. Provision may be necessary for gas cylinders near the bench, therefore, and also for a local compressor unit if compressed air is not piped in the building. Town gas for glass-blowing must be provided at a constant pressure of about 3·5 lb. per sq. in., and it is usually necessary to run a larger-bore pipe to the

glass-blowing position than that required for normal bench supply. Where oxygen is also used at the bench, the town gas line should be fitted with a non-return valve.

In laboratories where most of the glass apparatus is made on the site, the work is usually done in a special room or in part of a workshop. As well as good lighting, efficient ventilation is necessary for large-scale glass blowing. Acoustical treatment of the room may also be desirable to prevent the spread of noise from blast lamps and annealing flames.

It has been found advantageous in handling large lengths of glass to have a fairly long bench (6 ft. to 8 ft.) but for bending such lengths it has often been found convenient to reduce the bench length on either side of the gas and oxygen outlets. It is better therefore to provide a short length of fixed bench with a fold-down flap on either side of the working position.

Animal houses

Animals for experimental purposes are housed in most biological laboratories, and in the last few years a great deal of attention has been paid to animal housing. The need to have a ready and ample supply of laboratory animals convenient to the laboratory area has made it essential for the animal house to be considered as part of the laboratory.

Large animals, such as cows, pigs, sheep, &c., present housing problems different from those encountered with the smaller, more common experimental animals such as mice, rats, guinea-pigs, and rabbits. The use of large animals, however, is mainly confined to a few research establishments, dealing specifically with problems of disease or metabolism in such animals, and there is a tendency to use small animals in the more generalized biological research fields.

Animal care and husbandry are fully covered in the literature and particularly in the recently reissued handbook of the Universities Federation of Animal Welfare (3). The aim of the building designer should be to provide accommodation which will encourage proper animal care, a comfortable environment for the animals, and an efficient working pattern for the scientists and animal technicians.

Animal houses are designed either for breeding and maintaining a supply of animals, or to house animals on which experiments are being conducted. For the latter purpose each animal house is designed for a known technique, or a series of techniques, and the nature of these may vary widely, but similar principles apply to all.

PLANNING

It has been widely accepted in this country that where the scale of the work warrants it, animal houses should be in a separate block or wing, easily accessible to the laboratory workers concerned. There

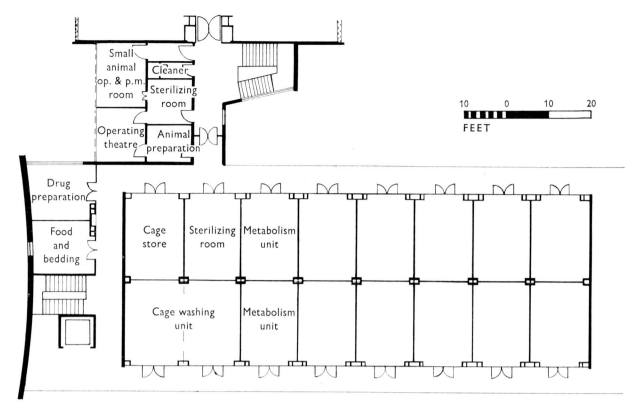

Fig. 52. Plan of the animal house for non-infected animals, Imperial Chemical Industries' Pharmaceuticals Division, Alderley Park.

are examples, however, of laboratories, especially on the Continent, where small animal units with their own animal housing accommodation form part of the more general laboratory accommodation. As the proper housing of most animals involves the provision of a special environment (see below) and may often require the practice of aseptic techniques as well as the provision of complete room and cage sterilization facilities, the former method of housing offers many advantages. The scientist's working area, however, must also be conveniently placed to prevent time-wasting movement between the animal house and the laboratory. In many cases the experimental procedures may be carried out on the animal in the animal room itself. The necessary equipment for carrying out the procedure is brought into the room on a trolley. The animal is prepared either on the bench provided in the room or in a nearby preparation room: the procedure is then carried out on the bench or on the trolley, and the animal returned to its cage. Animals will usually only be removed from the room for more complex operations involving special equipment, or if more rigorous aseptic procedure is necessary than can be provided in the animal room itself. It is becoming more common to provide operating theatres, dissecting rooms, &c., in the animal room suite rather than to allow the animals to be removed to the general laboratory areas.[1]

The layout of rooms within the animal house may be determined by the kind of work in progress. For example, great care is needed in the planning of circulation for scientists and technicians where infectious diseases or pathogenic organisms of any kind are involved. In such animal houses it is necessary to ensure that harmful bacteria cannot be carried from the animal rooms into the general laboratory areas. This may involve the provision of air-locks between communicating doors, and strict laboratory discipline to ensure that clothing worn in the animal rooms is not worn in any other parts of the building. Changing rooms and showers are needed. It may be necessary to provide separate circulation for food distribution, and dirty cages must be sterilized before bedding is removed and before scraping, washing, and storing for re-use.

For the animal rooms themselves, simple methods of planning have been successfully adopted, for example, rows of identical rooms on either side of a central corridor. There is a large measure of agreement that a number of small rooms is preferable to one large room.

Other solutions to the planning problem are possible as, for example, at the Imperial Chemical Industries' Pharmaceuticals Division Laboratories at Alderley Park (Fig. 52). In this building animal accommodation for both infectious and non-infectious animals is planned with two rows of small rooms placed back to back and surrounded by corridors or balconies open to the outside air on all sides. In the

---

[1] Centralized laboratory animal care in America has been described in a symposium held at the Royal Society of Medicine, London, in 1958 (4).

case of the animal house used for the study of non-infectious animals, the rooms associated with the animal accommodation such as post-mortem rooms, operating rooms, preparation rooms, &c., are housed in the block which links the animal house with the laboratories. The animal house for infectious diseases is linked to the laboratories with a covered way also open to the outside air.

Dr. Lane-Petter (5) has said that the ideal animal room is one which is long and comparatively narrow, accommodating cages on each of its long walls. Carpenter (6) recommends that animal rooms should not be more than 500 sq. ft. in area on the basis of his own experience in controlling epidemics. Small rooms, about 8 ft. wide, capable of taking two rows of cages are widely acceptable, though room size will, of course, depend on the size of the cages and the number to be accommodated.[1] Division into comparatively small rooms allows the use of individual rooms for a single species, reduces the area which has to be sterilized after the completion of an experiment, and, if the room size is carefully chosen, allows flexibility of use.

The work rooms associated with the animal house, i.e. animal operating rooms, post-mortem rooms, dissecting rooms, cage washing and sterilizing rooms, changing rooms, &c., vary in size and layout with the techniques practised in any particular establishment. In laboratories dealing with infectious diseases, these rooms must be accessible from the clean area and provision made for bringing infected animals to the treatment area by a separate route. The equipment of such rooms will be determined by the degree of strictness with which aseptic techniques are practised in the treatment of animals, ranging from an operating room which provides conditions and equipment comparable to those found in a hospital operating theatre to a simple, easily cleaned room with provision for handwashing and changing. It may be necessary in rooms such as dissecting rooms or rooms used for other specialized techniques such as metabolism experiments to provide a small volume of refrigerated storage space. This can usually be accommodated below bench level in order to keep the areas of such rooms to a minimum.

The service area of an animal house must provide for the efficient cleaning and sterilization of cages, the trolleys on which they are carried, and any incidental items of equipment such as water feeding bottles and bins for the storage and distribution of food and bedding. Clean-cage storage in the service area can be reduced to a minimum by storing a certain number of clean cages in the animal rooms themselves at high level on the racks where it is difficult to keep animals under proper supervision. The service area should, however, include provision for staff changing and washing. The cage-washing room is usually a wet and dirty area and animal technicians

must wear overalls and rubber boots. In large establishments consideration may also be given to the provision of showers in the changing rooms.

It may be uneconomical to store animal food and bedding in the service area in large animal houses or where the animal accommodation is on an upper floor of a multi-story building. Providing transport facilities are borne in mind there is no reason why the main storage of food and bedding should not be placed elsewhere in the building, or even in a separate building. It is usual to transport food and bedding directly to the animal rooms in mobile plastic or metal bins, parking space for which must be provided both in the vicinity of the store rooms and animal rooms. When this kind of food and bedding distribution is used only a limited amount of storage and bin parking space is required in the service area for the initial filling of clean cages before they are taken to the animal rooms.

The cleaning and sterilization of cages is of vital importance to the efficient running of the animal house. For non-infectious cages the first process is scraping and this can conveniently be carried out on a bench which is fitted with an open grille and a mobile bin below it for transporting the refuse to the incinerator. The cage may then be washed or sterilized by one of the methods described below, placed on drying racks, and finally removed to the clean-cage storage area. Infected cages must be sterilized immediately after removal from the animal room, i.e. before scraping or removal of bedding. When they have been sterilized they are handled in the same way as non-infected cages. In the past sterilization has usually been carried out by autoclaving (see Sterilization, above), but recently a new and effective method has been introduced (7). This is carried out by means of a proprietary solution called *Tego MHG*, a hot 1 per cent. solution of which is sprayed on the cages under pressure, or used as a bath through which the cages are passed.

Dry-heat sterilization is not effective except at temperatures which melt solder and which would therefore destroy most types of cage. Dry steaming in a dairy sterilizer is only effective where the cages are fairly clean to begin with as this process tends to bake dirt on to the cages and makes cleaning difficult.

Dirty non-infected cages should be taken into a separate room where intitial soaking and scraping is carried out before placing the cages in autoclaves which link the dirty area to the clean area where cages are dried and stored. In the case of infectious cages which must be autoclaved before scraping and washing, the autoclave should open into the washing room where the cages are scraped and washed before drying and storing. If steam is not available centrally, steam generators must also be accommodated in the cleaning area.

Where the volume of work warrants it, it may be advisable to provide in the cage-washing area separate sterilization equipment for water-feeding bottles. A

---

[1] UFAW have recommended an objective method of determining cage size (3).

washing bay into which trolleys can be wheeled for spraying and cleaning is also needed. An enclosure with waterproof surfaces and separate floor drainage is usually provided for this purpose.

With the *Tego* method, cages may be hosed and scrubbed manually in a washing bay, or may be allowed to soak in a *Tego* bath. Alternatively, the cages may be sprayed in the animal room itself. This method may be used also for the sterilization of racking and all other surfaces of the animal rooms before housing a new intake of animals, and simply requires hot-water hose points, to which portable spraying equipment is attached.

ENVIRONMENT

Animals are affected by noise, changes in temperature, draughts, and, to some extent, lighting. The heating and ventilation of animal houses is of the greatest importance to the animals' well-being. Temperature should not be allowed to vary more than $\pm 5°$ F., the normal temperature range being $65°$–$72°$ F., and there is some preference for temperatures towards the upper end of the range. Six to ten air-changes per hour are required depending on the size and number of animals housed in a room of a given volume. Humidity control is not essential, except for rooms housing monkeys. Some animal workers maintain that natural lighting is not essential in animal rooms and that seasonal variations in breeding can be eliminated by using only artificial lighting with pre-set time switches. If windows are used, they may be small and from the point of view of maintaining an even temperature, the smaller they are the better. Full air-conditioning with no recirculation is probably the most efficient way of obtaining the best conditions for animals and workers, but is an extremely expensive method of environment control. Warmed plenum input with balanced extraction is also efficient and may be combined with comparatively small radiant panels to balance fabric heat losses. Where air hygiene is of importance, the input air can be filtered and extraction near the floor will ensure a draught-free environment, particularly if there are no windows. Other methods of heating, either by means of radiators, radiant panels, or other methods of fabric heating, e.g. floor heating, are also used, but it should be remembered that where pipes or other heating equipment is exposed in the rooms, the collection and movement of dust in convection currents may be inimical to the control of cross-infection.

With plenum systems it is possible to maintain a positive pressure in the circulation areas in order to prevent the spread of bacteria from one room to another. This method of ventilation also has advantages where the animal house communicates directly with other accommodation as it prevents the spread of animal smells.

The principles of noise control generally are dealt with in Part II, Chapter 5.

Lighting fittings should be chosen with a view to minimizing dust collection and switching should be either outside the room or, if inside, waterproof equipment should be used.

FIXED EQUIPMENT AND FINISHES

The main item of fixed equipment in animal rooms is racking for cages. These must either be kept clear of the floor to allow easy cleaning or be completely mobile so that banks of cages can be easily moved when the floor underneath them is washed down. It has been recommended that racking whether hung on walls or suspended from the floor above should be demountable, and that all the parts should be of a size that they can be sterilized with equipment used for sterilizing cages. In some cases this may not be practicable and modern methods of sterilization (7) have made this less essential. The material from which racking is made must be corrosion resistant. Aluminium alloys have proved satisfactory for this purpose.

Where there is a very large through-put of cages, it may be economical to provide mechanical cage-washing equipment. Cage-washing machines are now available, and have been installed in some large establishments, e.g. at the Imperial Chemical Industries' Pharmaceuticals Division, Alderley Park. The machines seen by the team were for washing purposes only and not used for sterilizing infected cages.

It may be necessary in some animal rooms to provide a small bench and sink. Where this is done, the sink should be too small to allow cage washing and the benching should be kept to a minimum. Sturdy, movable tables are often used and should have impervious tops, which can be decontaminated.

Materials for laboratory finishes generally are discussed in Appendix II, and therefore only the special problems which arise in animal rooms are mentioned here. The main requirement in animal rooms is that surface finishes should be easily washable. Other precautions should be taken to ensure that there are no dust-collecting ledges and that every part of the room, walls, floors, &c., is easily accessible.

The floors of all animal rooms, service areas, and associated circulation spaces should be laid to fall to trapped gulleys which can be covered, or to drainage channels with removable grilles.

There are a number of impervious floors and wall finishes available, e.g. terrazzo, various asphaltic and bituminous finishes, floors of the oxychloride type, latex cements, granolithic finishes, &c. It cannot be too strongly emphasized that the recommendations for impervious membranes between floor finish and structural flooring are especially important in animal rooms where frequent washing down occurs. Hard continuous finishes tend to crack if laid in large areas and materials of the terrazzo type should be divided into small panels with brass or ebony strips. Impervious tiles are suitable material but present the usual jointing problems (see Appendix II, Materials and

Finishes). Tiled surfaces either for walls or floors may harbour dirt in the joints unless cleaned regularly. Plastered wall surfaces painted with high-quality alkyd paints have proved suitable in rooms with similar requirements, e.g. in hospital operating theatres. Glazed cement finishes are now available, and although still somewhat expensive may prove suitable for animal rooms as they give a hard smooth continuous surface.

Continuous-sheet materials have also be and proved suitable, e.g. PVC sheeting a nated rubber. The latter, however, must b a continuous impervious membrane turned up arou its outside edges to provide a shallow tank which will prevent any seepage of water to the structure. Doors may be lined with metal or plastic materials for ease of washing, door handles being replaced by simple push plates on the inside of the room.

REFERENCES

(1) HAINES, C. 'Planning the scientific laboratory.' *Archit. Rec.* **108,** 1950, p. 9.

(2) NUFFIELD PROVINCIAL HOSPITALS TRUST. *Present sterilizing practice in six hospitals.* London, 1958, p. 39.

(3) UNIVERSITIES FEDERATION FOR ANIMAL WELFARE. *UFAW handbook on the care and management of laboratory animals.* 2nd edition. London, 1957.

(4) LABORATORY ANIMALS CENTRE. *The organisation and administration of an animal division.* Carshalton, 1958, pp. 57–71. *Collected papers,* **7.**

(5) LANE-PETTER, W. Personal communication.

(6) COLEMAN, H. S. *Laboratory Design.* New York, 1951, p. 195.

(7) PERKINS, F. T., and SHORT, D. J. 'A new technique in the sterilisation of animal houses, racking and cages.' *Hospital Engineer,* **11,** 1957, pp. 270–6.

Chapter 3

ENGINEERING SERVICES

THE servicing of laboratory buildings is complex and expensive. Supplies of gas, electricity, water, compressed air, &c., must be piped to the scientist's working position whilst the design of heating and ventilating systems is complicated by requirements for closely controlled environments in special rooms and the high rates of extraction produced by fume cupboards and hoods. Piping, cables, and trunking for bench services, heating, ventilation, and fume extraction constitute a major planning problem.

Naturally, the services and special facilities incorporated in a new building will reflect the immediate demands as foreseen by the programming authority, but during the useful life of the building these demands will undoubtedly change. It follows that it is just as important to provide for easy and rapid addition and adaptation to the services installation as it is to meet the immediate demands. Also, constant maintenance is required to ensure efficient running. Complete and easy access to the services installation is essential.

In planning a new building, therefore, economy in first cost must be set against efficiency in terms of ease of maintenance and the possible loss of valuable time if improvisation is necessary. Inaccessibility or lack of space to accommodate new pipes, ducts, or equipment may even cause irreparable loss or damage if important work is interrupted when servicing changes have to be made.

Bench services and heating and ventilation are dealt with separately below, but both aspects of the problem must be drawn together and considered as a whole when planning a new building, so that the interrelation between them is fully taken into account.

The provision of services at the bench position

The services available at the bench are an essential part of the scientist's equipment, and, if they are inadequate, working efficiency is seriously impaired. On the other hand, economy in the services has a major effect on overall building cost. Analyses show that servicing is the most significant single item of cost in laboratory buildings, ranging from 21 per cent. to 47 per cent. of total cost in eight recent buildings (see Appendix I, Cost Analyses). A balance must

therefore be struck between working convenience and building economy.

There are three main factors which have a direct bearing on the efficiency and cost of services:

(1) the number and types of services to be piped to outlets at the bench;

(2) the routing of the services through the building from the point of entry of the main to the bench outlets;

(3) the number of outlets required at each bench position.

The last of these three items may have to be determined first in order to facilitate pipe-sizing calculations and to allow an assessment of the capital cost of different methods of distribution to be made. In designing the building, however, the architect will have to deal with them in this order when making his decisions. All three factors have a direct bearing on the degree of flexibility, on the ease and convenience of maintenance, as well as on the cost of the installation. They have been studied in various ways. The first, largely on the basis of experience and observation, the second by means of limited investigations and the application of data to the general planning problem, whilst the third item, the assessment of demand, formed an important part of the survey investigation (see Part I, Chapter 3).

The choice of piped services

In many laboratories building cost has been greatly increased by piping to the benches services which are rarely, if ever, used. Before installing more than the normal 'domestic' services (water, town gas, mains single-phase electricity, and drainage), it is advisable to study *actual needs* in terms of the scientific techniques likely to be practised in the building. It is not generally realized that local units, run from the 'domestic' piped supplies, can provide for many specialized service requirements. Unless the demand for a specialized service is consistently heavy over a large proportion of the building, local supply units are often more economical both in initial cost and in running cost. A special service piped throughout the building is paid for over the whole amortization period, and must be maintained whether it is used or not. Local units can be purchased as required and will add to running and maintenance costs only when in use.

Many units of this kind are now available and others are in course of development. For example, voltage stabilizers (up to 2 kilowatt stabilized to 0·1 per cent.), mains transformers and rectifiers can be run on single-phase A.C. supplies. Vacuum pumps, air compressors, equipment for producing the chemical equivalent of distilled water, and refrigeration plant are all available as local units.

The final choice of services to be supplied centrally and distributed to the working positions will, of course, be determined by the kind of work done in the laboratory. Whilst it may be necessary to reduce the number of piped services to a minimum on grounds of cost, it must be remembered that the serviced bench is as much a part of the scientist's equipment as his glassware or his instruments. For example, there is a trend towards greater use of compressed air, especially in chemical, biochemical, and biological disciplines, and in some cases it may be essential to pipe it to the bench in the interest of working efficiency.

Table 31[1] gives a list of the common services which may be found in various combinations in research laboratories. Recommended ratings and approximate levels of availability are also given. The range of services from which a choice must be made is discussed item by item below.

Water. The cold water-supply must be at an adequate pressure and remain constant when adjacent taps are in use. 30 to 40 p.s.i. pressure is needed for the efficient operation of water-driven vacuum pumps. Water-supply authorities rarely allow laboratory taps to be connected directly to the main and it is often impossible to get sufficient head of water from a storage tank to give the necessary pressure at the

tap. Usually, therefore, cold water is *pumped* from storage tanks, and some form of buffer tank or vessel and pressure-regulating device are needed to maintain the pressure at a *reasonably* steady level ($\pm$ 5 per cent.).

Hot water may be supplied either from a central calorifier or locally from gas or electric units. The use of local heaters may be preferable where only a few hot-water taps are required. A flow temperature of 150° F. is normally adequate.

Distilled or demineralized water. If only small quantities of distilled water are required, it may be preferable to produce it in local stills rather than to install plant, which in any case may not give water of the high purity required. Piping distilled water to the bench usually results in an increase in consumption. If it is too readily available it may be used for purposes for which it is not essential. In some laboratories, especially in Europe, distilled water is piped to a few taps conveniently placed in the corridors, so that it is always available near to, but not in the laboratory.

Demineralized water is more widely used nowadays and sometimes piped to the benches. The choice of plant depends entirely on the kind of work being done in the laboratory, and specialist firms produce apparatus to meet closely specified demands.

Steam. In laboratory disciplines where organic solvents are frequently used (organic chemistry, biochemistry, animal pathology, &c.), and also in some other kinds of chemical work, steam is used as a heat source. Although electric heating mantles are coming into wider use there are still many cases where they cannot take the place of steam. There is rarely the need for steam pressure greater than 15 p.s.i. at a normal laboratory bench cock. Higher pressures may, of course, be needed for special purposes, e.g. to run autoclaves for sterilizing (see Part II, Chapter 2, pp. 66–67).

Town gas. Town gas is used in most laboratories for heating purposes and the usual mains pressure (3·0 to 3·5 in. w.g.) is adequate for work at the bench. Gas should not be laid to rooms which are constantly used for the storage or for the handling of inflammable substances such as organic solvents.

Town gas for glass-blowing may have to be boosted to a constant 3·5 p.s.i. In this case a compressed-air supply of about the same pressue is needed, whilst for working harder types of glass it may be necessary to combine town gas with oxygen. With the latter, it is advisable to fit a non-return valve to the town gas line.

Inert gases. The use of inert gas is becoming more common in disciplines in which experiments are carried out under oxygen-free conditions. Nitrogen supplies are usually piped from high-pressure cylinders with reducing valves to give about 15 p.s.i. at the bench. Ventilated storage space is needed for the cylinders, and racks or stands are needed in or near the laboratory in which they are used. The transport

Table 31. Provision of Services.

Service	Availability (per outlet)	
COLD WATER	25–50 p.s.i.	3 gal./min.
HOT WATER . . .	10–30 p.s.i.	1 gal./min.
DISTILLED } water . DEMINERALIZED }	2–30 p.s.i.	1 gal./min.
STEAM { Steam baths { Special purposes .	5–15 p.s.i. 15–100 p.s.i.	100 lb./hr. 1,000 lb./hr.
GAS (Town) . . .	Above 3 in. w.g.	(Varied)
GASES inert e.g. { Argon . { Nitrogen	(12 in. w.g.)	or as required)
OXYGEN . . .	15 p.s.i.	(Varied)
COMPRESSED AIR . .	5 and 15 p.s.i.	20 ft.³/min.
VACUUM	10–15 mm. Hg	
ELECTRICITY { Public supply . { Stabilized . { Pulsing systems .	400/440 V. 3 ph. 50 cycle 230/250 V. 1 ph. 50 cycle 230/250 V. 1 ph. 50 cycle 1 sec. 6 sec.	60A. 13A. 13A. Earthed pulses for timing clocks and electronic counters, &c.

[1] Table 31 is reproduced from the British Standard 3202: 1959—*Recommendations on Laboratory furniture and fittings.* Copies of the standard may be obtained from the British Standards Institution, 2 Park Street, London, W. 1.

of gas cylinders raises difficult problems in large buildings. Special trolleys may be used which also serve as standing racks in the laboratory. Piping to benches generally from a central cylinder manifold can only be justified if inert gases are in constant use over a large area of the building.

Oxygen. Oxygen is often used for glass-blowing and is usually provided at the bench from high-pressure cylinders fitted with reducing valves. If oxygen lines are installed, they should be adequately drained and kept at least 6 in. clear of pipes carrying town gas or inflammable fluids. The whole of a piped oxygen installation including valves *must* be kept free from grease. The comments above on storage and handling of inert gases apply equally to oxygen.

Compressed air. The trend towards greater use of compressed air has been mentioned above. If a piped service is installed, provision should be made for drainage, adjacent to the compressor, or at the point of entry to the building in cases where compressed air is distributed through external mains.

Vacuum. A centralized rough vacuum service (10 m.m. to 30 m.m. Hg) can be quite satisfactory provided the installation is properly designed and a mechanical pump of *adequate* capacity is used. The capital and maintenance costs of such a service, however, can seldom be justified on economic grounds except in the case of a large laboratory where upwards of 50-100 outlets are required and the diversity factor is high.

For most laboratories, local electrically driven vacuum-pump units and water-operated ejector pumps fitted to the bench taps provide an adequate vacuum service. Water-operated pumps require a steady water pressure (see paragraph on water-supplies, above), and as they consume between 60 and 100 gallons of water an hour, excessive use of water pumps can also be quite costly.

Electrical supplies. The use of local conversion units to provide specialized electrical supplies has been discussed above. Ordinary single phase supply at domestic voltage will serve a very large proportion of laboratory needs. Special supplies (i.e. non-standard voltages, direct current, &c.) should not be installed unless there is a sufficiently widespread and frequent demand to make local units uneconomical. Where non-standard frequency is required, this may be supplied from a local motor alternator. Non-standard outlets should be used for the latter to ensure that apparatus is not inadvertently connected to a supply of the wrong frequency.

It is of some interest that one or two large industrial firms are encouraging the use of 50-volt equipment in the interests of safety and there may be a somewhat changed pattern of demand if this trend becomes common.

Identification of services. It is essential that service lines and outlets may be easily identified. In addition to colour coding and identification by the shapes of handwheels, as set out in the British Standards Institution's recommendations (1), it is suggested that a labelling system should also be used. The British Standards Institution's publication also contains recommendations on the types of valves and cocks for the various piped services.

Materials for piping and electric wiring. Materials for services piping and electric wiring are discussed in Appendix II, Materials and Finishes.

Distribution systems

The way in which service lines are routed through the building is the most important factor in determining the efficiency and cost of the servicing system. The ease with which the system can be adapted to changing needs and maintained in good working order depends wholly upon the method of distribution. The cost of the installation varies with pipe length, pipe size, the material used and the method of fixing, the number of bends and joints, the length and complexity of structural ducting, and the number and quality of the fittings needed at the bench.

The main differences in the commonly used distribution systems lie in the way in which the sub-mains (between the main supply and the points at which the bench lines proper begin) are carried through the building. There are two main methods of sub-main distribution, using vertical or horizontal sub-mains, and many variations within each method. Vertical sub-mains are fed from horizontal mains, carried either at low level (e.g. in the basement) or high level (e.g. above the top floor). Horizontal sub-mains are taken from vertical mains which are usually carried in structural ducts running vertically through the building at one or more points.

Figs. 53–58 show in diagrammatic form the principal common methods of service distribution. The horizontal and vertical structural duct work involved in each system is also indicated.

Vertical sub-mains. When sub-mains are run from a horizontal main at high or low level, each sub-main supplies a number of laboratories stacked one above the other, that is, corresponding rooms at each floor level. The length of the sub-main depends upon floor to floor height and the number of stories in the building (see Figs. 53, 54, and 55). It will be obvious that the greater the number of stories the greater the number of rooms which can be serviced from a single sub-main, and the more economical the system becomes.

Vertical sub-mains are normally carried at each grid point, either on the corridor wall or on the outside wall. Peninsular benches attached to either corridor walls or outside walls respectively constitute the most economical form of bench layout in conjunction with this type of servicing, as the pipe lines supplying the bench points can be taken directly from the sub-mains without further structural ducting.

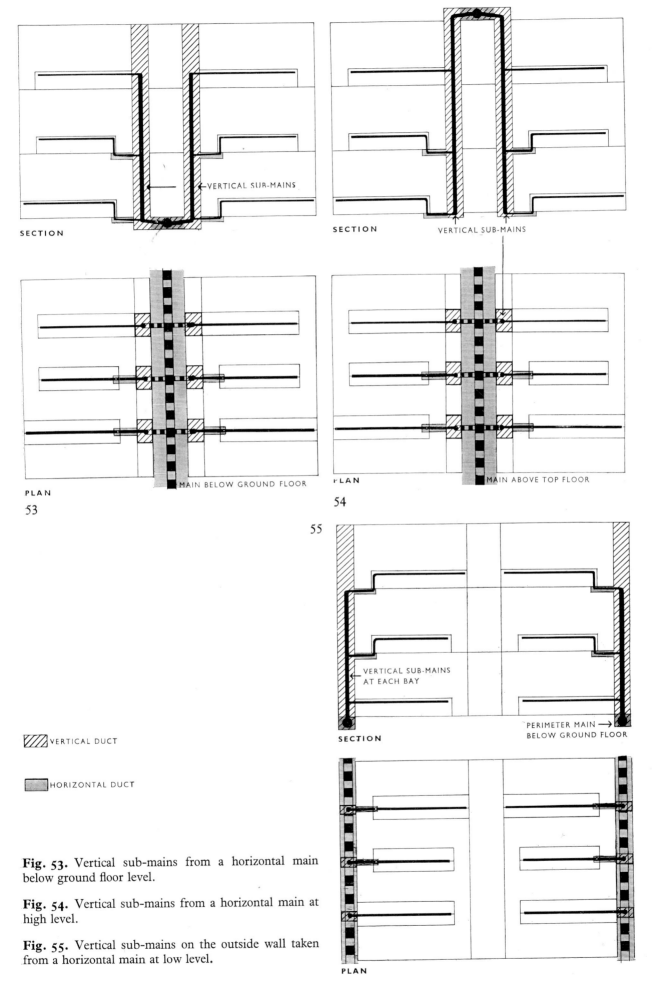

SECTION

←VERTICAL SUB-MAINS

PLAN

MAIN BELOW GROUND FLOOR

53

SECTION

VERTICAL SUB-MAINS

PLAN

MAIN ABOVE TOP FLOOR

54

55

SECTION

VERTICAL SUB-MAINS
AT EACH BAY

PERIMETER MAIN →
BELOW GROUND FLOOR

PLAN

▨ VERTICAL DUCT

▤ HORIZONTAL DUCT

Fig. 53. Vertical sub-mains from a horizontal main below ground floor level.

Fig. 54. Vertical sub-mains from a horizontal main at high level.

Fig. 55. Vertical sub-mains on the outside wall taken from a horizontal main at low level.

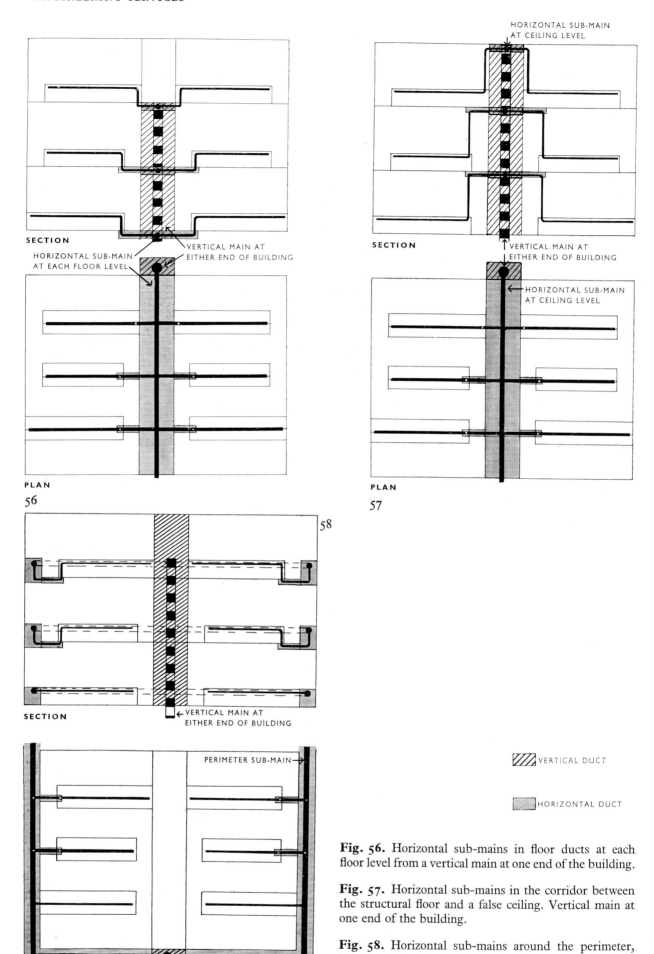

HORIZONTAL SUB-MAIN
AT CEILING LEVEL

SECTION

VERTICAL MAIN AT
EITHER END OF BUILDING

HORIZONTAL SUB-MAIN
AT EACH FLOOR LEVEL

PLAN

56

SECTION

VERTICAL MAIN AT
EITHER END OF BUILDING

HORIZONTAL SUB-MAIN
AT CEILING LEVEL

PLAN

57

58

SECTION

VERTICAL MAIN AT
EITHER END OF BUILDING

PERIMETER SUB-MAIN

PLAN

VERTICAL DUCT

HORIZONTAL DUCT

Fig. 56. Horizontal sub-mains in floor ducts at each floor level from a vertical main at one end of the building.

Fig. 57. Horizontal sub-mains in the corridor between the structural floor and a false ceiling. Vertical main at one end of the building.

Fig. 58. Horizontal sub-mains around the perimeter, below window level. Vertical main at one end of the building.

78

Fig. 59. Vertical sub-mains on outside walls at alternate grid points, distributed to benches by pipes under the windows. ASEA Laboratory, Västerås, Sweden.

Fig. 59 shows a Swedish laboratory in which vertical sub-mains run on the outside walls at alternate grid points and are distributed to the benches by means of pipes running under the windows. In this laboratory the heating system, which is a high-velocity air input installation fed through heating units under the windows, is supplied from vertical air ducts on the outside walls, also at alternate grid points. The illustration suggests that even when the installation is carried out neatly and efficiently, overcrowding (with consequent maintenance difficulties) can result when all the servicing, including the heating, is carried on one side only of the laboratory unit. There are obvious advantages in placing the heating units in any building on the outside walls, and it can be argued that vertical service sub-mains should be carried on the corridor side of the laboratories in order to simplify the pipe work, and to make maintenance as easy as possible. Fig. 60 shows a German example of vertical servicing on the corridor walls. This method of servicing is also common in America and there are examples in this country, notably Messrs. Courtauld's Acetate and Synthetic Fibres Laboratory at Coventry and the I.C.I. Pharmaceuticals Laboratory at Alderley Park. Repairs and additions may be made without interference to the laboratory worker. Also it enables the services to be turned off from the corridor in the event of fire. The depth of the vertical ducts is

sufficient to contain outward-opening laboratory doors, a desirable safety feature which is difficult to achieve if doors open out and obstruct the main corridor.

This method of distribution can also be used with island benches and the bench pipe runs fed either at low level through a short length of floor duct as in both the examples mentioned above, or at high level with vertical drops (see Fig. 61).

Horizontal sub-mains. In this method of distribution the sub-mains supply a number of adjacent rooms at each floor level. Pipes and cables run either at high level or low level, in floor ducts, or between the structural floor and a false ceiling (see Figs. 56 and 57). Horizontal sub-mains may also run around the perimeter of the building below window level (Fig. 58). The latter method has been widely used in the past, especially where rooms were shallow in depth and benches were placed mainly under windows.

In visiting laboratories the team heard many complaints about floor ducts. They are difficult to waterproof, and to maintain, causing a great deal of disturbance and inconvenience when the duct covers are removed. It should also be mentioned that if pipes are carried either in the floor or ceiling, greater floor to floor heights may be needed. Floor ducts should be avoided wherever possible and if horizontal sub-mains are used, they should be carried

Fig. 60. Services in a vertical duct on the corridor wall. Institute of Chemistry and Pharmacy, University of Munich.

Fig. 61. Exposed service pipes at the Battelle Institute, Frankfurt.

Fig. 62. Section showing service ducts. The Wellcome Research Laboratories, Beckenham.

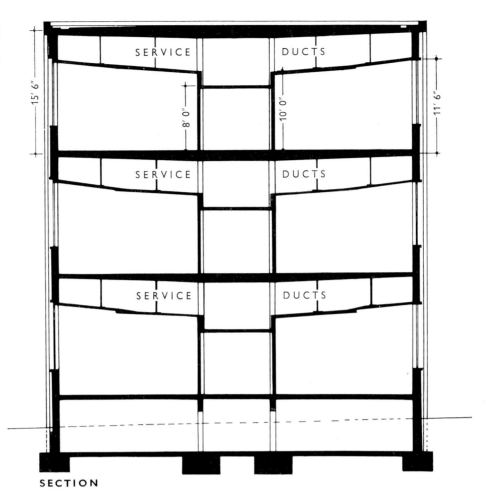

SECTION

above a false ceiling in the corridor and distributed in the laboratories themselves without further ducting.

One of the disadvantages of perimeter servicing has been mentioned above, namely the difficulties which ensue when the piped services and the heating system are all carried along the same area of wall. Peninsular benches attached to the window walls are the most suitable kind of layout with this type of distribution, but whatever bench layout is adopted with services on outside walls, alterations or repairs to the pipe lines cannot be carried out without a great deal of disturbance in the laboratory itself.

A recent development of the horizontal sub-main system is shown in Fig. 62. This is the method adopted in the Wellcome Foundation's new laboratories at Beckenham. Here the services are distributed from horizontal sub-mains in a gallery above the corridor, and out to bench positions through an accessible, wedge-shaped space between floor and ceiling. Whilst this is efficient in that it allows service points to be placed anywhere in the rooms above or below, it involves excessive floor to floor height (in this case 15 ft. 6 in.). In the Wellcome research building this is justified because of the need to eliminate pipes and ducts in a large number of rooms where sterile conditions are essential.

Drainage. So far, in discussing alternative methods of distribution, only the supply services have been considered. In choosing the method to be used in a particular building, however, account must also be taken of waste disposal. By far the simplest method of running waste lines is to place them entirely above floor level and running directly into a vertical stack. This is usually only possible in conjunction with vertical sub-mains, where the structural duct work for the drainage stacks is already available. Island benches are more difficult to service when vertical sub-mains are used as the bench wastes must be taken through a short length of floor duct and this may not be possible without thickening the structural floor, or underslinging the wastes immediately below the structural floor. With horizontal sub-mains there are usually only one or two vertical ducts carrying the service mains and in larger buildings it will be found necessary to have drainage stacks at other points in the building where no vertical ducts are available.

Two main conclusions can be drawn. First, that vertical stacks must be provided for drainage, whichever type of distribution system is used, and it is more convenient to have these stacks in an easily accessible service duct. Second, that the most convenient method of carrying the bench waste line, i.e.

G

wholly above the floor, is not usually possible with horizontal sub-mains. In the latter case it is usually necessary to take the bench lines below the structural floor in order to reach either a horizontal branch drain or a vertical stack.

Fume disposal ducts. It has become almost standard practice to place fume cupboards as near to the corridor walls as possible. From the point of view of accommodating the necessary duct work this is reasonable, whether vertical or horizontal sub-mains are used. Fume extract ducts are usually large in cross-section and in a multi-story building, if each cupboard has a separate trunking system, large structural ducts are necessary to accommodate them. Direct vertical extract ducts are more efficient than those which have considerable horizontal runs. Therefore a vertical sub-main system is also advantageous in this respect, in that the fume ducts can run vertically over their whole length. Where horizontal sub-mains are used, the extract trunking must be separately accommodated in vertical ducts, or some restriction on the efficiency of the system must be accepted, in consequence of carrying the trunking horizontally over considerable distances.

Similar considerations also affect the routing of ventilation ducts. These are discussed in the section below dealing with heating and ventilation.

Cost comparisons between the distribution systems

For the purpose of studying comparative costs for different methods of servicing, a total building size was assumed of 120 unit cells each 20 ft. deep from corridor walls to window walls, 11 ft. wide, and 11 ft. floor to floor height, and that the cells or rooms were grouped on either side of a central corridor. A six-story building would contain 20 cells on each floor (i.e. 10 structural bays on each side of a central corridor), a four-story building would contain 30 cells on each floor (15 on either side of the corridor), and a two-story building, 60 cells (30 on either side of the corridor). For each building, four sets of comparative figures were obtained (see Part I, Chapter 3, p. 37) covering the following methods of servicing:

1. vertical sub-mains fed from mains at low level, using one vertical riser for each cell (Fig. 53);
2. vertical sub-mains fed from main at low level but using only one vertical riser for each pair of cells, i.e. one cell on either side of the corridor;
3. horizontal sub-mains at each floor level fed from one vertical main placed at one end of the building (Figs. 56 and 57);
4. perimeter sub-mains at bench level fed from two vertical mains at one end of the building (Fig. 58).

Figs. 63, 64, 65, and 66 show diagrammatically the four methods of distribution.

In preparing the comparative costs, only the cost of piping, jointing, and fixing was taken into account, beginning at the point of supply and ending at the point where the bench spur or run-out began. The cost of the related supply equipment was not included, as it was thought that this factor could be regarded as common for comparable laboratories. For the purpose of pipe-sizing an average number of bench outlets was assumed, the same number per bench run being used in each case. Table 32 gives comparative figures for the four types of servicing. Horizontal sub-mains were found to be the cheapest for any number of stories. The cost of all types of servicing is greater for the smaller number of stories. The figures in Table 32 are all referred to the lowest cost per bay, namely that for horizontal sub-mains in a six-story building: this datum has been given the value of 100 units to allow easy comparison between the distribution methods. The figures given are comparative only and do not show the actual cost.

Whilst a horizontal sub-main system is the cheapest method, the difference between it and method 2 (i.e. single vertical sub-mains serving each pair of cells) is marginal but both the other methods are considerably more expensive. These figures, given in Table 32, cannot be regarded as giving a complete picture of the comparative costs of the various methods of distribution, however, because no account has been taken of the structural ducting involved in each case, nor of the comparative efficiency in terms of flexibility and ease of maintenance. On the one hand, a horizontal sub-main system requires long lengths of floor ducting, or if the pipes are carried at high level, a demountable suspended ceiling. Both of the latter present maintenance difficulties, and it is costly to make the horizontal ducts large enough to allow for the addition of other pipe lines after the building is occupied. Vertical sub-mains, on the other hand, require the provision of vertical structural ducts at frequent intervals through-

Table 32. Cost per bay based on lowest cost (Method 3) which has been given the value of 100 units.

Method of distribution	No. of stories		
	6	4	2
1. Vertical sub-mains from mains at low level using one vertical riser for each cell	149·43	164·73	192·78
2. Vertical sub-mains from mains at low level using only one vertical riser for each *pair* of cells, i.e. one cell on either side of the corridor . . .	113·73	141·27	142·80
3. Horizontal sub-mains at each floor level fed from one vertical main . . .	100·00	109·65	130·05
4. Perimeter sub-mains at bench level fed from two vertical mains at one end of the building . . .	151·98	172·38	176·46

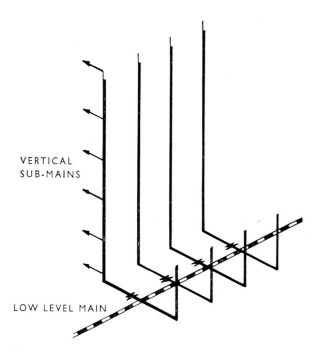

Fig. 63. Vertical sub-mains fed from a main at low level using one vertical riser for each cell.

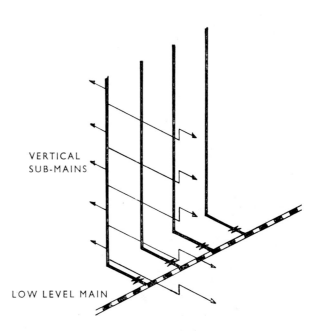

Fig. 64. Vertical sub-mains fed from a main at low level using one vertical riser for each pair of cells, one on either side of the corridor.

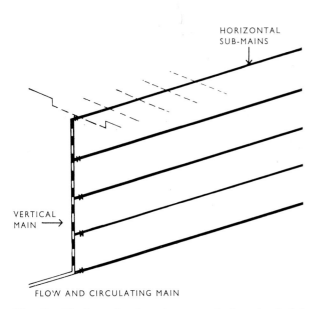

Fig. 65. Horizontal sub-mains at each floor level fed from one vertical main.

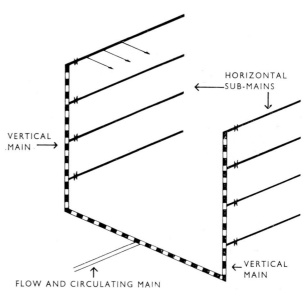

Fig. 66. Perimeter sub-mains at bench level fed from two vertical mains.

out the building, and these occupy valuable floor area. It has been found impossible to arrive at valid comparative costs for vertical and horizontal ducting, but taking some account of the fact that floor ducts may necessitate higher floor to floor heights and require costly water-proofing treatment, the overall cost per foot of ducting whether vertical or horizontal may work out roughly the same in both cases.

The most expensive servicing method in terms of piping, i.e. perimeter sub-mains, is the only system which does not require structural ducting and this must be considered in comparing the costs. It seems

probable, for example, that perimeter servicing is cheaper than the normal vertical sub-main system using a vertical riser to each laboratory cell when the cost of structural ducting is taken into account.

The final choice of a services distribution system may, however, have to be made on grounds of efficiency and ease of maintenance, and with reference to the degree of flexibility required in any particular laboratory. For example, if it can be foreseen that additional pipe runs will be required, they can be installed in vertical ducts without any disturbance to laboratory work, but serious dislocation of

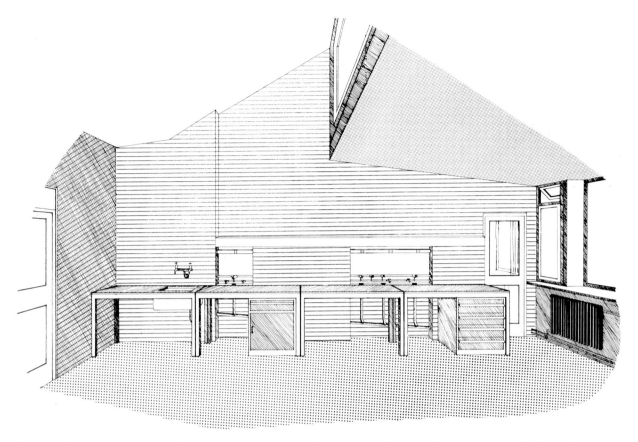

Fig. 67. Interior of a typical laboratory unit in the extension to the Agricultural Research Council's Animal Research Station, Cambridge.

circulation and communication in the building may result if these changes have to be made in horizontal floor or ceiling ducts. As already mentioned above, even routine maintenance work may cause inconvenience in the laboratory where perimeter sub-mains are used.

Broadly, horizontal sub-mains are cheapest in terms of first cost, perimeter servicing and vertical sub-mains are both more expensive, but vertical servicing has great advantages in being adaptable and easy to maintain.

The experimental laboratory designed by the team at the Animal Research Station, Cambridge (see Fig. 42), is a single-story building in which the services sub-mains are carried in the ceiling above the corridor. The bench lines are brought down on the surface of the partition walls between laboratory units. The bench services run above bench level through a cranked brick wall and are left exposed for half their length alternately on either side of the wall. This enables a single pipe run to serve benches on both sides of the wall. Full use is therefore made of each service run in terms of the number of outlets, and as each pipe appears on the surface in each room, taps can be screwed directly to the pipe without bends or off-sets. The arrangement of pipes and furniture is shown in Fig. 67.

In the new laboratories for the Imperial Cancer Research Fund in London (see Fig. 44), vertical sub-mains are used to service five laboratory floors and one floor devoted to animal accommodation. Demountable partitions are used between the laboratory units, the panels being supported on permanent vertical struts which incorporate a patent channel-fixing device on each side. The channels are used to carry the bench services, to support the covered service spine, and also to carry shelves, cupboards, and small items of equipment above the bench. The servicing layout and the unit furniture, which was also designed to fit the partition module, are shown in Fig. 68.

Scale of provision

At present there is very little uniformity of provision in terms of the number of points or outlets provided at the scientist's working position. Very wide variations were found by the team in the establishments visited and even in individual rooms within the same building. W. H. Pritchard has said that surveys show frequent over-provision of gas taps and under-provision of electric outlets (2). The number of points is usually determined individually for each room, usually in accordance with the stated requirements of one worker. There has been a con-

Fig. 68. Servicing layout, unit partitioning, and furniture designed for the new Laboratories of the Imperial Cancer Research Fund, London.

tinuous increase in the number of points installed over the last few years, and the tendency today is towards installing sufficient outlets to meet still further increases in demand. This is especially true of electrical outlets, the aim being to reduce the amount of valuable working time spent in improvising to meet the increasing demand for electrical equipment.

The design of the pipe lines to a laboratory bench depends upon the number of outlets, the size of the outlets, and the nozzle pressure required, the whole system being calculated with reference to a diversity or use factor. The number of taps or outlets in use in laboratory buildings at any one time is unlikely ever to approach the total number of outlets provided, and therefore the diversity factor is applied to pipe-sizing calculations to take account of this. Usually for the electrical services it is assumed that not more than 20 per cent. of the points are in use at any one time and, for the other services, not more than 40 per cent. It would appear from some of the tables prepared

from the survey data that these diversity factors might possibly be reduced in the future. For example, in the case of hot-water taps the proportion of total working time during which one tap is in use is very small indeed (see Table 41).

The assessment of the number of outlets for the common services, for individuals and teams of various sizes working in different disciplines, formed a major part of the laboratory survey (see also Part I, Chapter 3, The Scope and Methods of the Investigation). The results of the survey on the provision of services are given below.

Use of cold-water taps

For cold-water taps the results are in terms of the basic demand for direct access to the water-supply. No data are available from the survey on the actual volume of water drawn off, but a rough estimate can be made in terms of gallons per minute where the pressure at the tap is specified (see above, p. 75) and the nozzle size is known.

85

Table 33. Frequency distributions, shown as percentages of total working time taken over whole year, of number of cold-water taps used by *Scientific Officers*.

Discipline	Total no. of obs.	Percentage of total working time during which cold-water taps (0–9) were in use									
		None	1	2	3	4	5	6	7	8	9
Chemistry	406	96·1	3·7	0·2	0·0	0·0	0·0	0·0	0·0	0·0	0·0
Physics	429	95·1	4·7	0·2	0·0	0·0	0·0	0·0	0·0	0·0	0·0
Biochemistry	429	73·2	15·1	6·8	2·6	0·9	1·2	0·2	0·0	0·0	0·0
Biophysics	170	95·3	4·1	0·6	0·0	0·0	0·0	0·0	0·0	0·0	0·0
Microbiology	439	98·4	1·4	0·2	0·0	0·0	0·0	0·0	0·0	0·0	0·0
Entomology	399	96·7	1·0	2·3	0·0	0·0	0·0	0·0	0·0	0·0	0·0
Animal Physiology	418	98·3	0·7	1·0	0·0	0·0	0·0	0·0	0·0	0·0	0·0
Plant Physiology	327	94·8	4·9	0·3	0·0	0·0	0·0	0·0	0·0	0·0	0·0
Botany	421	100·0	0·0	0·0	0·0	0·0	0·0	0·0	0·0	0·0	0·0
Zoology	344	98·0	1·7	0·3	0·0	0·0	0·0	0·0	0·0	0·0	0·0
Pathology	384	90·9	5·2	3·4	0·3	0·2	0·0	0·0	0·0	0·0	0·0

Table 34. Frequency distributions, shown as percentages of total working time taken over whole year, of number of cold-water taps used by *Experimental Officers*.

Discipline	Total no. of obs.	Percentage of total working time during which cold-water taps (0–9) were in use									
		None	1	2	3	4	5	6	7	8	9
Chemistry	428	68·5	20·1	6·3	3·0	0·5	1·4	0·2	0·0	0·0	0·0
Physics	239	90·8	9·2	0·0	0·0	0·0	0·0	0·0	0·0	0·0	0·0
Biochemistry	414	82·9	12·8	3·1	1·2	0·0	0·0	0·0	0·0	0·0	0·0
Microbiology	425	97·4	2·6	0·0	0·0	0·0	0·0	0·0	0·0	0·0	0·0
Entomology	321	94·7	5·0	0·3	0·0	0·0	0·0	0·0	0·0	0·0	0·0
Animal Physiology	304	86·2	8·5	5·3	0·0	0·0	0·0	0·0	0·0	0·0	0·0
Plant Physiology	106	97·2	2·8	0·0	0·0	0·0	0·0	0·0	0·0	0·0	0·0
Botany	441	98·6	1·4	0·0	0·0	0·0	0·0	0·0	0·0	0·0	0·0
Zoology	410	97·8	2·0	0·2	0·0	0·0	0·0	0·0	0·0	0·0	0·0
Pathology	131	70·2	22·9	6·9	0·0	0·0	0·0	0·0	0·0	0·0	0·0

Table 35. Frequency distributions, shown as percentages of total working time taken over whole year, of number of cold-water taps used by *Assistants*.

Discipline	Total no. of obs.	Percentage of total working time during which cold-water taps (0–9) were in use									
		None	1	2	3	4	5	6	7	8	9
Chemistry	331	74·6	20·9	4·2	0·3	0·0	0·0	0·0	0·0	0·0	0·0
Physics	284	91·5	8·1	0·4	0·0	0·0	0·0	0·0	0·0	0·0	0·0
Biochemistry	337	86·6	12·5	0·6	0·3	0·0	0·0	0·0	0·0	0·0	0·0
Biophysics	143	82·5	16·8	0·7	0·0	0·0	0·0	0·0	0·0	0·0	0·0
Microbiology	359	97·8	2·2	0·0	0·0	0·0	0·0	0·0	0·0	0·0	0·0
Entomology	327	93·0	6·7	0·3	0·0	0·0	0·0	0·0	0·0	0·0	0·0
Animal Physiology	363	91·5	7·4	0·8	0·3	0·0	0·0	0·0	0·0	0·0	0·0
Plant Physiology	221	99·1	0·9	0·0	0·0	0·0	0·0	0·0	0·0	0·0	0·0
Botany	260	86·5	10·8	2·7	0·0	0·0	0·0	0·0	0·0	0·0	0·0
Zoology	348	94·8	4·9	0·3	0·0	0·0	0·0	0·0	0·0	0·0	0·0
Pathology	285	84·2	11·6	3·5	0·7	0·0	0·0	0·0	0·0	0·0	0·0

Tables 33, 34, and 35 give the basic frequency distributions for all grades and disciplines, based on the whole of a man's time. Tables 36, 37, and 38 exhibit the corresponding distributions based only on the time during which one or more cold-water taps were actually in use (see Part I, Chapter 3, pp. 32–33).

In Table 39 the data have been averaged over all disciplines, and Scientific Officers and Experimental Officers are combined under the general title 'Scientists'.

Table 40 shows the percentage satisfaction of demand when small groups of Scientists and Assistants are supplied with different numbers of taps.

Table 36. Frequency distributions, shown as percentages of time that some cold-water taps were in use, for *Scientific Officers*.

Discipline	Total no. of obs.	Percentage of time during which some cold-water taps (1–9) were in use								
		1	*2*	*3*	*4*	*5*	*6*	*7*	*8*	*9*
Chemistry . . .	406	94·9	5·1	0·0	0·0	0·0	0·0	0·0	0·0	0·0
Physics	429	95·9	4·1	0·0	0·0	0·0	0·0	0·0	0·0	0·0
Biochemistry . . .	429	56·3	25·4	9·7	3·4	4·5	0·7	0·0	0·0	0·0
Biophysics . . .	170	87·2	12·8	0·0	0·0	0·0	0·0	0·0	0·0	0·0
Microbiology . . .	439	87·5	12·5	0·0	0·0	0·0	0·0	0·0	0·0	0·0
Entomology . . .	399	30·3	69·7	0·0	0·0	0·0	0·0	0·0	0·0	0·0
Animal Physiology . . .	418	41·2	58·8	0·0	0·0	0·0	0·0	0·0	0·0	0·0
Plant Physiology . . .	327	94·2	5·8	0·0	0·0	0·0	0·0	0·0	0·0	0·0
Botany	421	0·0	0·0	0·0	0·0	0·0	0·0	0·0	0·0	0·0
Zoology	344	85·0	15·0	0·0	0·0	0·0	0·0	0·0	0·0	0·0
Pathology . . .	384	57·1	37·4	3·3	2·2	0·0	0·0	0·0	0·0	0·0

Table 37. Frequency distributions, shown as percentages of time that some cold-water taps were in use, for *Experimental Officers*.

Discipline	Total no. of obs.	Percentage of time during which some cold-water taps (1–9) were in use								
		1	*2*	*3*	*4*	*5*	*6*	*7*	*8*	*9*
Chemistry . . .	428	63·8	20·0	9·5	1·6	4·5	0·6	0·0	0·0	0·0
Physics	239	100·0	0·0	0·0	0·0	0·0	0·0	0·0	0·0	0·0
Biochemistry . . .	414	74·9	18·1	7·0	0·0	0·0	0·0	0·0	0·0	0·0
Microbiology . . .	425	100·0	0·0	0·0	0·0	0·0	0·0	0·0	0·0	0·0
Entomology . . .	321	94·3	5·7	0·0	0·0	0·0	0·0	0·0	0·0	0·0
Animal Physiology . . .	304	61·6	38·4	0·0	0·0	0·0	0·0	0·0	0·0	0·0
Plant Physiology . . .	106	100·0	0·0	0·0	0·0	0·0	0·0	0·0	0·0	0·0
Botany	441	100·0	0·0	0·0	0·0	0·0	0·0	0·0	0·0	0·0
Zoology	410	90·9	9·1	0·0	0·0	0·0	0·0	0·0	0·0	0·0
Pathology . . .	131	76·8	23·2	0·0	0·0	0·0	0·0	0·0	0·0	0·0

Table 38. Frequency distributions, shown as percentages of time that some cold-water taps were in use, for *Assistants*.

Discipline	Total no. of obs.	Percentage of time during which some cold-water taps (1–9) were in use								
		1	*2*	*3*	*4*	*5*	*6*	*7*	*8*	*9*
Chemistry . . .	331	82·3	16·5	1·2	0·0	0·0	0·0	0·0	0·0	0·0
Physics	284	95·3	4·7	0·0	0·0	0·0	0·0	0·0	0·0	0·0
Biochemistry . . .	337	93·3	4·5	2·2	0·0	0·0	0·0	0·0	0·0	0·0
Biophysics . . .	143	96·0	4·0	0·0	0·0	0·0	0·0	0·0	0·0	0·0
Microbiology . . .	359	100·0	0·0	0·0	0·0	0·0	0·0	0·0	0·0	0·0
Entomology . . .	327	95·7	4·3	0·0	0·0	0·0	0·0	0·0	0·0	0·0
Animal Physiology . .	363	87·1	9·4	3·5	0·0	0·0	0·0	0·0	0·0	0·0
Plant Physiology . .	221	100·0	0·0	0·0	0·0	0·0	0·0	0·0	0·0	0·0
Botany	260	80·0	20·0	0·0	0·0	0·0	0·0	0·0	0·0	0·0
Zoology	348	94·2	5·8	0·0	0·0	0·0	0·0	0·0	0·0	0·0
Pathology . . .	285	73·4	22·2	4·4	0·0	0·0	0·0	0·0	0·0	0·0

Table 39. Frequency distributions, shown as percentages of total working time taken over whole year, of number of cold-water taps used by *Scientists and Assistants* (averaged over all disciplines).

Staff grade	Total no. of obs.	Percentage of total working time during which cold-water taps (0–6) were in use						
		None	*1*	*2*	*3*	*4*	*5*	*6*
Scientists .	7,385	91·9	5·7	1·7	0·4	0·1	0·1	0·0
Assistants .	3,258	89·6	9·1	1·2	0·2	0·0	0·0	0·0

Table 40. Percentage satisfaction of demand for cold-water taps in groups of *Scientists and Assistants* (averaged over all disciplines).

No. of Scientists and Assistants	Percentage satisfaction of demand for cold-water taps (1–5)				
	1	*2*	*3*	*4*	*5*
1 Scientist + 1 Assistant .	74·5	92·5	97·5	99·2	100·0
1 Scientist + 2 Assistants .	73·9	93·0	98·0	99·4	100·0
2 Scientists + 2 Assistants .	68·1	89·7	96·4	98·7	99·8

Use of hot-water taps

Tables 41, 42, and 43 give the frequency distributions, shown as percentages of total time taken over the whole year, of the number of hot-water taps used by Scientific Officers, Experimental Officers, and Assistants. In only one instance was more than one tap used, and in some disciplines no hot-water taps were used at all. It would appear from the distribution tables that the demand for hot water is small, and that providing hot water is available in the laboratory at some point the demand would be largely met. It was thought that in this case further analysis in terms of the satisfaction of demand by groups of workers was unnecessary.

Table 41. Frequency distributions, shown as percentages of total working time taken over whole year, of number of hot-water taps used by *Scientific Officers*.

Discipline	Total no. of obs.	Percentage of total working time during which hot-water taps (0–2) were in use		
		None	1	2
Chemistry . .	406	100·0	0·0	0·0
Physics . .	429	99·5	0·5	0·0
Biochemistry .	429	99·1	0·9	0·0
Biophysics . .	170	99·4	0·6	0·0
Microbiology .	439	98·6	1·4	0·0
Entomology . .	399	99·5	0·5	0·0
Animal Physiology	418	99·5	0·5	0·0
Plant Physiology .	327	99·7	0·3	0·0
Botany . .	421	100·0	0·0	0·0
Zoology . .	344	100·0	0·0	0·0
Pathology . .	384	98·7	1·3	0·0

Use of gas taps

Tables 44, 45, and 46 provide the basic distributions for all grades and disciplines, based on the whole of a man's working time, while Tables 47, 48, and 49 are based only on the time during which some gas points were in use (see Part I, Chapter 3, pp. 31–33).

Table 42. Frequency distributions, shown as percentages of total working time taken over whole year, of number of hot-water taps used by *Experimental Officers*.

Discipline	Total no. of obs.	Percentage of total working time during which hot-water taps (0–2) were in use		
		None	1	2
Chemistry . .	428	97·4	2·6	0·0
Physics . .	239	100·0	0·0	0·0
Biochemistry .	414	96·9	3·1	0·0
Biophysics . .	..	..	..	..
Microbiology .	425	97·9	2·1	0·0
Entomology . .	321	100·0	0·0	0·0
Animal Physiology	304	96·4	3·6	0·0
Plant Physiology .	106	100·0	0·0	0·0
Botany . .	441	99·5	0·5	0·0
Zoology . .	410	99·3	0·7	0·0
Pathology . .	131	97·7	2·3	0·0

Table 43. Frequency distributions, shown as percentages of total working time taken over whole year, of number of hot-water taps used by *Assistants*.

Discipline	Total no. of obs.	Percentage of total working time during which hot-water taps (0–2) were in use		
		None	1	2
Chemistry . .	331	97·0	3·0	0·0
Physics . .	284	99·6	0·4	0·0
Biochemistry .	337	93·8	5·9	0·3
Biophysics . .	143	98·6	1·4	0·0
Microbiology .	359	95·0	5·0	0·0
Entomology .	327	98·5	1·5	0·0
Animal Physiology	363	98·1	1·9	0·0
Plant Physiology .	221	98·6	1·4	0·0
Botany . .	260	97·7	2·3	0·0
Zoology . .	348	99·4	0·6	0·0
Pathology . .	285	94·4	5·6	0·0

Table 44. Frequency distributions, shown as percentages of total working time taken over whole year, of number of gas taps used by *Scientific Officers*.

Discipline	Total no. of obs.	Percentage of total working time during which gas taps (0–9) were in use									
		None	1	2	3	4	5	6	7	8	9
Chemistry . .	406	90·4	5·4	2·7	1·5	0·0	0·0	0·0	0·0	0·0	0·0
Physics . .	429	94·9	4·4	0·5	0·2	0·0	0·0	0·0	0·0	0·0	0·0
Biochemistry .	429	83·7	12·8	2·6	0·9	0·0	0·0	0·0	0·0	0·0	0·0
Biophysics . .	170	97·6	2·4	0·0	0·0	0·0	0·0	0·0	0·0	0·0	0·0
Microbiology .	439	64·2	30·3	4·6	0·9	0·0	0·0	0·0	0·0	0·0	0·0
Entomology .	399	97·2	2·8	0·0	0·0	0·0	0·0	0·0	0·0	0·0	0·0
Animal Physiology .	418	97·9	1·9	0·2	0·0	0·0	0·0	0·0	0·0	0·0	0·0
Plant Physiology .	327	98·5	1·2	0·3	0·0	0·0	0·0	0·0	0·0	0·0	0·0
Botany . .	421	99·0	1·0	0·0	0·0	0·0	0·0	0·0	0·0	0·0	0·0
Zoology . .	344	96·5	3·2	0·3	0·0	0·0	0·0	0·0	0·0	0·0	0·0
Pathology . .	384	86·2	7·3	6·2	0·3	0·0	0·0	0·0	0·0	0·0	0·0

Table 45. Frequency distributions, shown as percentages of total working time taken over whole year, of number of gas taps used by *Experimental Officers.*

Discipline	Total no. of obs.	Percentage of total working time during which gas taps (0–9) were in use									
		None	1	2	3	4	5	6	7	8	9
Chemistry . .	428	81·1	11·5	5·6	1·6	0·2	0·0	0·0	0·0	0·0	0·0
Physics . .	239	92·9	6·3	0·4	0·4	0·0	0·0	0·0	0·0	0·0	0·0
Biochemistry .	414	84·8	8·5	5·3	1·0	0·0	0·0	0·0	0·0	0·2	0·2
Microbiology .	425	71·5	23·1	4·5	0·9	0·0	0·0	0·0	0·0	0·0	0·0
Entomology .	321	94·1	5·6	0·3	0·0	0·0	0·0	0·0	0·0	0·0	0·0
Animal Physiology .	304	80·3	17·1	2·6	0·0	0·0	0·0	0·0	0·0	0·0	0·0
Plant Physiology .	106	99·1	0·9	0·0	0·0	0·0	0·0	0·0	0·0	0·0	0·0
Botany . .	441	98·6	1·4	0·0	0·0	0·0	0·0	0·0	0·0	0·0	0·0
Zoology . .	410	97·1	2·7	0·2	0·0	0·0	0·0	0·0	0·0	0·0	0·0
Pathology . .	131	58·0	26·7	12·2	2·3	0·8	0·0	0·0	0·0	0·0	0·0

Table 46. Frequency distributions, shown as percentages of total working time taken over whole year, of number of gas taps used by *Assistants.*

Discipline	Total no. of obs.	Percentage of total working time during which gas taps (0–9) were in use									
		None	1	2	3	4	5	6	7	8	9
Chemistry . .	331	86·4	10·9	2·4	0·3	0·0	0·0	0·0	0·0	0·0	0·0
Physics . .	284	96·1	3·9	0·0	0·0	0·0	0·0	0·0	0·0	0·0	0·0
Biochemistry .	337	89·3	9·5	0·6	0·6	0·0	0·0	0·0	0·0	0·0	0·0
Biophysics . .	143	94·4	5·6	0·0	0·0	0·0	0·0	0·0	0·0	0·0	0·0
Microbiology .	359	68·0	26·5	2·8	1·4	0·8	0·5	0·0	0·0	0·0	0·0
Entomology .	327	94·2	5·5	0·3	0·0	0·0	0·0	0·0	0·0	0·0	0·0
Animal Physiology .	363	93·9	5·0	1·1	0·0	0·0	0·0	0·0	0·0	0·0	0·0
Plant Physiology .	221	98·6	1·4	0·0	0·0	0·0	0·0	0·0	0·0	0·0	0·0
Botany . .	260	85·0	6·5	5·4	0·0	0·0	0·0	2·7	0·0	0·4	0·0
Zoology . .	348	98·0	1·7	0·0	0·3	0·0	0·0	0·0	0·0	0·0	0·0
Pathology . .	285	81·8	16·1	2·1	0·0	0·0	0·0	0·0	0·0	0·0	0·0

Table 47. Frequency distributions, shown as percentages of time that some gas taps were in use, for *Scientific Officers.*

Discipline	Total no. of obs.	Percentage of time during which some gas taps (1–9) were in use								
		1	2	3	4	5	6	7	8	9
Chemistry . . .	406	56·3	28·1	15·6	0·0	0·0	0·0	0·0	0·0	0·0
Physics . . .	429	86·3	9·8	3·9	0·0	0·0	0·0	0·0	0·0	0·0
Biochemistry . .	429	78·5	16·0	5·5	0·0	0·0	0·0	0·0	0·0	0·0
Biophysics . .	170	100·0	0·0	0·0	0·0	0·0	0·0	0·0	0·0	0·0
Microbiology . .	439	84·6	12·9	2·5	0·0	0·0	0·0	0·0	0·0	0·0
Entomology . .	399	100·0	0·0	0·0	0·0	0·0	0·0	0·0	0·0	0·0
Animal Physiology . .	418	90·5	9·5	0·0	0·0	0·0	0·0	0·0	0·0	0·0
Plant Physiology . .	327	80·0	20·0	0·0	0·0	0·0	0·0	0·0	0·0	0·0
Botany . . .	421	100·0	0·0	0·0	0·0	0·0	0·0	0·0	0·0	0·0
Zoology . . .	344	91·4	8·6	0·0	0·0	0·0	0·0	0·0	0·0	0·0
Pathology . . .	384	52·9	44·9	2·2	0·0	0·0	0·0	0·0	0·0	0·0

Table 48. Frequency distributions, shown as percentages of time that some gas taps were in use, for *Experimental Officers.*

Discipline	Total no. of obs.	Percentage of time during which some gas taps (1–9) were in use								
		1	2	3	4	5	6	7	8	9
Chemistry . . .	428	60·8	29·6	8·5	1·1	0·0	0·0	0·0	0·0	0·0
Physics . . .	239	88·7	5·6	5·7	0·0	0·0	0·0	0·0	0·0	0·0
Biochemistry . .	414	55·9	34·9	6·6	0·0	0·0	0·0	0·0	1·3	1·3
Biophysics . .	..	..	..	..	..	..	..	..	..	..
Microbiology . .	425	81·0	15·8	3·2	0·0	0·0	0·0	0·0	0·0	0·0
Entomology . .	321	94·9	5·1	0·0	0·0	0·0	0·0	0·0	0·0	0·0
Animal Physiology . .	304	86·8	13·2	0·0	0·0	0·0	0·0	0·0	0·0	0·0
Plant Physiology . .	106	100·0	0·0	0·0	0·0	0·0	0·0	0·0	0·0	0·0
Botany . . .	441	100·0	0·0	0·0	0·0	0·0	0·0	0·0	0·0	0·0
Zoology . . .	410	93·1	6·9	0·0	0·0	0·0	0·0	0·0	0·0	0·0
Pathology . . .	131	63·6	29·0	5·5	1·9	0·0	0·0	0·0	0·0	0·0

Table 49. Frequency distributions, shown as percentages of time that some gas taps were in use, for *Assistants*.

Discipline	Total no. of obs.	Percentage of time during which some gas taps (1–9) were in use								
		1	2	3	4	5	6	7	8	9
Chemistry . . .	331	80·2	17·6	2·2	0·0	0·0	0·0	0·0	0·0	0·0
Physics . . .	284	100·0	0·0	0·0	0·0	0·0	0·0	0·0	0·0	0·0
Biochemistry . .	337	88·8	5·6	5·6	0·0	0·0	0·0	0·0	0·0	0·0
Biophysics . .	143	100·0	0·0	0·0	0·0	0·0	0·0	0·0	0·0	0·0
Microbiology . .	359	82·8	8·7	4·4	2·5	1·6	0·0	0·0	0·0	0·0
Entomology . .	327	94·8	5·2	0·0	0·0	0·0	0·0	0·0	0·0	0·0
Animal Physiology .	363	82·0	18·0	0·0	0·0	0·0	0·0	0·0	0·0	0·0
Plant Physiology .	221	100·0	0·0	0·0	0·0	0·0	0·0	0·0	0·0	0·0
Botany . . .	260	43·3	36·0	0·0	0·0	0·0	18·0	0·0	2·7	0·0
Zoology . . .	348	85·0	0·0	15·0	0·0	0·0	0·0	0·0	0·0	0·0
Pathology . .	285	88·5	11·5	0·0	0·0	0·0	0·0	0·0	0·0	0·0

Table 50. Frequency distributions, shown as percentage of total working time, of number of gas taps used by *Scientists and Assistants* (averaged over all disciplines).

Staff grade	Total no. of obs.	Percentage of total working time during which gas taps (0–6) were in use						
		None	1	2	3	4	5	6
Scientists	7,385	88·9	8·4	2·2	0·5	0·0	0·0	0·0
Assistants	3,258	89·0	8·9	1·4	0·3	0·1	0·1	0·2

Table 51. Percentage satisfaction of demand for gas taps in groups of *Scientists and Assistants* (averaged over all disciplines).

No. of Scientists and Assistants	Percentage satisfaction of demand for gas taps (1–6)					
	1	2	3	4	5	6
1 Scientist + 1 Assistant .	72·3	91·3	96·5	98·3	99·3	100·0
1 Scientist + 2 Assistants .	67·8	88·0	94·5	97·0	98·6	99·8
2 Scientists + 2 Assistants .	64·7	87·2	94·8	97·6	99·0	99·8

Table 52. Frequency distributions, shown as percentages of total working time taken over whole year, of electric current used by *Scientific Officers* in each discipline.

Discipline	Total no. of obs.	Percentage of total working time during which current (0–30 amps.) was in use							
		None	0–5	6–10	11–15	16–20	21–25	26–30	> 30
Chemistry	406	75·9	15·5	3·2	4·7	0·3	0·2	0·0	0·2
Physics	429	70·6	21·7	4·4	2·6	0·7	0·0	0·0	0·0
Biochemistry . . .	429	57·3	23·5	12·4	3·7	0·7	0·0	0·5	1·9
Biophysics . . .	170	91·2	8·2	0·0	0·6	0·0	0·0	0·0	0·0
Microbiology . . .	439	59·2	35·6	5·0	0·2	0·0	0·0	0·0	0·0
Entomology . . .	399	72·2	25·6	2·0	0·2	0·0	0·0	0·0	0·0
Animal Physiology . . .	418	82·5	11·3	4·8	1·4	0·0	0·0	0·0	0·0
Plant Physiology . . .	327	80·1	18·4	0·6	0·9	0·0	0·0	0·0	0·0
Botany	421	91·9	7·9	0·2	0·0	0·0	0·0	0·0	0·0
Zoology	344	85·5	13·9	0·6	0·0	0·0	0·0	0·0	0·0
Pathology	384	44·0	29·9	17·2	7·8	1·1	0·0	0·0	0·0

In Table 50 the demand has been averaged over all disciplines. Experimental Officers and Scientific Officers have been grouped together as Scientists. Percentage satisfaction of demand for small groups of Scientists and Assistants supplied with different numbers of taps are given in Table 51.

Electric services

USE OF CURRENT

Tables 52, 53, and 54 have been compiled showing the frequency distribution of current used (in 5-amp. increments) by the three grades of worker in different disciplines.

It was found possible to group the disciplines into three classes:

HIGH users of current:
Biochemistry, Chemistry, Pathology.

MEDIUM users of current:
Physics, Microbiology, Animal Physiology, Botany.

LIGHT users of current:
Biophysics, Entomology, Plant Physiology, Zoology.

It should be noted that the composition of the three classes is not the same for *electric current* as for *bench length*.

Table 53. Frequency distributions, shown as percentages of total working time taken over whole year, of electric current used by *Experimental Officers* in each discipline.

Discipline	Total no. of obs.	Percentage of total working time during which current (0–30 amps.) was in use							
		None	0–5	6–10	11–15	16–20	21–25	26–30	>30
Chemistry	428	48·4	32·0	11·2	5·8	1·2	1·4	0·0	0·0
Physics	239	68·2	30·6	0·4	0·4	0·4	0·0	0·0	0·0
Biochemistry	414	64·5	23·2	8·0	2·2	1·7	0·4	0·0	0·0
Microbiology	425	62·1	31·5	4·0	2·1	0·3	0·0	0·0	0·0
Entomology	321	77·9	19·3	2·5	0·3	0·0	0·0	0·0	0·0
Animal Physiology	304	63·5	25·3	9·6	1·3	0·3	0·0	0·0	0·0
Plant Physiology	106	67·0	24·5	0·9	6·6	1·0	0·0	0·0	0·0
Botany	441	67·1	19·3	12·9	0·0	0·0	0·0	0·7	0·0
Zoology	410	80·5	18·0	0·5	1·0	0·0	0·0	0·0	0·0
Pathology	131	38·9	52·7	8·4	0·0	0·0	0·0	0·0	0·0

Table 54. Frequency distributions, shown as percentages of total working time taken over whole year, of electric current used by *Assistants* in each discipline.

Discipline	Total no. of obs.	Percentage of total working time during which current (0–30 amps.) was in use							
		None	0–5	6–10	11–15	16–20	21–25	26–30	>30
Chemistry	331	62·9	20·9	6·3	6·0	2·1	1·2	0·6	0·0
Physics	284	70·1	22·5	4·9	1·4	1·1	0·0	0·0	0·0
Biochemistry	337	60·5	26·1	10·1	2·1	1·2	0·0	0·0	0·0
Biophysics	143	79·0	18·2	1·4	1·4	0·0	0·0	0·0	0·0
Microbiology	359	49·6	32·6	14·7	2·5	0·3	0·3	0·0	0·0
Entomology	327	71·6	23·5	1·8	0·0	3·1	0·0	0·0	0·0
Animal Physiology	363	81·8	13·2	5·0	0·0	0·0	0·0	0·0	0·0
Plant Physiology	221	89·6	10·0	0·0	0·4	0·0	0·0	0·0	0·0
Botany	260	81·2	11·2	0·4	3·1	1·5	0·4	1·1	1·1
Zoology	348	72·7	24·4	2·9	0·0	0·0	0·0	0·0	0·0
Pathology	285	49·8	32·6	14·4	2·1	0·7	0·4	0·0	0·0

Table 55. Frequency distributions, shown as percentages of total working time taken over whole year, of electric current used by *Scientists and Assistants* in high, medium, and low groups of disciplines.

Staff grade	Discipline class	Percentage of total working time during which current (0–30) amps. was in use							
		None	1–5	6–10	11–15	16–20	21–25	26–30	>30
Scientists	High	57·0	26·5	10·2	4·5	0·9	0·4	0·1	0·4
	Medium	71·0	22·4	5·3	1·0	0·2	0·0	0·1	0·0
	Low	79·4	18·6	1·1	0·8	0·0	0·1	0·0	0·0
Assistants	High	58·1	26·2	10·1	3·5	1·4	0·5	0·2	0·0
	Medium	69·9	20·4	6·8	1·7	0·6	0·2	0·2	0·2
	Low	76·8	20·2	1·7	0·3	1·0	0·0	0·0	0·0

Table 56. Frequency distributions, shown as percentages of time during which some current was in use, for *Scientists and Assistants* in high, medium, and low groups of disciplines.

Staff grade	Discipline class	Percentage of time during which some current (0–30 amps.) was in use						
		0–5	6–10	11–15	16–20	21–25	26–30	>30
Scientists	High . . .	61·6	23·7	10·5	2·1	0·9	0·2	0·9
	Medium . . .	77·2	18·3	3·4	0·7	0·0	0·3	0·0
	Low . . .	90·3	5·3	3·9	0·0	0·5	0·0	0·0
Assistants	High . . .	62·5	24·1	8·4	3·3	1·2	0·5	0·0
	Medium . . .	67·8	22·6	5·6	2·0	0·7	0·7	0·7
	Low . . .	87·1	7·3	1·3	4·3	0·0	0·0	0·0

For the purpose of comparison between the three user groups Scientific Officers and Experimental Officers have been taken together as Scientists, although in some disciplines, e.g. physics, there seems to be an appreciable difference in the usages of the two grades. Analysis on the basis of user groups is useful for the very general comparison it affords between disciplines, and as a basis for subsequent cal-culations on estimating total load, with its variations, for differently constituted groups of workers. Tables 55 and 56 show the frequency distributions of current used by Scientists and Assistants in each of the three user classes. Table 55 is based on the whole of a man's time, while Table 56 refers only to that portion of it during which some current was actually used.

Tables 57 and 58 show the level of satisfaction achieved for a given degree of provision.

A man working with two available outlets from a ring main (each with a fuse rating of 13 amps.) could draw on up to 26 amps. This would give rise to nearly 99 per cent. satisfaction, based on the time he actually required some current, even if he were in the 'high' class (Table 58).

For small groups of four or fewer Scientists, with each individual working independently, the separate distributions can be compounded, and Table 59 gives the current requirements of Scientists for various levels of satisfaction. It may be seen that one Scientist in the 'medium' class requires 10 amps. to meet his need for 98 per cent. of all his working time. The corresponding figure for a group of four is, however, only 20 amps., which is no more than double the figure for one man. Such results have immediate relevance to the design of electric supply services to separate rooms or units in the laboratory.

The estimation of the total fluctuating load for a large group, say a whole laboratory, is useful in deciding the size of cables and the capacity of transformers. It is impracticable to compound the relevant distributions for large groups, but it is possible to use the statistical approximation that distributions built up in this way tend in general to follow the normal or Gaussian form. It is first necessary to calculate the means and variances of the individual distributions. This has been done from the frequency distributions of electric current used by Scientists and Assistants shown as percentages of total time in Table 55, and the resultant means and variances are shown in Table 60.

Taking as an example a laboratory in the 'medium' class with 25 Scientists and 25 Assistants, it may be assumed that each individual can draw on as much current as he needs, although in practice he will be slightly limited by local fuse capacities. The means and variances in this class are 1·3 and 6·9 amps. for

Table 57. Electric current required to give various degrees of satisfaction based on the whole of a man's time for *Scientists and Assistants* in high, medium, and low groups of disciplines.

Staff grade	Discipline class	Current in amps. to give levels of satisfaction between 90 and 99 per cent.									
		90	91	92	93	94	95	96	97	98	99
Scientists	High	8·7	9·2	9·7	10·2	10·8	11·9	13·1	14·2	15·3	19·9
	Medium	4·7	5·0	5·2	5·4	6·1	7·0	8·0	8·9	9·8	12·0
	Low	3·1	3·4	3·7	4·0	4·3	4·6	4·9	5·2	5·5	10·0
Assistants	High	8·3	8·8	9·2	9·8	10·3	11·4	12·8	14·2	15·9	19·4
	Medium	5·4	6·0	6·8	7·5	8·2	9·0	9·7	10·4	13·1	17·2
	Low	3·6	3·9	4·1	4·4	4·7	5·0	5·2	5·5	8·4	15·5

Table 58. Electric current required to give various degrees of satisfaction, based on the time during which some current was in use, for *Scientists and Assistants* in high, medium, and low groups of disciplines.

Staff grade	Discipline class	Current in amps. to give levels of satisfaction between 90 and 99 per cent.									
		90	91	92	93	94	95	96	97	98	99
Scientists	High	12·7	13·2	13·6	14·1	14·6	15·1	15·7	18·1	20·5	28·0
	Medium	9·0	9·2	9·5	9·8	10·1	10·3	11·1	12·6	14·0	15·5
	Low	5·5	6·2	7·1	8·0	9·0	9·9	11·0	12·3	13·6	14·9
Assistants	High	12·5	13·1	13·7	14·3	14·9	15·5	17·0	18·5	20·0	23·4
	Medium	10·4	11·1	12·0	12·9	13·8	14·7	15·7	18·3	21·2	25·5
	Low	7·5	8·2	8·9	9·5	10·2	10·9	12·8	15·5	15·5	15·5

Table 59. Electric current required to give various degrees of satisfaction based on the whole of a man's time, for *groups of Scientists* up to 4.

Discipline class	No. of scientists	Current in amps. to give levels of satisfaction between 90 and 99 per cent.									
		90	91	92	93	94	95	96	97	98	99
High	1	8·7	9·2	9·7	10·2	10·8	11·9	13·1	14·2	15·3	19·9
	2	14·6	15·1	15·6	16·8	17·9	19·0	20·2	22·3	25·0	31·2
	3	19·1	19·7	20·3	21·3	22·6	23·8	25·1	27·7	31·0	36·2
	4	22·9	23·7	24·5	25·3	26·8	28·5	30·2	32·8	35·9	40·5
Medium	1	4·7	5·0	5·2	5·4	6·1	7·0	8·0	8·9	9·8	12·0
	2	8·6	9·0	9·4	9·8	10·2	10·8	12·1	13·4	14·7	17·5
	3	10·8	11·5	12·2	12·9	13·5	14·2	14·9	15·7	18·0	20·3
	4	13·4	13·9	14·3	14·8	15·2	16·0	17·4	18·7	20·1	24·0
Low	1	3·1	3·4	3·7	4·0	4·3	4·6	4·9	5·2	5·5	10·0
	2	5·0	5·2	5·4	5·9	6·8	7·8	8·8	9·7	11·1	14·0
	3	7·7	8·1	8·6	9·0	9·5	10·0	10·4	12·0	14·0	16·8
	4	9·3	9·5	9·8	10·1	10·4	11·4	12·8	14·1	15·5	19·1

Scientists and 1·7 and 13·5 amps. for Assistants (Table 60). When the distributions are independent, the means and variances are additive. Therefore in this case the mean and variance for the whole laboratory are 75·0 amps. and 510·0 amps. respectively. Thus the fluctuating load for the whole group of 50 Scientists and Assistants would have approximately a normal distribution of 75·0 amps. with a standard deviations of 22·6 amps. For example, a load in excess of 1·96 standard deviations (i.e. 75·0+ (1·96 × 22·6) = 119·3 amps.) would occur only 2½ per cent. of the time. This is sufficient to calculate from

standard statistical tables the fluctuating load for any required percentage of satisfaction to the users, providing that the number of individuals in a group is sufficiently large.

It is not proposed to illustrate this method further here but more detailed applications to specific instances could be made.

USE OF ELECTRIC POINTS

Apart from the actual quantity of electricity required, the number of points or sockets available is also an important factor in the design of the installation. Unfortunately, information on the number of points in use is not available for the whole of the survey period. Complete recordings were made in only one quarter, and partial recordings in each of two others. There is, therefore, some possibility of the data being affected by seasonal variations, which would have averaged out in complete records. The basic figures set out in Tables 61, 62, and 63 should be considered with this in mind.

One important feature stands out in these tables. A large number of points is required on occasion, even though for most of the time a smaller number is sufficient. Take, for example, microbiology Assistants: practically all their demand is for four points

Table 60. Means and variances of electric current used by *Scientists and Assistants* in high, medium, and low groups of disciplines.

Staff grade	Discipline class	Mean	Variance
Scientists	High	2·6	20·0
	Medium	1·3	6·9
	Low	0·8	3·4
Assistants	High	2·5	17·4
	Medium	1·7	13·5
	Low	1·0	5·6

Table 61. Number of electric points in use: basic observations for *Scientific Officers*.

Discipline	Number of electric points in use									Total no. of obs.
	None	1	2	3	4	5	6	7	8	
Chemistry . . .	160	14	10	17	..	..	..	..	..	201
Physics	144	32	7	6	1	..	1	2	..	193
Biochemistry . .	122	35	22	15	3	1	6	3	1	208
Biophysics . . .	81	2	..	..	..	..	..	..	..	83
Microbiology . .	139	37	20	41	10	1	7	..	..	255
Entomology . . .	162	35	18	..	..	..	..	..	..	215
Animal Physiology . .	196	19	4	2	..	..	..	..	2	223
Plant Physiology . .	135	29	6	4	..	..	..	..	..	174
Botany	162	8	1	1	..	..	..	..	..	172
Zoology . . .	89	8	..	..	..	..	..	..	..	97
Pathology . . .	62	33	24	12	6	3	1	12	2	155
TOTAL	1,452	252	112	98	20	5	15	17	5	1,976

Table 62. Number of electric points in use: basic observations for *Experimental Officers*.

Discipline	Number of electric points in use							Total no. of obs.
	0	1	2	3	4	5	6	
Chemistry	95	56	31	14	2	1	..	199
Physics .	53	17	6	..	..	8	..	84
Biochemistry	108	24	17	10	10	1	1	171
Biophysics	..	..	..	..	..	..	..	..
Microbiology .	120	38	12	23	4	1	..	198
Entomology	138	31	12	1	..	..	..	182
Animal Physiology	77	21	4	..	8	1	..	111
Plant Physiology	20	25	..	..	..	..	..	45
Botany .	109	15	7	21	..	..	..	152
Zoology .	70	26	3	..	..	1	..	99
Pathology .	20	15	13	13	1	..	..	62
TOTAL .	810	268	105	82	25	12	1	1,303

Table 63. Number of electric points in use: basic observations for *Assistants*

Discipline	Number of electric points in use							Total no. of obs.
	0	1	2	3	4	5	9	
Chemistry	101	40	16	5	1	..	..	163
Physics .	75	20	6	..	..	..	..	99
Biochemistry	117	43	14	4	..	..	..	178
Biophysics	49	3	6	4	..	..	..	62
Microbiology .	85	58	21	13	14	..	10	201
Entomology	133	45	11	4	..	..	..	193
Animal Physiology	162	10	6	3	1	1	..	183
Plant Physiology	101	5	5	..	..	..	..	111
Botany .	95	9	..	..	..	..	..	104
Zoology .	63	21	..	5	14	1	..	104
Pathology .	50	23	2	16	3	..	..	94
TOTAL .	1,029	277	87	54	33	2	10	1,492

Table 64. Frequency distributions, shown as percentages of time that some electric points were in use, of the numbers of points required by *Scientific Officers, Experimental Officers and Assistants*, averaged over all disciplines.

Staff grade	Percentage of time during which electric points (1–9) were in use								
	1	2	3	4	5	6	7	8	9
Scientific Officers	48·1	21·4	18·7	3·8	1·0	2·9	3·2	1·0	0·0
Experimental Officers . . .	54·4	21·3	16·6	5·1	2·4	0·2	0·0	0·0	0·0
Assistants	59·8	18·8	11·7	7·1	0·4	0·0	0·0	0·0	2·2

Table 65. Number of points and amperage in use: basic observations for *Scientific Officers*.

Amperage	Number of points in use								Total no. of obs.
	1	2	3	4	5	6	7	8	
0–0·9 . . .	104	6	..	..	..	1	..	..	111
1–1·9 . . .	75	8	3	..	..	..	2	..	88
2–4·9 . . .	46	70	49	1	1	..	..	..	167
5–9·9 . . .	16	19	28	18	4	7	..	..	92
10–14·9 . . .	9	8	11	1	..	1	12	4	46
15–19·9 . . .	2	1	7	..	..	..	..	..	10
20–24·9 . . .	..	..	..	..	..	..	..	..	..
25–29·9 . . .	..	..	..	..	..	2	..	..	2
30–35·0 . . .	..	..	..	..	..	4	3	1	8
TOTAL . . .	252	112	98	20	5	15	17	5	524

Table 66. Number of points and amperage in use: basic observations for *Experimental Officers*

Amperage	Number of points in use						Total no. of obs.
	1	2	3	4	5	6	
0–0·9 .	84	11	..	1	8	..	104
1–1·9 .	88	10	1	..	..	..	99
2–4·9 .	72	45	13	2	..	..	132
5–9·9 .	16	27	55	19	..	..	117
10–14·9 .	7	8	7	2	3	..	27
15–19·9 .	1	3	3	..	1	1	9
20–24·9 .	..	1	3	1	..	..	5
25–30·0 .	..	..	..	..	..	..	..
TOTAL .	268	105	82	25	12	1	493

or less, except for a concentration at nine points. This pattern can be discerned, on close inspection, in many parts of the three tables.

Table 64 gives the frequency distributions of working times during which given numbers of points were used by Scientists and Assistants, averaged over all disciplines and based on the time during which some points were in use. Again the frequencies for Scientific Officers fall steadily from 'one point in use', with a small peak around about '6' and '7'. Similarly, the percentages for Assistants have dropped to zero at 6 points, but there is an isolated 2·2 per cent. at '9'.

These figures suggest that the economical solution is to provide four or five outlets, which would satisfy the main demand for points directly, and to regard the small demand for larger numbers of points as a special requirement to be met separately. If these large demands entailed only a small amount of current there would be little objection to expecting the extra outlets to be made up as required by the worker concerned. If, however, heavy current were involved the position would be more difficult. In order to examine the relation between amperage and number of points in use, two-way analyses were made for each grade. These are described below.

USE OF POINTS IN RELATION TO SUPPLY OF CURRENT

The basic observations on amperage and number of points in use for the three grades are shown in Tables 65, 66, and 67. Considering first Scientific Officers, it is clear that there are a number of occasions—about 6 per cent. of the total—when both

Table 67. Number of points and amperage in use: basic observations for *Assistants*.

Amperage	Number of points in use									Total
	1	2	3	4	5	6	7	8	9	
0–0·9 . .	100	4	..	..	..	..	..	..	..	104
1–1·9 . .	72	13	2	..	..	..	..	..	..	87
2–4·9 . .	66	29	29	21	2	..	..	..	..	147
5–9·9 . .	32	22	19	12	..	..	..	..	4	89
10–14·9 . .	4	10	..	..	..	..	..	..	5	19
15–19·9 . .	3	8	2	..	..	..	..	..	..	13
20–24·9 . .	..	..	1	..	..	..	..	1	..	2
25–30·0 . .	..	1	1	..	..	..	..	..	..	2
TOTAL . .	277	87	54	33	2	..	..	..	10	463

large numbers of points and fairly heavy currents are required. Thus, one observation in 500 revealed a man using 8 points with a total of between 30 and 35 amps. The requirements of Experimental Officers and Assistants can be examined in a similar fashion, and they can be seen to be of no greater magnitude.

Suppose that outlets from a ring-main are provided at about 4-ft. intervals, so that with about 12 ft. of bench length each man has 3 outlets available to him. Taking Scientific Officers and Experimental Officers together, this would give about 90 per cent. satisfaction so far as the number of points was concerned, and would permit the maximum observed total of current to be used provided that the number of outlets per ring were assessed with this in mind. With 4 outlets, at 3 ft. intervals, the demand satisfied would rise to about 95 per cent. The corresponding satisfaction for Assistants would be 90 per cent., and 97 per cent. for 3 and 4 outlets, respectively, and again there would be no trouble in drawing off the maximum observed amount of current. With the scale of provision envisaged here, a worker would be able to obtain the outlets he wanted directly from wall sockets for a large proportion of his time. Only occasionally would he require more: these would have to be obtained by multiple connexions or by using points left free by adjacent workers, but the total current needed would be still within the capacity of the installation.

The position of bench outlets

There is a great deal of differing opinion on what is the best position for bench outlets and their controls. Mention was made of this in the section dealing with bench width and spacing, and there seems to be little doubt that providing bench widths are not excessive, the nearer the controls are placed to a horizontal arm-reach position, the easier they are to manipulate. Nevertheless, in some laboratories where large arrays of glassware are in use on the bench, or where framed rigs are used to support complex apparatus, there are valid reasons for bringing the controls to the front of the bench. Arguments levelled against this method are that the mechanical transmission systems below the bench are liable to failure and that control knobs may become entangled with clothing. Both of these disadvantages can be overcome. In Germany front controls are attached direct to a valve, the service pipe being brought forward under the bench and then returned via the valve to the bench outlet. Control knobs can be designed in such a way that accidental operation becomes virtually impossible.

The quality of the fittings used on the bench and the material from which they are made can have an important bearing on the initial and running cost of the services system. This is discussed in Appendix II, Materials and Finishes.

Heating and ventilating

The design problems of heating and ventilating systems for laboratory buildings fall naturally into two categories. On the one hand, a comfortable working environment must be provided in rooms such as normal bench laboratories where the scientific worker spends most of his time, and, on the other, closely specified conditions must be provided in special rooms to meet the needs of the techniques they are designed to house. The latter category includes rooms in which temperatures must be held above those required for human comfort, cold rooms for short- or long-term use in carrying out special kinds of work or merely for cold storage, and many other rooms for housing techniques which require special conditions of temperature or humidity such as chromatography rooms, I.R. spectrophotometer rooms, and tissue-culture rooms.

It is not proposed to deal in detail with the provision of controlled environment rooms in this report, except in so far as the servicing of such rooms is affected by the type of heating and ventilating system chosen for the general laboratory areas. Detailed design for controlled environment is highly specialized and each example must be dealt with separately by the heating and ventilating engineer. The engineer's task may, however, be greatly complicated by thoughtless positioning of special rooms. The planning of them in relation to the general laboratory area is dealt with in Part II, Chapter 2. The choice of a heating and ventilating system for the general laboratory area as it relates to human comfort, conditions of safety and fume extraction is discussed below.

Heating the general laboratory area

Whilst it is impossible to consider the heating system without reference to the method of ventilation, it is convenient to discuss particular problems as they relate to various kinds of heating systems. The end point, as in all other work places, is to provide a comfortable and healthy environment for those who occupy the building. In many research laboratories the achievement of this aim is made more difficult by the nature of the work which may produce unpleasant, irritating, or even toxic or inflammable fumes. To a large extent, therefore, the heating system must be chosen with the efficiency of the ventilation system in mind. Where fume cupboards are used, large quantities of air will be drawn from the room, and if this air is not replaced by artificial means, the heating system will be called upon to raise the air temperature at a much higher rate than in other types of building. This is especially the case where a laboratory building is divided into small units, each of which may have to house a fume cupboard.

The heating system for the general laboratory area may also have to be chosen with reference to the kind of work likely to be carried out. For example, systems which rely on large radiant sources may be unsuitable for certain types of biological work and any system which creates a considerable temperature gradient within the room may be unsuitable if moderately even temperatures are required in the vertical as well as the horizontal plane.

In every case the overall planning of the building will be seriously affected by the choice of heating system and it is at an early stage in design that informed decisions must be taken. The aim of the discussion which follows is to give guidance in the making of such decisions.

FLOOR HEATING

The general principles of floor heating are now well known and the system has been well tried in schools and houses. Heating is by means of either hot-water coils or electrical elements placed below the floor surface, the controlling factor in design being the floor surface temperature which may be used consistent with foot comfort. For most types of room it is necessary to cover almost the whole floor area with the heating elements in order to achieve the necessary room temperatures without raising the surface temperature to an unacceptable degree. Most laboratories have a large proportion of their floor area taken up with permanent items of furniture and equipment, and the proportion of floor area remaining uncovered may well be less than half the total area. To achieve an adequate room temperature therefore, with a reduced area of heating surface, a high surface temperature would be needed and this might produce uncomfortable standing and walking conditions.

The need to move laboratory benches and equipment within the services grid has been discussed above. Even though room shapes and sizes are not changed, it is very likely that internal arrangements will be altered from time to time. The implications are obvious: floor heating restricts change and movement of equipment.

Whilst the possibility of penetration of liquids through the floor finish can probably be dealt with satisfactorily (see Appendix II, Materials and Finishes), great care must be taken in the design of the membrane which is placed between the heating elements and the floor surface.

The main characteristic of fabric-heating systems, namely the slow response to regulation, may also be used as an argument against floor heating for laboratories where fairly rapid control of room temperature is required. On the other hand, it is convenient to include the heating system in the floor, thus reducing the number of service pipes which have to be dealt with in the laboratory space itself.

CEILING HEATING

Some of the considerations outlined above for floor heating also apply to ceiling heating installations. Whilst ceiling heating does not restrict planning changes, it may complicate the laboratory services system to an unacceptable degree. Ceiling heating has, however, been used in a number of recent laboratories where the laboratory bench servicing is carried in floor ducts or where the design is such that bench service runs are not carried in ceiling spaces and therefore do not have to penetrate the heating areas.

Perforated or continuous metal panels are used as the surfacing material for most ceiling heating installations. Large lengths of piping as well as the metal panels themselves may be subjected to highly corrosive atmospheres, particularly in chemical and biochemical laboratories. Exposed ceiling panels with sharp edges and perforations are particularly difficult to protect.

The difficulties inherent in fabric-heating systems generally have already been mentioned above. Objections to large radiant sources apply particularly to ceiling heating installations. Also, in some laboratories, it may be necessary to reduce ceiling heights on the grounds of economy to such an extent that ceiling heating becomes inappropriate.

In the laboratories at the Atomic Energy Research Establishment in Denmark, the ceiling is made of perforated panels and the space between it and the structure above is used as a pressurized duct for warm air which is pushed through the perforations into the rooms below. This is combined with radiant sources, around the perimeter of the building designed to deal with fabric heat losses only.

RADIATORS

It will be seen from Part II, Chapters 1 and 2, that the work of the team points to a method of design based on rationalized bench and services layouts, which would often lead to rooms of greater depth than those generally used hitherto. Lighting studies suggest that such layouts are practicable. Simplified bench layouts with benches placed only at right angles to the window walls allow great freedom in window design whilst leaving the wall area below sill level clear for radiators or other heating units. Where laboratory services are piped to benches from centrally placed vertical or horizontal ducts, the heating system can be planned around the perimeter of the building, thus divorcing it from the bench services and simplifying the centralized laboratory servicing system.

Radiator systems are of course cheaper in first cost than fabric-heating installations, and have obvious advantages if they can be conveniently placed on clear external walls. They give equal efficiency without restricting the floor layouts in any way, and with benches at right angles to the window wall do not become entangled with benches and their service runs. Perimeter heating may involve certain difficulties with internal rooms, which will almost certainly occur if greater depths from corridor to window wall are used. Most of the internal rooms, however, will be special rooms, often requiring special treatment both from the point of view of heating and ventilation.

WARMED-AIR SYSTEMS

Unit heaters blowing warmed air, whether heated by hot water or electricity, have been installed in a few recent laboratories. The same considerations apply to this method of heating in laboratories as in other types of building. The system allows for a rapid warm-up where intermittent heating is required. In most research laboratories, however, the heating system will be running continuously at least over the whole working week, if not over the whole of the heating season. Warmed-air unit heaters are probably best suited to large rooms and will become uneconomic if used in large numbers. For example, in order to provide for future adaptability, it might be necessary to install one unit in each structural bay.

The usual difficulties in achieving subjective comfort may also arise in rooms with single-glazed windows, and, in addition, there may be some objection to stirring up fume-laden air if no general extract system is used. To some extent, normal heating methods provide a safety factor in naturally ventilated laboratories in so far as the temperature gradient will encourage heavy fumes to fall to the floor and light fumes to rise to the ceiling. With forced warmed-air systems if there is no artificial extract to ensure a regular pattern of air movement this is not the case. Unless there is good secondary air movement induced by the natural ventilation system, extremely unpleasant working conditions might result.

Ducted warmed-air systems are dealt with below in the section on ventilation.

Ventilation

The general planning of laboratory areas is affected even more by the choice of ventilation system than by the choice of heating system, although of course both must be considered together. Unlike most other buildings, laboratories require good ventilation for direct reasons of safety as well as comfort, particularly in the case of chemical, biochemical, and other laboratories where fumes are generated during the course of the work. Although the most objectionable techniques from the point of view of fume production may be carried out in fume cupboards, quite high rates of air change (of the order of eight to ten air changes per hour) may still be required in the laboratory itself. Even with high air-change rates, however, the amount of air drawn through a normal fume cupboard may well represent a larger volume than that required for efficient ventilation of the room in which it is placed. When this is the case difficult problems of input and extract balance may arise. The difference in volume must either be made up by secondary air input to rooms with fume cupboards, or the resulting pressure differential between different parts of the building must be accepted. Air transfer of this kind may be undesirable or even dangerous, depending upon the kind of work involved.

The ventilation problem, therefore, is twofold: the system must cater for safe, comfortable, and flexible working conditions and also for any special air requirements related to the scientist's work. Moreover, there are usually rooms in a large laboratory building where specialized ventilation is needed. For example, in microbiological work or in radioactive counting rooms it may be essential to provide filtered air to prevent dust build-up. It is rare to find a research building in which artificial ventilation is not needed for special purposes in a few rooms, and therefore ventilation plant of some kind is usually required.

Systems of ventilation range from those in which the whole of the space heating and the required air change are provided by artificial warmed-air input and mechanical extract to those in which only limited amounts of unwarmed air are put into the building or in which some form of mechanical extract is used. At one end of the scale is complete air conditioning, which implies cooling in summer as well as heating in winter, and at the other end the small special room which has normal heating and an axial-flow extract fan to provide a somewhat higher rate of air change than would normally be obtained with natural ventilation. It is rare in this country that full air conditioning can be justified, as the need for summer cooling is only spasmodic, and cooling plant is extremely expensive. A wholly mechanical air-heating system, however, may be justified where some form of mechanical ventilation would in any case be required in parts of the building, or where the nature of the work demands high rates of air change. High-pressure air-input systems are now available, and trunking sizes can be kept within manageable limits. There are two high-pressure systems in common use. One of these uses hot and cold air in separate ducts; each room is fed through a box in which the hot and cold air are mixed automatically in order to provide a room temperature determined by a thermostat setting. The other makes use of hot-water pipes over which more or less air is blown to provide the required room temperature. For laboratory use the latter has the disadvantage that it involves both hot-water pipes and air ducts and may complicate even further the complex array of service lines. With either, double glazing is desirable and it should be possible to run the laboratories without opening windows. Low-pressure warmed-air systems of the conventional kind are of course possible, but may have a considerable effect on economy if room heights have to be adjusted to house trunking of large cross-sectional area. The pressurizing of the space between the false ceiling and the structure above, as in the Danish Atomic Energy Establishment at Risø, is a modified version of this, in which virtually the whole space above the ceiling acts as a duct and the perforated ceiling itself as the input grille. Low-pressure systems of warmed-air input would normally be combined with radiant heating to overcome fabric losses.

With all forms of mechanical input ventilation it is necessary to use mechanical extraction. In laboratories this may be of the normal kind, namely through high- or low-level extract grilles connected to trunking, the size of which will vary in proportion to the amount of air to be extracted. If there are fume cupboards, however, the decision must be taken either to use the fume cupboard as the only means of extraction from the room or to interlock the fume-cupboard extract fan with normal room extract, so that the rate of air change remains constant whether or not the fume cupboard is in use. The latter method is more satisfactory but may be difficult to achieve if flexibility is to be maintained. It may be necessary, for example, to provide for future fume cupboards in rooms where they are not required immediately, in which case the extract trunking must be arranged so that a fume cupboard can be connected in the future, and so that normal room extract works satisfactorily in the meantime. The interlocking of fume extract and room extract is further complicated by two other aspects of ventilation design. First, it may be necessary to provide some room extract at low level to deal with heavy vapours, e.g. solvent fumes of all kinds. Secondly, it will usually be found essential to provide some supplementary make-up air at room temperature where fume cupboards are in use, in order to prevent the system being thrown out of balance by high rates of fume extraction. For example, it is not uncommon for fume cupboards to draw as much as 500 to 700 cu. ft. per minute from the room, and in a room 12 ft. wide by 25 ft. long by 10 ft. high, 500 cu. ft. per minute represents ten air changes per hour. The required air-change rate may be only eight air changes per hour and the difference must be made up by means of some secondary air input if air transfer from one part of the building to another is to be avoided.

Whilst a wholly mechanical air heating and ventilation system may be complex in a building where fume cupboards are in use or may be used in future, the advantages are great in so far as room conditions may be closely designed to give proper air-change rates for human comfort and safety. The cost is high but it may not be very much higher than a normal heating system with which it is necessary to combine some form of tempered air input to replace the air drawn out by fume cupboards. In other words, where controlled air conditions are required, owing to the nature of the work, it may also be economical to use an air-input system over the whole building. A completely flexible scheme of this kind has been designed for the new laboratories of the Imperial Cancer Research Fund at Lincoln's Inn Fields. Here a high-pressure input system is combined with low-pressure make-up air which serves both to replace air drawn out by fume cupboards and also to supply internal rooms. A single system of extract ducts serves for both fume cupboard and room extraction. A proportion of low-level extract is always provided and is combined with either high-level room extraction through grilles or through the fume cupboard. A fume cupboard can be placed in any bay in the future and connected to the extract system, or any fume cupboard may be removed and normal room extract substituted for it.

REFERENCES

(1) BRITISH STANDARDS INSTITUTION. *Recommendations on laboratory furniture and fittings.* London, 1959. *British Standard,* 3202.

(2) PRITCHARD, W. H. 'Materials and services.' ROYAL INSTITUTE OF BRITISH ARCHITECTS. *Report of a symposium on design of teaching laboratories in universities and colleges of advanced technology.* London, 1958. p. 19.

LIGHTING AND COLOUR

LIGHTING and colour are determining factors in the design of laboratory rooms and thus of the laboratory building as a whole. The quantity and quality of natural and artificial illumination affect the efficiency and comfort of those who work in the laboratory. To a large extent window design determines the external appearance of the building, and the distribution of light in the rooms in relation to surface colours largely determines the character of the working environment. If natural lighting only is to be relied upon for a large proportion of the working hours as it has been in this country in the past, the depth to which daylight can penetrate imposes limits on the depth of rooms and may affect ceiling height, and thus the cost of the structure.

Levels of illumination

Artificial-lighting installations have for many years been designed to achieve illumination levels suitable for the various activities carried on in buildings. Recent developments in daylight calculation techniques (1) enable the architect to design natural lighting also within reasonable limits of accuracy. A complete assessment can therefore be made of the amount of light available at any point in a room, from natural or artificial sources. Quantitative criteria for different kinds of building are usually taken from the *Code for Lighting in Buildings* published by the

Table 68. Recommended Illumination Levels for Laboratories (extract from I.E.S. *Code for Lighting in Buildings*).

Type of laboratory	Illumination level (lumens per sq. ft.)	Corresponding daylight factor level*
Laboratories and testing rooms Extra fine instruments, scales . . .	50	10%
General . . .	20	4%
Balance rooms . .	Special	..
Hospital pathological and research laboratories .	20	4%
School laboratories .	15	3%

* Corresponding levels of daylight factor have been added here. These are obtained by expressing illumination level as a percentage of outdoor illumination, for which a value of 500 lm. per sq. ft. is usually assumed in this country.

Illuminating Engineering Society of Great Britain (2). The I.E.S. Code recommendations for laboratories are given in Table 68. Neither balance rooms, which require special lighting, nor school laboratories are included in this study. There are, therefore, two broad categories, 50 lumens per sq. ft. (10 per cent. daylight factor) for reading extra fine instruments and 20 lumens per sq. ft. (4 per cent. daylight factor) for research laboratories generally.

Unlike many other work places, in research laboratories tasks of widely varying visual difficulty may be performed in the same room. In view of this it was thought that the drastic simplification implicit in the I.E.S. Code recommendations for laboratory lighting might lead to uneconomic room design, especially from the point of view of daylighting. The Code, however, also gives scales of illumination for tasks of specified visual difficulty. Any kind of work which can be defined in terms of visual difficulty can, therefore, be placed on the illumination scales. It was decided to study laboratory tasks with a view to placing them on these scales, and in order to discover the frequency of occurrence of the varying degrees of visual difficulty. As part of the main laboratory survey, therefore, observations were made on the visual characteristics of the work being carried out by each scientist (see Part I, Chapter 3).

The amount of light needed to carry out any visual task with a stated degree of efficiency (assessed on speed and accuracy of performance) depends upon the size of the relevant task detail and the contrast between the detail and its background. The I.E.S. Code gives six categories of size and in order to simplify the work of the observers these were combined in pairs as follows:

A—Minute (includes I.E.S. Code categories 'minute' and 'very small')

B—Small (includes I.E.S. Code categories 'small' and 'fairly small')

O—Ordinary (includes I.E.S. Code categories 'ordinary' and 'large').

Three degrees of contrast between task detail and background were used, corresponding to those used in the I.E.S. Code:

2—Good   3—Average   4—Poor

Table 69. Percentages of total working time (excluding microscopy and dark-room work) for which various combinations of detail and contrast occurred in the work of laboratory staff.

Classification of task	A2	A3	A4	B2	B3	B4	O2	O3*	O4	R & W Reading & writing	A Micro-scopy	I Dark room
Size of detail	Minute	Minute	Minute	Small	Small	Small	Ordi-nary	Ordi-nary	Ordi-nary			
Contrast	Good	Average	Poor	Good	Average	Poor	Good	Average	Poor			
Discipline												
Plant Physiology	0·0	1·6	2·6	0·9	7·1	4·5	0·6	22·7	0·0	60·0	2·9	0·0
Physics	0·0	2·2	5·1	1·3	20·5	3·5	0·0	28·7	0·0	38·7	7·9	0·3
Chemistry	0·0	0·3	1·5	1·2	29·2	7·3	0·0	35·5	0·0	25·0	0·0	0·0
Zoology	0·0	2·6	11·4	0·1	15·5	2·4	0·5	25·3	0·1	42·1	19·0	0·0
Biophysics	0·0	0·0	6·9	0·9	20·9	5·2	0·0	20·9	0·0	45·2	1·7	0·0
Entomology	0·3	1·0	10·0	0·9	19·8	3·2	0·3	28·0	0·0	36·5	23·9	0·0
Biochemistry	0·0	0·7	2·0	1·5	34·4	5·5	0·0	33·2	0·0	22·6	0·2	0·0
Pathology	0·0	1·1	4·8	0·0	29·8	8·2	3·4	32·9	0·0	19·8	8·2	0·0
Botany	1·0	3·0	3·6	0·0	26·8	3·9	0·2	26·4	0·0	35·1	6·4	0·8
Microbiology	0·0	2·6	4·4	1·6	29·6	5·9	0·1	30·7	0·0	25·1	7·4	0·0
Animal Physiology	0·0	1·6	7·9	2·0	30·1	6·3	0·0	26·0	0·0	26·1	4·8	0·0
Average	0·1	1·5	5·2	1·0	25·6	5·3	0·4	29·6	0·1	31·2	7·4	0·1

* General activities (cleaning down benches, sweeping floors, washing glassware, &c., included in O3).

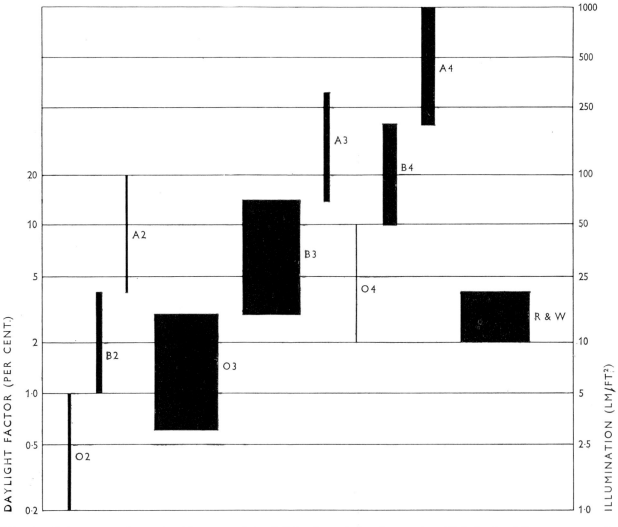

Fig. 69. Laboratory tasks analysed in terms of visual difficulty and placed on scales of lighting level (lumens per sq. ft. and daylight factor). Each solid rectangle represents one task category, the height of which gives the recommended range of illumination for that grade of visual task and the width of which is proportional to the percentage of total working time spent on tasks in that category.

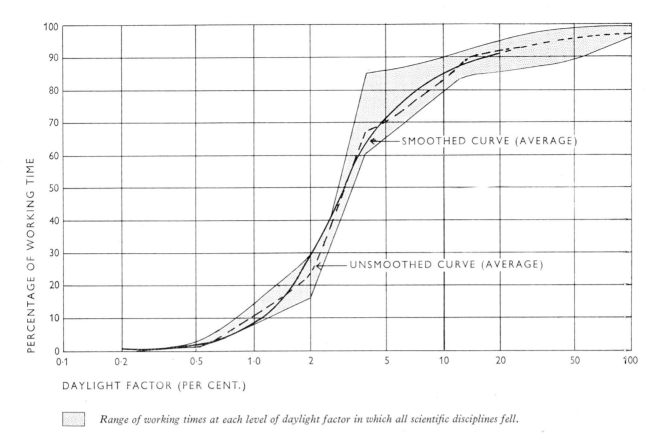

PERCENTAGE OF WORKING TIME

SMOOTHED CURVE (AVERAGE)

UNSMOOTHED CURVE (AVERAGE)

DAYLIGHT FACTOR (PER CENT.)

Range of working times at each level of daylight factor in which all scientific disciplines fell.

Fig. 70. Daylight factors required to give adequate lighting for any proportion of total laboratory working time (averaged for eleven disciplines). The coverage of task categories for given percentages of working time are given in Table 69.

Work carried out in dark rooms and other rooms where daylight is excluded was given a separate category, 1. A further category, A (without a contrast number), was allocated to microscope work, which was difficult to place on the scales. Time spent in reading and writing was separately analysed in the survey, and comes under the heading R & W.

Task classifications shown in Table 69 cover the full range of categories used by the observers, who were instructed at the Building Research Station and allowed a training period to give them proficiency in placing the tasks on the category scale.

The survey data have been analysed in terms of the percentage of total working time spent on each grade of work in eleven disciplines. These are shown in Table 69.

In Fig. 69[1] the percentages averaged for all eleven disciplines have been placed on scales of lighting level (lumens per sq. ft. and daylight factor) derived from those given in the I.E.S. Code. Each solid rectangle represents one task category. The height of the rectangle gives the range of illumination recommended for that kind of work. The width of the rectangle is proportional to the percentage of total working time (averaged for eleven disciplines) spent on tasks

within that category. For example, Grade B3, which requires illumination in the range 15 to 70 lumens per sq. ft. or a daylight factor in the range 3 to 14 per cent., occupied 25·6 per cent. of total working time. Categories B3, O3, and R & W account for about 85 per cent. of all working time and three of the remaining grades occur very rarely. The pattern of distribution of visual difficulty is similar for all disciplines and suggests that criteria can be established which will cater for the whole range of laboratory work.

In Fig. 70 the data are presented in the form of a curve relating percentage of total working time (averaged for 11 disciplines) to the daylight factor which would be adequate for that portion of the working time. A smoothed and an unsmoothed curve are shown, and the shaded area shows the range of working times at each level of daylight factor within which all disciplines fell. The curves are shown in a broken line at levels above 20 per cent. daylight factor, this being the highest level economically obtainable at a useful depth of penetration in a room lit by a window in one wall. There is rapid flattening of the curves at 4 per cent. daylight factor, due to the fact that above this level the percentages of working time covered by proportional increases in daylight factor become very much smaller. For example, an increase from 3 to 4 per cent. covers an additional

[1] Similar figures can be drawn for any individual discipline using the relevant column in Table 69.

19·2 per cent. of working time, whereas a proportionally equal increase from 4 to 5·3 per cent. covers only a further 4·9 per cent. of working time. Unsmoothed curves similar to those in Fig. 70 were drawn for each discipline and the tables in the section dealing with the assessment of criteria were derived from them.

Derivation of design criteria

(a) Daylight

In the past, recommendations and regulations concerning levels of natural lighting have been made in terms of minimum daylight factor. Daylight levels, however, are much higher than the minimum over most of the room area, being lowest at the back of a side-lit room and highest near the windows. If the recommended minimum level is adequate for the most difficult visual task to be performed in the room, it follows that the rest of the room could have its daylighting reduced to this minimum without disadvantage. This approach to the quantitative appraisal of lighting levels is justified in some types of building. For example, in school classrooms, where all the pupils would normally be engaged on the same visual work at the same time in positions all over the room, it is essential that the recommended minimum should be adequate for the most difficult visual task. In laboratories, however, although the range of visual difficulty is great, the research worker is not usually restricted to one small portion of the room, and, with few exceptions, exacting visual work can be done near to a window in good light. It seems reasonable, therefore, to assess daylighting criteria for laboratories with due regard to the fact that a room designed to a nominal minimum has daylight factors higher than the minimum over most of its area.

The data in Table 69 and curves for each discipline similar to the unsmoothed curve in Fig. 70 have been analysed in a number of ways in order to relate requisite daylight factors to each discipline individually, and, in view of the regular distribution pattern amongst the disciplines, to the average for all disciplines. Table 70 shows for individual disciplines (and for the average, cf. unsmoothed curve, Fig. 70) the daylight factors required to cater for percentages of total working time from 10 per cent. to 85 per cent.

Unsmoothed curves for each discipline were used to compile Table 71, which shows the percentages of total working time covered by minimum daylight factors of 2 per cent., 3 per cent., 4 per cent., 5 per cent., and 6 per cent. These disciplines can be placed in order of difficulty to daylight: the order is shown in Table 70. Plant Physiology is the least difficult and Animal Physiology is the most difficult to light; Physics and Chemistry are amongst the more easily lit disciplines.

The daylight factors shown in the tables are minima. For example, referring to Table 70, in rooms with these daylight factors, work occupying the stated percentages of total working time could be carried out in the worst-lit areas of the rooms, in other words, anywhere in such rooms. In practice, however, a great deal more than these percentages of working time would be covered, because work of greater visual difficulty (i.e. outside the given percentages of total working time) could be carried out in parts of the rooms nearer the windows, where daylight factors would be higher than the minimum values given in the tables.

In his work on the specification of illumination levels Weston (3) has stated that it is advisable to recommend one level rather than to specify a range, provided that the recommended level is known to be nearer the probable optimum than to the tolerable minimum. If this is done, then it matters little whether these values are departed from by as much as 30 per cent. in either direction, because curves relating efficiency of visual performance to levels of illumination flatten out for high levels of perfor-

Table 70. Levels of daylight factor required to cater for given percentages of laboratory working time.

Discipline	Order of difficulty to light*	Daylight Factor required to cater for percentages (10–85) of total working time									
		10	20	30	40	50	60	70	75	80	85
Plant Physiology	1	1·2	2·0	2·3	2·6	2·8	3·1	3·4	3·6	3·7	4·0
Physics	2	1·0	1·8	2·3	2·6	3·0	3·4	3·8	4·6	6·6	10·0
Chemistry	3	0·9	1·4	2·1	2·5	3·0	3·5	4·6	5·6	7·6	10·0
Zoology	4	1·1	2·0	2·4	2·7	3·0	3·4	3·9	5·7	9·5	18·5
Biophysics	5–6	1·3	2·2	2·4	2·8	3·1	3·4	3·9	5·4	7·8	11·0
Entomology	5–6	1·0	1·8	2·4	2·7	3·0	3·4	4·2	6·0	8·8	13·0
Biochemistry	7	1·0	1·6	2·2	2·6	3·2	3·7	5·1	6·4	8·1	10·0
Pathology	8	0·8	1·4	2·0	2·6	3·1	3·8	6·0	7·6	10·0	13·0
Botany	9	1·0	1·9	2·4	2·8	3·2	3·6	4·7	6·2	8·3	11·0
Microbiology	10	1·0	1·6	2·3	2·8	3·2	3·7	5·6	7·2	9·2	12·0
Animal Physiology	11	1·1	2·0	2·5	3·0	3·4	4·0	6·5	8·4	11·0	13·7
Average (unsmoothed curve—Fig. 70)		1·0	1·8	2·3	2·6	3·1	3·6	4·6	6·2	8·4	11·0

* Order of difficulty to light is represented as follows: number 1 in the table is the least difficult (i.e. needing the lowest lighting levels) and number 11 is the most difficult (i.e. needing the highest lighting levels).

Table 71. Percentages of laboratory working time catered for by daylight factors of 2, 3, 4, 5, and 6 per cent. (excluding microscopy and dark-room work).

Discipline	Percentage of working time catered for by 2 per cent. D.F.	Percentage of working time catered for by 3 per cent. D.F.	Percentage of working time catered for by 4 per cent. D.F.	Percentage of working time catered for by 5 per cent. D.F.	Percentage of working time catered for by 6 per cent. D.F.
Plant Physiology	19	57	85	87	88
Physics	23	51	73	76	79
Chemistry	28	51	68	72	76
Zoology	20	50	70	73	76
Biophysics	16	46	71	74	77
Entomology	22	49	69	72	75
Biochemistry	26	47	64	69	74
Pathology	29	48	62	66	70
Botany	21	46	67	71	75
Microbiology	25	46	63	68	72
Animal Physiology	21	41	60	65	68
Average (unsmoothed curve—Fig. 70) .	24	48	68	71	74

mance. In assessing the proportion of working time which may be covered by a given illumination level, therefore, some tolerance may be allowed, and it is reasonable to specify levels in terms of minima, as in the above tables, knowing that a safety factor has been allowed, as the minimum levels are rated on a high degree of efficiency of performance.

A typical room lit from a window in one of its walls is shown in Fig. 71. On one side, daylight factor contours have been drawn and on the other three zones representing areas in which tasks occupying various percentages of total working time could be

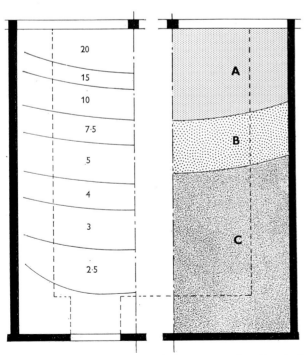

ZONE A. *Visually most critical tasks (15 per cent of working time)*
ZONE B. *Somewhat less critical tasks (10 per cent of working time)*
ZONE C. *Least critical tasks (75 per cent of working time)*

Fig. 71. Equal daylight factor contours for a side-lit laboratory, showing zones in which tasks of different visual difficulty could be satisfactorily performed.

carried out. If the room is assumed to be a chemistry laboratory, it will be seen by reference to Table 70 that with a minimum daylight factor of about 2·5 per cent., work occupying rather less than 40 per cent. of total working time could be done anywhere in the room. The minimum daylight factor would need to be increased from 2·5 per cent. to 5·6 per cent. to light adequately work occupying 75 per cent. of the total working time if the work was distributed at random about the room. As explained above, however, most of the room has daylight factors greater than 2·5 per cent., so that by zoning the work, visual tasks which take much more than 40 per cent. of total working time could be adequately lit. Tasks which occupy 75 per cent. of the total working time could be carried out anywhere in the room nearer to the window than about the mid-point, i.e. in zones A or B (Fig. 71), but by zoning the most difficult visual tasks (which occupy about 15 per cent. of the total working time) to the front quarter of the room (zone A) and relegating tasks of medium difficulty (which occupy 10 per cent. of total working time) to zone B, the available daylight can be fully utilized and all tasks adequately lit, the least visually difficult naturally being located towards the back of the room. This zoning system calls for careful planning of benches, services, &c. If full zoning by visual difficulty proves inconvenient or impossible, either the levels of daylight must be raised all round or supplementary local daylight or artificial light must be supplied where it is needed. For example, if a laboratory bench is placed in the middle of a room, parallel with the window, the illumination level along its whole length is fairly even, and therefore tasks of vastly varying visual difficulty must all be performed under equal lighting conditions. Greater choice and flexibility of use is achieved if benches are placed at right angles to the window wall, thus providing a good range of illumination level so that a more exacting task can be taken nearer to the window.

Taking full account of the diverse nature of the visual tasks carried out in research laboratories and the natural distribution of daylight in a conventional side-lit room, a 3 per cent. minimum daylight factor appears to be a reasonable criterion for such rooms. With zoning, it is adequate on grounds of visual efficiency and it is attainable at moderate room depths in side-lit rooms. Referring to Table 71 it will be seen that on average a 3 per cent. daylight factor will cater for approximately 50 per cent. of total working time, the remaining 50 per cent. being well covered in areas of the room nearer to the window (see Fig. 71).

It will be seen that the validity of the 3 per cent. minimum depends to a very great extent on the diversity of illumination level from the front to the back of side-lit rooms. If a room is top-lit or partially top-lit, higher minimum levels of illumination may be achieved, but the diversity of illumination is less marked. For example, in a deep room with partial top lighting and a reduced amount of side lighting in relation to floor area, the proportion of room area having high daylight factors would be reduced. A higher criterion must be chosen for such rooms if the same proportion of working time is to be catered for. In a previously published report on this aspect of the work (4) the criterion chosen was based on a 75 per cent. coverage of total working time. This is still considered to be suitable under conditions of less diverse natural illumination. From Table 70 it will be seen that it results in a minimum design criterion of 6 per cent. daylight factor. It is suggested that this value is suitable for wholly top-lit rooms and that it will not usually be any more difficult to achieve in such rooms than the 3 per cent. value in side-lit rooms. The criterion adopted for a given laboratory room should depend upon how diverse will be the illumination occurring over its area. Rooms with side lighting only should have a daylight factor minimum of 3 per cent., rooms with evenly distributed top light only should have a minimum of 6 per cent. Where the two methods of lighting are combined, values between 3 per cent. and 6 per cent. should be chosen, due regard being paid to the uniformity of daylight distribution within the room.

(b) Artificial light

Fig. 69 shows lighting levels in both daylight factor and lumens per square foot. The tables in the section concerning daylighting criteria above were drawn up in terms of daylight factor for convenience in dealing with the natural diversity problems inherent in daylighting work, but similar tables could be prepared substituting values in lumens per square foot of artificial lighting for values of daylight factor referred to a sky of 500 lumens per square foot (see footnote to Table 68).

The arguments relating to coverage of working time are applicable to artificial lighting as to daylighting. In assessing artificial lighting criteria, also, the distribution of illumination should be considered.

Well designed artificial-lighting installations for work places would aim at uniform levels of illumination over the whole of the working area. Artificial lighting is, in this respect, similar to natural lighting from roof lights only. No criterion which can be equated to the suggested 3 per cent. daylight factor can therefore be evolved and a single criterion of 30 lumens per square foot (equivalent to 6 per cent. daylight factor) is thought to cover a sufficiently large proportion of total working time. Where tasks of extreme visual difficulty have to be performed under artificial light, special local lighting can be used. Other factors must be considered in assessing illumination criteria for deep rooms in which artificial lighting is to be used at the back of the rooms during daylight hours. These are discussed below.

Reflection factors of laboratory surfaces

In calculating levels of illumination it is essential to know the reflection factors of surfaces within the room from which incident light will be reflected (5). In daylighting computations the proportional contribution to overall illumination which is obtained by inter-reflection inside the room is greater towards the back of a side-lit room, where daylight factor values are critical. Light-coloured surfaces reflect more light than dark ones and account must be taken of this in lighting calculations. In order to facilitate

Table 72. Reflection factors of some materials used for ceilings, walls, floor finishes, and bench tops.

Surface	Material	Reflection factor (per cent.)		
		Max.	Min.	Representative
Ceilings	Acoustical materials	82	26	50
	Paints	90	9	60
Walls	Acoustical materials	82	26	50
	Wall boards	89	5	20
	Asphalt wall tiles	78	5	30
	Ceramic wall tiles	88	5	50
Floor finishes	Asphalt floor tiles	60	4	10
	Ceramic floor tiles	71	8	20
	Rubber floor tiles	54	19	30
	Linoleum	63	4	15
	Oak flooring	29	13	20
Bench tops	Polished dark hardwoods (teak)	..	..	5–10
	Cork linoleum	..	..	10–15
	Medium oak or similar stained wood	..	..	12–16
	Black slate	..	..	4
Miscellaneous	Stainless steel (in use)	..	..	40
	Bookshelves (dark timber, shelves full of books)	..	..	12–16
	Shelves (white tile backing, bottles of liquids)	..	..	35
	Shelves carrying brown bottles	..	..	22

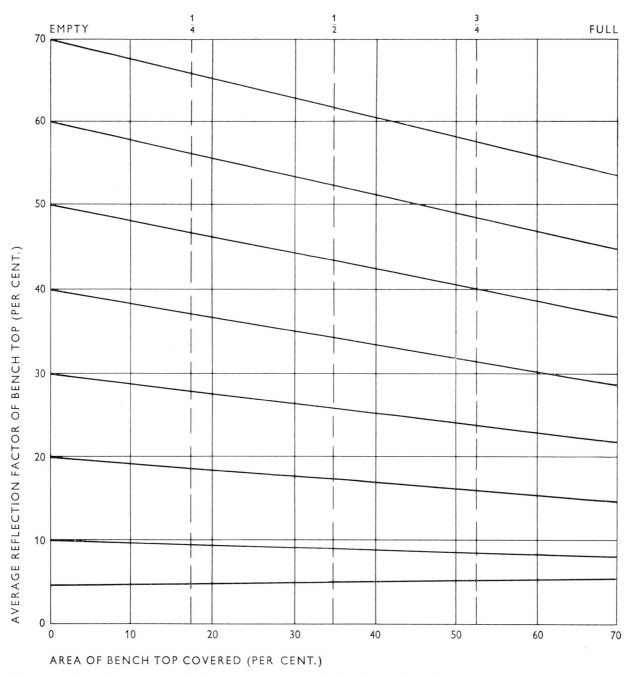

Fig. 72. Effect of the presence of glassware on average reflection factor of bench tops.

such calculations a study of typical laboratory surfaces was made.

For applied colours, that is paints, &c., the increasing use of the Munsell system of colour identification makes it possible to derive the reflection factor quite easily from the Munsell reference.[1]

Table 72 shows reflection factors of a number of materials and finishes for ceilings, walls, floors,

[1] The recently published British Standard 2660: 1955 (6) gives Munsell references for a range of 101 standard colours. An approximation for the reflection factor value can be obtained from the Munsell reference by means of the following formula:

$$\rho = V(V-1)$$

where ρ = the required reflection factor (per cent.) and V = Munsell Value.

timber fittings, &c. It is given as a guide for use in conjunction with current daylight calculation techniques (1), (7). Some allowance should be made for deterioration of surface finishes and it can be deduced from studies conducted by the Building Research Station that a correction factor of the order of 0·8 should be applied in order to obtain a reflection factor more representative of the average during the life of the building.

A further difficulty arises in lighting calculations for laboratory rooms. Benches and other surfaces are often covered with apparatus and glassware and the normal reflection factor of the clear surface may not give a true representation of the reflection factor of the surface in use. A number of studies were carried out at the Building Research Station to assess the effect of conditions found in normal practice. Fig. 72 has been evolved from the collected data and shows the effect on reflection factor of various degrees of coverage.

Daylight reaches the work place directly from the sky (the sky component) and indirectly after reflection (the indirect component). It is the latter which is affected by changing the reflection factors of walls, ceiling, and floor. Indirect component is calculated by means of the Building Research Station inter-reflection formula (8) or with the aid of nomograms or tables derived from it (1), (7), (8), (9). Average and minimum indirect components are calculated, the former being applicable to the central areas of side-lit rooms, the latter to the parts of the room farthest from the window.

Laboratory furniture occupies a considerable proportion of the floor area and the colour of bench tops and sides may vary considerably. In order to apply the calculation technique to laboratory rooms with confidence, it was thought advisable to check the inter-reflection formula against measurements made in a model room, using two alternative bench layouts and various combinations of reflection factors for tops and sides of the benches.

Fig. 73 shows alternative bench layouts and Table 73 the calculated and measured values of average and minimum indirect components together with the various colour combinations of bench tops and sides, the latter modifying the average reflection factor of the room as a whole. The reflection factors of room surfaces other than bench tops and sides remained constant throughout the experiment and were as follows:

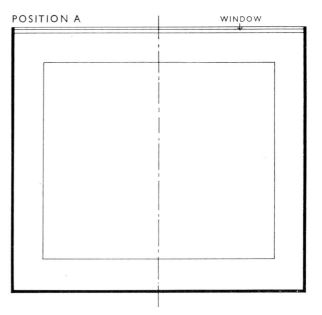

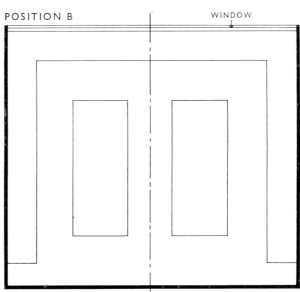

Fig. 73. Plan of model room showing the alternative positions of laboratory benches used in preliminary measurement and calculation of the indirect component of daylight factor (see Table 73).

	Reflection factor per cent.
Wall under window .	34
Side and rear walls .	41
Ceiling . . .	69
Floor . . .	29
Window glass . .	15

Table 73. Comparison between measured and calculated values of average and minimum indirect component showing effect of bench position.

Colour of top	Colour of sides	Position (see Fig. 73)	Average r.f. of interior	Average indirect component (per cent.)		Minimum indirect component (per cent.)	
				Calculated	Measured	Calculated	Measured
N	N	A	49	3·0	2·5	2·3	1·7
N	N	B	50	3·0	2·6	2·3	1·8
W	G	A	46	2·6	2·5	1·9	1·7
W	G	B	45	2·4	2·8	1·8	1·8
B	N	A	43	2·0	1·8	1·4	1·3
B	N	B	43	2·0	1·7	1·4	1·2
G	G	A	40	1·8	2·0	1·2	1·3
G	G	B	39	1·6	2·0	1·1	1·3
B	G	A	39	1·6	1·7	1·1	1·2
B	G	B	37	1·4	1·6	0·9	1·1

Key: N = Natural, reflection factor 65 per cent.
     B = Black, reflection factor 4 per cent.

G = Grey, reflection factor 20 per cent.
W = White, reflection factor 75 per cent.

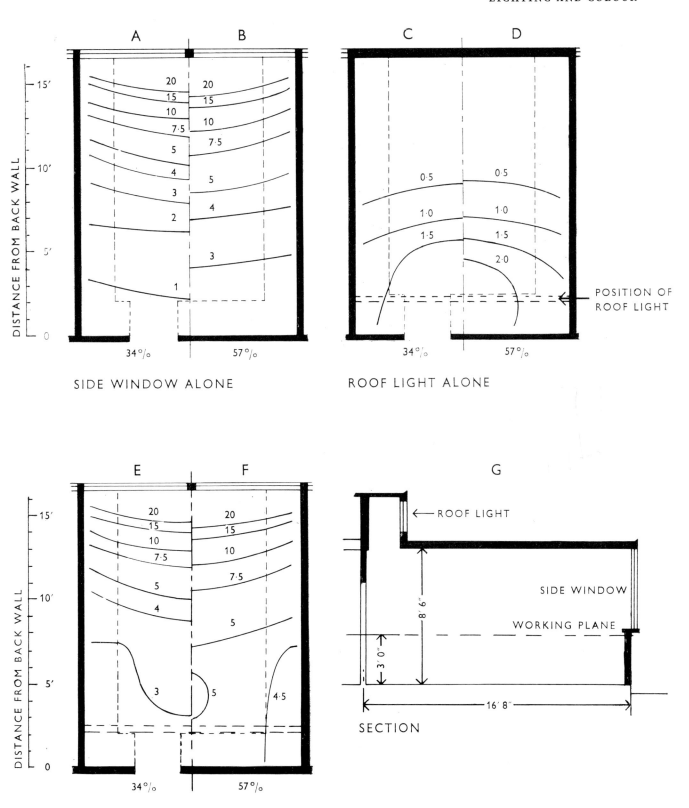

Fig. 74. Comparison between equal daylight factor contours obtained by calculation for laboratory rooms having average interior reflection factors of 34 and 57 per cent. (Reflection factor of roof outside roof light is 40 per cent.)

It will be seen from Table 73 that indirect component of daylight factor is not significantly affected by variation of bench position. The values in the table show the improvement in natural-lighting level that can be effected by making bench tops of light-coloured material. The value of minimum measured

indirect component given in Table 73 for BGB (1·1 per cent.) would apply to a black slate bench top, whilst the value for NNA (1·7 per cent.) would apply to a light-coloured plastic finish. A teak bench top would fall somewhere between the values given for BGB (1·1 per cent.) and GGB (1·3 per cent.).

Comparison of calculated and measured values shows that the Building Research Station inter-reflection formula gives reasonably good results for minimum indirect component except for conditions NNA and NNB, but for the average indirect component the calculated values vary slightly more in relation to the measured values, especially with lighter coloured benches. In room positions where the indirect component is critical in achieving a day-lighting criterion, mainly in positions farthest from the window, the minimum indirect component is, however, applicable, and thus in most practical applications reasonably accurate results may be expected by using the formula.

This study serves to stress the importance of reflected light in rooms lit from one side only. In some parts of the working area the achievement of a specified minimum daylight factor may often depend upon the darkness or lightness of the surfaces within the room. This interdependence of lighting level and surface treatment is further emphasized when the colours of room surfaces generally are considered. Studies in the application of the suggested daylight-factor criteria are described below and it will be seen that in one case an increase in average reflection factor from 34 to 57 per cent. more than trebled the minimum daylight factor (from 0·75 to 2·75 per cent. daylight factor).

The lightness of the interior of a laboratory will also affect the efficiency of the artificial-lighting installation. With properly designed fittings, advantage can be taken of light surfaces in order to integrate and diffuse the light output and to increase the uniformity of distribution on the bench.

The application of lighting criteria to the design of laboratory rooms

Only the provision of an adequate amount of light has so far been considered. This is, however, merely one aspect of lighting design. The more subjective aspects such as directional quality, the avoidance of discomfort glare, and the choice of colour are also of major importance. They determine not only the degree of comfort and pleasantness in the visual environment but also the character of the rooms. These aspects were of course taken into account in studies on the application of the quantitative criteria which were carried out using both calculation and model techniques.

The first example studied was a small room, part of a project designed by the team for the Agricultural Research Council as an addition to the Grasslands Research Station at Hurley. The room was designed at a fairly early stage in the team's work, making use of the results of the pilot survey; it was 13 ft. wide and 16 ft. deep.[1] For the purposes of the first calculations, reflection factors of interior surfaces typical

[1] These are the approximate inside dimensions of the room: the building was designed on a 3 ft. 4 in. grid, the room grid being 13 ft. 4 in. by 16 ft. 8 in.

of current practice were specified by the team after making observations in a number of existing laboratories. They were as follows:

	Reflection factor per cent.
Walls . . .	40
Ceiling . . .	75
Floor . . .	12
Window glass . .	15

Computations of daylight factor with a window the full length of the 13 ft. wall and reaching from a 3 ft. sill to the ceiling in each case showed that little more than 1 per cent. daylight factor was obtained at the back of the room even with a 10 ft. ceiling.

Fig. 74A shows equal daylight factor contours for a similar room with an 8 ft. 6 in. ceiling, a window in one wall only, and with a 34 per cent. average interior reflection factor. Certain general conclusions could be drawn from this preliminary study. It was obvious that with average reflection factors of this order (34 per cent.) it would be impossible to achieve the 3 per cent. daylight factor for side-lit rooms in an economical way. With each ceiling height for which calculations were made, the window was assumed to be as large as possible, maintaining a 3 ft. high sill. For ceiling heights of the order of 10 or 11 ft. the criterion could not be met. It appeared, therefore, that further calculations should be made using a higher average interior reflection factor, the value of which could be assessed by means of a subjective model study (see Part I, Chapter 3). Observers were able to change the colours of walls, floor, and ceiling and inspect them under conditions similar to those experienced in a full-sized building.

It was found possible and practical to improve the average reflection factor to a considerable degree, using combinations of suitable and available materials. The value eventually chosen for the calculations was 57 per cent. Equal daylight factor contours using this value are shown in Fig. 74B. Three per cent. daylight factor was achieved 4 ft. from the back of the room with a ceiling height as low as 8 ft. 6 in.

Fig. 75 relates daylight factors 1 ft. from the back of the room (on the centre line and at a point near the side wall) to ceiling height. Again, for each ceiling height, the window reached from side wall to side wall and from ceiling to a 3 ft. high sill.

Fig. 76 shows the relationship between average interior reflection factor and daylight factor near the back wall of the room. The daylight factor is markedly dependent on the reflection factor, and it is clear that the lightness of the interior colours is highly important in relation to daylighting which comes from the side window. Values calculated for the small room described above were used in preparing Fig. 6, but the relationship would not be significantly different for other configurations of room size and shape. On the evidence, it would appear that for economic lighting design, average interior reflection factor for

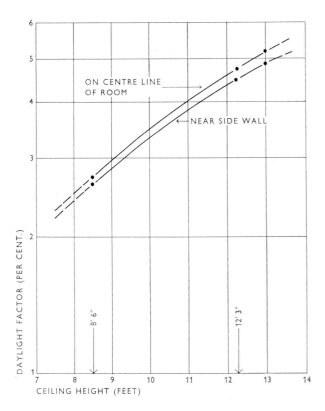

Fig. 75. Variation of daylight factor (1 ft. from the back wall of a laboratory room) with ceiling height. Room lit by side window only.

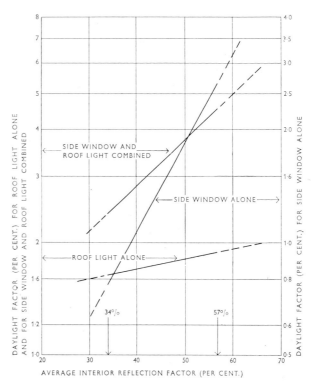

Fig. 76. Variation of daylight factor with average interior reflection factor in a 16 ft. deep room. (Daylight factors are averages for five positions near back wall of room.)

laboratories should not be allowed to fall below about 50 per cent.

The depth of this room (16 ft.) is of the order commonly found in many existing laboratories, but the results of the survey indicated that fairly long runs of continuous bench (up to 25 ft.) would be preferable for many disciplines. For economy in building layout and more especially in servicing as well as for convenience in zoning of tasks, it is better if these continuous runs of benching are placed at right angles to the windows.

The satisfactory results obtained in the small room with surfaces of high reflection factor suggested that efforts should be made to design rooms deeper than 16 ft., which could nevertheless be properly lit. It was realized that these studies would have to include both rooms for single-story buildings which could be top-lit and rooms for multi-story buildings, where no top lighting was possible.

As a first step it was decided to see what could be achieved in the small room dealt with above by adding a roof light towards the back of the room. Several kinds of roof lights were tried in the model and the arguments in favour of the indirect, vertically glazed type chosen (Fig. 74G) are set out in the section dealing with model studies below. The contribution to natural lighting from the roof light, for both 34 per cent. and 57 per cent. values of average reflection factor, is shown in Figs. 74CD and 74EF, and curves showing the variation with reflection factor

for the room with a roof light have been added in Fig. 76.

When assessing these results the variation of day-lighting criterion with diversity of illumination (see pp. 102 and 104) must be borne in mind. For this combination of roof light and side lighting, a minimum daylight factor of about 4 per cent. is thought to be suitable and could be adequately met in the room as shown.

The daylight factor contours in Fig. 74EF encouraged the team to think in terms of much deeper rooms, up to 24 ft. from window to rear wall. The lighting studies from this point onwards, therefore, were concerned with daylighting of deep single-story rooms by means of side lighting and supplementary top lighting, and the design of similar rooms for multi-story buildings, using supplementary artificial lighting. It has been assumed in these studies that as much use as possible should be made of natural light. In some laboratories, however, particularly those in which bacteriological work is carried out, sun penetration and thermal solar gain must be controlled. These problems are discussed below in relation to the experimental laboratory at Cambridge.

Deep rooms in single-story buildings

The distribution of natural light in a 16 ft. deep room with side lighting only was shown in Fig. 74B. This may be compared with Fig. 77A which shows the distribution of daylight from a side window only in a

109

room 24 ft. deep, a typical laboratory in the experimental building designed by the team as an extension to the Animal Research Unit at Cambridge. The daylight factor values were measured in the unit model (Fig. 37). With side lighting only the daylight level at the back of the room fell off rapidly beyond mid-depth to about 0·5 per cent. daylight factor at the rear wall. The room was only 8 ft. high at the side window. Higher values of daylight factor could, of course, be obtained in a similar room with a greater ceiling height and a larger window area (see Figs. 75 and 79).

Interior reflection factors were as follows:

	Reflection factor per cent.	Colour	
		Munsell ref.	B.S. no.
Side walls . .	72	5Y 9·25/1	4–046
Back wall . .	56	10Y 8/2	5–058
Floor . . .	44	N7	9–095
Bench tops . .	21	2·5Y 5/2	3–037
Openings (e.g. window into corridor) .	14	2·5Y 4/0·5	9–101
Ceiling and window wall . . .	78	white	

In order to supplement the daylight at the back of the room, it was decided to develop further the indirect type of roof lighting originally used in the smaller laboratory (see section, Fig. 74C). The diagrammatic sections (Fig. 78) show two types of permanent sun control louvres. It will be seen from the section through the finished building (Fig. 42), that the outside horizontal louvres were eventually chosen. The model measurements given in Fig. 77 were made with the latter type of louvre system in position. The relative merits of the louvre systems are discussed below from the point of view of sun glare and the reduction of solar heat gain.

The addition of the roof light raises the illumination levels from the centre to the back of the room as shown in Fig. 77B and c. The 3 per cent. daylight factor criterion is achieved about 8 ft. from the rear wall. Most of the rear portion of the room is, however, taken up by a fume cupboard on one side and the wash-up sink and draining board on the other. The fume cupboard is equipped with built-in lighting, and no exacting visual tasks are performed at the wash-up sink. Satisfactory levels of illumination were obtained in this case in spite of a louvre system which reduced considerably the amount of direct light obtained at the back of the room from the roof light. The building faces south-west, a condition dictated by the site and the existing buildings. The model studies showed that with a less exacting sun condition (e.g. without louvres), the 3 per cent. criterion would be met over the whole of the room. No great daylighting problems are raised by deepening rooms in single-story buildings. Quite high levels of illumination can be provided by roof lighting as, for example, in many recent factory buildings.

In most disciplines exacting visual tasks must be performed for quite long periods of time, for example, reading dials, handling of small amounts of material with delicate instruments, &c. In work of this kind double shadows, or shadows which are reversed when moving from one bench position to another, are confusing and may result in reading errors.

The type of roof light used in the model studies described above was chosen as the best solution to glare and shadow reversal problems.

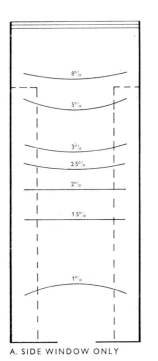
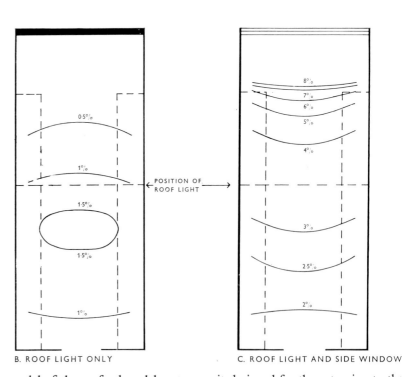

A. SIDE WINDOW ONLY   B. ROOF LIGHT ONLY   C. ROOF LIGHT AND SIDE WINDOW

Fig. 77. Daylight factors measured in a model of the 24 ft. deep laboratory unit designed for the extension to the Animal Research Station, Cambridge, for the Agricultural Research Council.

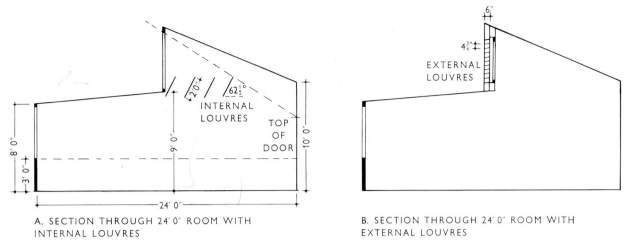

A. SECTION THROUGH 24′ 0″ ROOM WITH
INTERNAL LOUVRES

B. SECTION THROUGH 24′ 0″ ROOM WITH
EXTERNAL LOUVRES

Fig. 78. Diagrammatic sections of the 24 ft. deep room showing internal and external louvre systems.

Deep rooms in multi-story buildings

It is obvious from Fig. 77A that in a deep room in a multi-story building lighting from a side window only would fall off too rapidly to allow efficient use of the room in natural light only. Calculated daylight factor values for a room of similar depth, but with a ceiling 12 ft. high, are shown in Fig. 79. It will be seen that even with a room of this height, the lighting criteria are not achieved over a large enough proportion of the room. Moreover, in cost studies (Part II, Chapter 6) room height is shown to be an important factor in overall cost. It is essential therefore to economic laboratory design to keep ceiling heights down to the absolute minimum, consistent with efficient room use (i.e. height of apparatus) and good ventilation (see Part II, Chapter 3, Engineering Services).

Deep rooms facilitate efficient working and lend themselves to simple and economical servicing. The lighting criteria suggested in this report, however, cannot be met by natural lighting only, in such rooms in multi-story buildings, unless excessively expensive high rooms and very large areas of glazing are used, with their attendant sky glare and heat loss problems. Supplementary artificial lighting, which can be used during the day as well as after dark, must be provided if the lighting levels necessary to visual efficiency are to be achieved.

Fundamental research on the concept of artificial lighting as a supplement to daylight is at present being carried out at the Building Research Station, and the model studies of the Cambridge laboratory building form part of this work. In terms of initial building cost, daylight is not free. To make use of it in rooms of economic and efficient plan shape, it must be paid for as building volume (added room height) and heat loss in winter and solar heat gain in summer

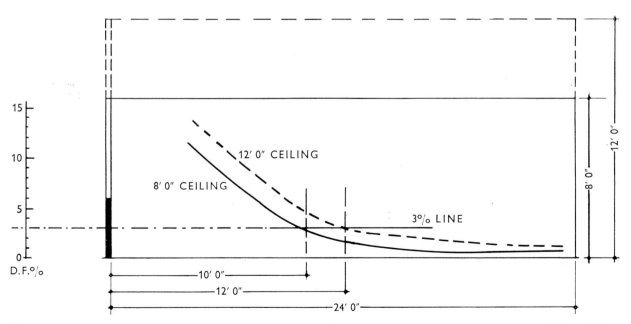

Fig. 79. Daylight factors from side window only on a 3 ft. working plane in a 24 ft. deep room. Ceiling heights 8 ft. and 12 ft.: windows 11 ft.×5 ft. and 11 ft.×9 ft. respectively.

(excessive heating costs or double glazing with some form of air conditioning). For a group of six school laboratories it has been shown (10) that on a thirty-five year amortization (5 per cent.) of building cost, a supplementary artificial-lighting installation (including maintenance and running costs) is a cheaper method of achieving a required minimum level of illumination in deep rooms.

The provision of an adequate illumination level for efficient seeing is, of course, only the beginning of good lighting design. The brightness pattern of the interior in relation to the light source (whether natural or artificial) determines visual comfort (11); glare must be avoided and a pleasant as well as an efficient lighting character achieved. It is a simple matter to determine how much artificial illumination is required on the working plane to supplement daylight at the back of a room, but to be satisfactory, supplementary artificial lighting must overcome the feeling of gloom and achieve a balance between the brightnesses of naturally and artificially lighted surfaces. This requires an appreciation of subjective apparent brightness, as opposed to photometric brightness, and demands that natural and artificial light sources be designed together. For example, a surface of known photometric brightness will *appear* darker or lighter according to the adaptation level of the eye of the observer. Adaptation is determined by the brightnesses of *all* the surfaces in the field of view, and therefore a very bright surface of large area such as a large window, through which a bright sky is visible, raises the adaptation level and will reduce the *apparent* brightness of less bright surfaces in the room. Window size and design must be related to the design of the brightness pattern in the room as well as illumination levels for efficient seeing.

Observational studies are still in progress, and only the conclusions so far reached are available for inclusion in this report. Although the Cambridge laboratory is a single-story building, the model was also used to study lighting for a room of similar depth in a multi-story building and forms part of the general investigation of supplementary artificial lighting at the Building Research Station.

A 3 ft. 4 in. wide louvred laylight, the full width of the room, was used in the observations. This was dropped 6 in. below ceiling level, the exposed edge being in translucent material, in order to light the ceiling. Observations were made with the laylight in two positions, adjacent to the rear wall of the room and 3 ft. 4 in. from it. Observers were given control of a dimmer which raised or lowered the output of light from the laylight. They were asked to vary the level so that the appearance of gloom at the back of the room was dispelled, and to produce a pleasing lighting environment, eliminating the effect of glare from the window as far as possible while maintaining a brightness balance in the room as a whole. The brightness of the sky seen through the window was varied by means of neutral

filters placed over the window, in order to assess the effects of changing sky conditions. Results so far show that the levels chosen are directly proportional to sky brightness, and thus it is necessary to choose a sky brightness or a range of brightnesses on which to base recommended artificial lighting levels. The brightness chosen was 1,500 ft. lamberts (average sky brightness), which occurs frequently during the working day at most times of the year (10), (12). For a simple side window such as that used in the model, and with room depths of the order of 24 ft., the available data indicate that illumination levels on the working plane at the back of the room should be 40–50 lumens per sq. ft. Somewhat lower levels were chosen when the laylight was placed away from the rear wall. This suggests that the artificial lighting influenced the character of the whole room, even to some slight extent near the windows. Other side effects were noted but require further study before conclusions can be drawn from them. For example, darker colours towards the back of the room required higher levels of artificial illumination, and at low levels of sky brightness there was a tendency for the observer to use the artificial lighting to brighten up the whole room environment, rather than to balance the brightness with that of the reduced daylight. This is a further reason for choosing a commonly occurring, moderately high sky brightness for design purposes.

Although these levels of supplementary lighting are high, they are not unreasonably so, especially in laboratories where, as already shown above (p. 104), illumination levels of the order of 30 lumens per sq. ft. are needed for visual efficiency. With illumination levels of this order it is essential to design the artificial and natural lighting in conjunction with each other in order to produce a suitable visual environment in which the character of the lighting is appropriate to function, and at the same time efficient and comfortable.

In laboratories, windows and supplementary lighting must produce working conditions which are stimulating but glare-free. The choice of colour for laboratory surfaces is somewhat restricted, but nevertheless can contribute a great deal in this respect. Colour is discussed in the section dealing with subjective studies below.

The variation in the spectral quality of mixed sunlight and skylight is considerable, throughout the day and the seasons, but in an environment lit only by daylight is unnoticed. When artificial lighting is superimposed on daylight, however, the variations may be more apparent owing to the constant quality of the artificial light, which serves as a reference point for comparison. Insufficient experience of supplementary lighting has been gained to make firm recommendations on the best type of fluorescent lamp for all situations. Observers who took part in the model studies at the Building Research Station raised no complaints about either 'Northlight' or 'Daylight' tubes, but the blend was not perfect. It has been suggested (10) that if supplementary artificial lighting is used increasingly in deep buildings, lamp manufacturers may wish to design lamps specially for this purpose. For the moment 'Daylight' tubes are probably best on the score of efficiency and compatibility with mixed sunlight and daylight.

The remaining problem of supplementary artificial lighting is the integration of the sources used in daytime with the general artificial lighting for use when darkness falls. In laboratories this difficulty is less marked than in other types of building, where fairly low levels of general artificial lighting are normally acceptable after dark. Artificial lighting levels of the order of 30 lumens per sq. ft. are needed in laboratories, and to provide supplementary lighting for daytime use of 40–50 lumens per sq. ft. does not raise insuperable economic difficulties. A number of methods of change over have been suggested. Danish workers in this field would prefer a completely separate artificial lighting system for use after dark, introducing a different quality of light with different spectral composition. The main argument for such a system is that it maintains the subjective effect occasioned by the complete change of visual character which occurs when the lights are switched on in a room normally lit only by daylight. The added cost would probably be prohibitive for normal purposes in this country. Switching can be arranged so that a number of lamps in the supplementary system are put out when the normal artificial lighting comes into use. If only small changes of illumination are involved (of the order of 10 lumens per sq. ft.), the improvement in overall brightness balance would probably compensate for the slight loss at the back of the room. This method is to be tried by the Ministry of Education (10), but the change over will be made when the classrooms are empty, and the pupils entering the wholly artificially lit environment will automatically adapt their vision to the new conditions. No immediate comparison with the daytime character of the rooms will then be possible.

For laboratories it is suggested that when permanent supplementary lighting is to be used the system should be designed to give 40 to 50 lumens per sq. ft. over the whole working area, and that switching should be arranged so that artificial light can be brought into use progressively from the back wall towards the window wall of the room. The daytime lighting should dispel any subjective feeling of gloom and balance the light from the window so that neither artificial nor natural source is dominant. The system should also be glare-free when the whole room is artificially lit after dark.

One of the laboratory units in the experimental laboratory at Cambridge is to be equipped with a translucent laylight over the part of the room occupied by the roof light. For the purposes of the trial the roof light will be temporarily blacked out and an artificial level of 40 lumens per sq. ft. at the back of the room will be provided by fluorescent tubes mounted above the laylight. The same level of illumination for use after dark will be provided by fluorescent tubes fitted with clip-on louvres mounted parallel with and above the forward edges of the benches. The system will be studied under actual working conditions and adjustments made if necessary.

Model studies

The model illustrated in Part I, Chapter 3, was used for three main purposes apart from direct illumination measurements and supplementary artificial lighting assessments:

Assessment of window and roof light design.
Colour studies.
Sun-penetration studies.

These are dealt with separately below.

Assessment of window and roof light design

The work of the team has led generally to the conclusion that benches at right angles to the window-wall are conducive to compact planning and are more economic to service. Windows of various sizes and shapes were tried in the model, bearing in mind that it may be better to maintain a solid panel of outside wall below window level against which a radiator may be placed or beside which a writing table or piece of equipment may stand. There is every advantage in having windows immediately adjacent to the ends of the benches, rather than a solid wall, provided that adequate sun protection is given in south-facing rooms. For workers at benches near the window it may be desirable to reduce the visible area of high sky in order to prevent glare if exacting visual work is to be carried out without discomfort. Horizontal baffles, roof overhangs, and outrigged vertical baffles were all found to help in this respect in the model studies, but all reduced the daylight levels in the room. The uses of various types of blind for this purpose are discussed below in the section on sun penetration.

Assessments of several kinds of roof light for single-story buildings were made in the model. Model laboratory benches were arranged in the rooms and the observers were asked to look at instrument scales, glassware, &c., on the bench with each type of roof light. The general character of the lighting was also considered in relation to glare, distribution of illumination, and the general brightness pattern of the interior. The observers were asked to consider comfort and pleasantness in the working environment as well as illumination levels on the visual tasks.

Normal clerestory lighting (Fig. 80A) allows direct penetration of sunlight over a considerable area of benching and also brings a direct view of sky to a worker at almost any point at the bench. A strong bright pattern is produced over a large area of the

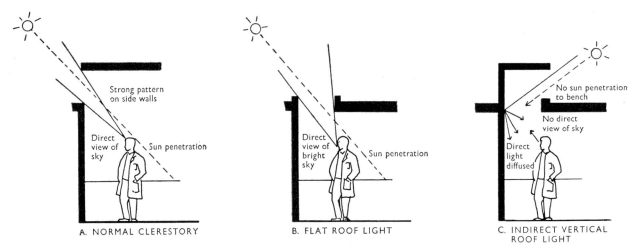

Fig. 80. Comparison of toplighting systems.

side wall and a reversal of shadow occurs along the bench. This was found to be disturbing and makes the reading of fine scales and other visual alignment tasks difficult. Horizontal roof lights (Fig. 80B) have similar disadvantages, except that some diffusion may be possible in order to prevent shadow reversal. The type of roof light chosen for the Cambridge building as a result of this work (a modified version of that shown in Fig. 80C) gives indirect lighting from a reversed clerestory window. Incident daylight is either from the same direction as that from the main window, or is diffused by inter-reflection, and therefore produces no shadow reversal. Sun penetration can be more easily controlled either by internal or external louvres and a direct view of sky is only possible from positions very near the rear wall of the room.

An attempt is usually made to arrange for laboratories for biological and microbiological work to have a northerly aspect. Where this is done, there is no sunlight problem if a roof light faces in the same direction as the main windows. The southerly aspect of the experimental building in Cambridge was largely determined by site considerations and in this case the design of the roof light was chosen mainly on the grounds of non-reversal of shadows. Under other circumstances, however, other solutions might have to be considered and the problems of lighting balanced against those of solar gain and shadow reversal.

Colour studies

The first colour studies carried out in the model were aimed at discovering how far reflection factors could reasonably be raised above those found by the team in existing laboratories, in order to obtain a higher proportion of reflected light towards the back of the rooms. It was found possible to raise the average reflection factor of a laboratory interior quite considerably, as described in the section on the application of lighting criteria (see pp. 108 et seq. above), and the effect of this on daylight factor levels has

been discussed above and is shown in Fig. 76, with reference to the original 16 ft. deep room.

The extent to which interior design generally and the integration of colour and lighting in particular can be rationalized has received a great deal of attention in recent years and particularly since the publication of colour studies for hospital interiors by the Nuffield Provincial Hospitals Trust (13), and for school interiors by the Ministry of Education (14). The work on colour and reflection factors in interiors which has been done at the Building Research Station is described in a series of papers, to which reference can be made (8), (9), (15). This work also led to the publication of British Standard 2660 (6), which places at the designer's disposal a tool which combines the ready control of the Munsell system with a more practical approach based on a limited number of colours agreed with the principal paint manufacturers. All the colours used in the model studies are defined both by Munsell references and the relevant reference number from British Standard 2660 (see also footnote on p. 105).

Whilst the effect of lightness (Munsell value) of interior finishes on the amount of daylight obtained in a room by inter-reflection can be calculated with considerable accuracy, the effect of this and other attributes of colour on the quality of daylighting and room character is still to be explored. For example, the overall subjective impression experienced in a room may be changed by varying the hue and chroma of the surface finishes, while maintaining the average value or reflection factor constant. Effects of this kind were studied in the model in relation to the method of daylighting for small laboratory rooms. It is not claimed that the colours mentioned here are the only possible ones, for this type of room, but it is hoped that a discussion of the principles will give some guidance to those choosing colour schemes for laboratories. Coloured papers were used to vary the colours of walls and ceiling; timber veneers were applied to benches and other furniture and coloured linoleum used for floor coverings.

In order to study more closely the shortcomings of several colour schemes seen by the team in existing laboratories, the colours were reproduced in the model. The dull and depressing appearance which had been noted in the actual buildings appeared to be caused by lack of contrast between floor, walls, and bench fronts and tops, and by the predominance of dark hardwoods. The first attempt to improve upon this kind of room was made by raising the values of the colours, but using only greys and whites. A light-grey lino was used, walls were coloured in a pale grey (Munsell N.9), the ceiling was white, the window wall a darker grey (N.4) and a similar colour for bench tops with bench fronts painted white. The window frame, mullions, &c., were also painted white in order to reduce the contrast between the window bars and the sky. Apart from the general cold and flat effect of the monochromatic arrangement, observers noted that the high contrast between dark bench tops and very light walls was insistent and disturbing and that there was too great a contrast between the brightnesses of the rear and side walls due to the high brightness induced on the rear wall by the roof light. The dark-grey colour on the window wall, receiving no direct light, gave too marked a contrast with the white window frames and gave an impression of dullness near the window. The brightness contrast created on the side walls by the roof light was reduced by using a very light colour and was much more comfortable visually for a person working at a bench near the back of the room than the darker colours previously used.

It was decided that bench tops in the final scheme for the 16 ft. deep room should be in timber, this being the most common benching material, and the choice of colours was made with this as a starting point. A number of floor colours were tried: a light coloured floor was found to improve the diffusion of light in the room and was a major factor in brightening the room as a whole. The colours finally chosen were as follows:

	Colour	
	Munsell ref.	B.S. no.
Hardwood benches and furniture	2·5Y 5/2	3–037
Light-grey P.V.C. floor covering	N7	9–095
Ceiling and interior surface around roof light . .	matt white	
Window frames, door, and architrave . . .	gloss white	
Side walls—reduced yellow .	5Y 9·25/1	4–046
Rear wall—reduced yellow .	5Y 8/2	4–047
Window wall—blue . .	7·5B 3/4	7–085

The choice of wall colours was made in accordance with the preliminary colour study, the high-value colours on the side walls being maintained, the rear wall being slightly darkened in order to equalize the apparent brightness of rear and side walls. It was also found that high-chroma colours can be used to advantage on window walls, especially below sill

level. Their brilliance is considerably reduced in this situation but nevertheless adds stimulation to the general environment.

The colour of benches in relation to walls against which they are seen has an important effect upon the visual comfort of the worker. Dark-coloured bench tops provide good contrast with glassware and light-coloured objects generally, but cause a strong contrast with light-coloured side walls. This was considerably improved by introducing a lighter coloured timber skirting between the bench top and the wall. Many laboratory workers prefer a light-coloured wall behind the bench to give good colour discrimination in relation to substances being handled in the course of their work. Lightening the colour of under-bench cupboards and drawers brightened the room environment generally.

Some observers preferred light-coloured bench tops which gave a less dominant contrast with the wall surface and allowed the use of contrasting dark-coloured timbers for the under-bench units, which, in turn, contrasted with a light-coloured floor. Where glassware is in use, however, it was generally agreed that light-coloured bench tops were less comfortable visually, and the team found this was corroborated in practice, many scientists complaining that breakages were much more frequent on light-coloured bench tops. Nevertheless, the team is of the opinion that where this disadvantage is of no account, light-coloured benches are an important factor in brightening the laboratory environment.

It has been shown above (see pp. 104 et seq.) that they also give a slight quantitative improvement in daylight levels.

The choice of timber was shown to play an important part in the interior character of laboratories of this kind. Observers were against introducing colour as such where it was seen in simultaneous contrast with items of apparatus on the bench. Bright colour in small well-defined areas, however, added interest to the environment when placed away from the normal line of vision of the worker at his bench position.

In studying the 24 ft. deep room a number of variations of this colour scheme have been tried and the following broad principles seem to hold good: high-value colours of low chroma on walls against which items of apparatus, bottles, &c., are seen, provide a neutral background against which the paraphernalia of research can create its own pattern. Harsh contrasts between large masses of dark and light colour can be reduced by interposing a moderately light colour between them. This produces a less visually distracting environment and is important when such contrasts occur in the worker's immediate field of view.

The light distribution on walls and ceilings must be considered when choosing surface colours. Where exacting visual tasks are performed in many positions in the room, marked brightness contrasts are

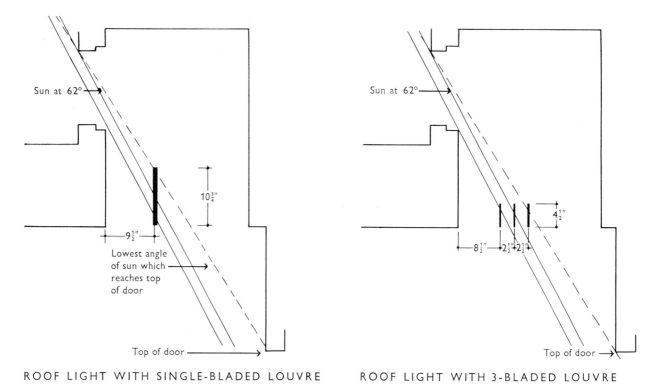

ROOF LIGHT WITH SINGLE-BLADED LOUVRE   ROOF LIGHT WITH 3-BLADED LOUVRE

Fig. 81. Alternative louvre systems used in sun penetration studies.

disturbing and may cause inaccuracies in observation. By varying the lightness of a single colour, such contrasts can often be eliminated without making the environment dull and uninteresting.

The studies of permanent supplementary artificial lighting were not specifically designed to take account of colour preferences but some of the observers were asked to note any disturbing features when viewing the room for the purpose of assessing illumination levels. Light and dark colours were placed on the side walls and the darker colours were of fairly high chroma. It was generally agreed that the contrast between the colour rendering of natural and artificial light was least marked with high-value low-chroma colours. Although matt surfaces were preferred generally, observers were particularly critical of specular finishes in supplementary artificial lighting. Specular bench-top finishes should be avoided in order to prevent reflected glare from light sources, especially where glassware is in constant use.

Sun penetration

Sun control may be of major importance in laboratories. In some bacteriological techniques, for example, sun cannot be tolerated on the bench because it affects the samples under investigation: microscope slides may be affected, colours of samples changed on exposure to sunlight, &c. This constitutes a further argument against placing benches under windows. With benches at right angles to the window wall, even without effective sun control, it is usually possible to remove the sensitive work out of sunlight range.

There are two aspects of sun control—control of light and control of solar heat gain. Account must be taken of both aspects in laboratory design. Sunlight patches on interior surfaces which are otherwise of low brightness cause discomfort glare if they occur in the immediate field of view of a worker at his bench. Solar heat gain may make working conditions intolerable in summer in buildings where there are overriding reasons for keeping the windows closed.

Sun penetration and solar gain problems are particularly acute in rooms with roof lights in addition to side windows, and a special study was undertaken to assess the sunlight problem in the 16 ft. deep room, and later in the 24 ft. deep room designed by the team for the experimental building at Cambridge. The photometric brightnesses were measured in the 16 ft. room and the Building Research Station glare formula was used to calculate the glare factor for patches of sunlight on the rear wall of the model [surface colour 5Y 8/2 (B.S. 4–047)]. The measurements were made with the sun at an altitude of 62° (equivalent to summer solstice) when sunlight penetrated to within 2 ft. of the bench top. A glare factor of 850 was obtained, corresponding to a degree of discomfort worse than 'just intolerable' on the multiple criterion scale (11). With the sun at 54° altitude (corresponding to noon—local solar time—on about 3 May or 10 August), the sunlight patch was just below door-head height, and in this case glare to a person working in a normal position on the bench was assessed at 105, or somewhat better than 'just uncomfortable'. It was concluded that if the sunlight patches could be kept above door height

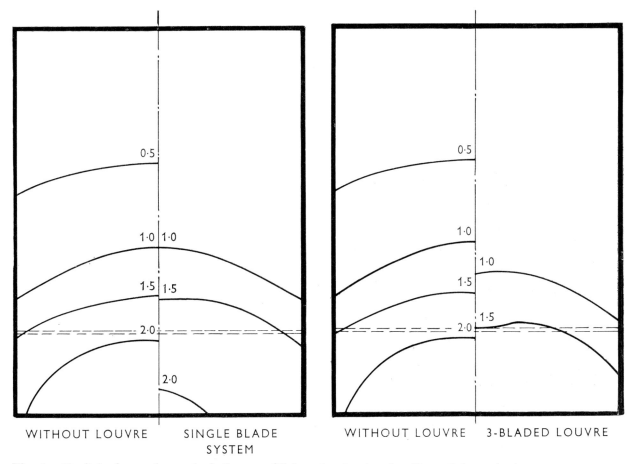

Fig. 82. Daylight factors due to the indirect roof light only, showing the effects of alternative louvre systems.

(or if they were considerably reduced in size) discomfort would be negligible.

Two permanent internal louvre systems were designed to prevent sun penetration lower than door height (see Fig. 81). Both are equally effective against sunlight, and measurements were made to discover how much they affected the amount of daylight reaching the back of the room through the roof light. The results are shown in Fig. 82. The single blade system has little effect on daylighting except within about 3 ft. of the back wall (0·25 per cent. daylight factor reduction), the three-blade system produces a similar reduction between 8 ft. and 4 ft. from the back wall, and a greater reduction (0·5 per cent. daylight factor) within 4 ft. of the wall.

For the Cambridge building two louvre systems were designed. The first, an internal louvre system (Fig. 78A) was designed on the principles outlined above, to prevent sun penetration below door-head level. This produced satisfactory illumination levels and an acceptable working environment in terms of brightness distribution. It took no account of solar heat gain, however, and would have necessitated the use of blinds in the high-level windows. High-level blinds are difficult to control and it was therefore decided to design an external louvre system in conjunction with double glazing to reduce to a minimum the heat gain from solar radiation in summer (Fig. 78B). A slightly lower standard of light control was accepted—small areas of sunlight will appear on the

rear wall below door-head level with low-angle sun. The worst condition, with a south-west orientation, produces 'just acceptable' contrast conditions. Solar gain through normal side windows may also be controlled with permanent louvre systems or just as effectively with blinds. A number of types of blind are available which are effective against heat and light. The following list (16) gives percentage heat transmission for a number of these placed either between the glazing of double windows or mounted externally.

	Av. solar heat transmission (per cent.)
Pleated paper blind, white, between glass panes	35
Pleated paper blind, dark blue, between panes	50
Flat paper blind, with aluminium foil surface facing inwards, between panes . . .	28
Flat paper blind, with aluminium foil surface facing outwards, between panes . .	21
Flat paper blind, with aluminium foil facing both ways between panes	14
Venetian blind with glossy aluminium slats set vertical between panes	25
Venetian blind with lacquered slats set vertical between panes	31
Exterior white sun blind, set at 45° inclination from the upper edge of a closed double-glazed window	26
Exterior red sun blind, set at 45° inclination from the upper edge of a closed double-glazed window	24
Exterior blue sun blind, set at 45° inclination from the upper edge of a closed double-glazed window	22

Aluminium-faced opaque blinds and venetian blinds are effective, as are roller sun blinds of various colours. The white paper blinds, although somewhat less effective against heat, allow light to reach the room and are useful for workrooms such as laboratories, in that they allow ample light to enter the room while preventing the disturbing glare conditions described above.

REFERENCES

(1) DEPARTMENT OF SCIENTIFIC AND INDUSTRIAL RESEARCH. *The prediction of levels of daylight in buildings.* London, 1955. *Building Research Station digest,* no. 80.

(2) THE ILLUMINATING ENGINEERING SOCIETY. *I.E.S. Code for lighting in buildings.* London, 1955.

(3) WESTON, H. C. *Determination of recommended values of illumination.* COMMISSION INTERNATIONALE DE L'ECLAIRAGE. *Proceedings, 2, Paper O.* Stockholm, 1951.

(4) LLEWELYN DAVIES, R. 'Design of research laboratories.' *J.R. Inst. Chem.* **81,** 1957, pp. 5–15.

(5) DEPARTMENT OF SCIENTIFIC AND INDUSTRIAL RESEARCH. *A study of the interreflection of daylight using model rooms and artificial skies.* London, 1954. *National building studies. Research paper,* no. 24.

(6) BRITISH STANDARDS INSTITUTION. *Colours for building and decorative paints.* London, 1955. *British Standard,* 2660.

(7) DEPARTMENT OF SCIENTIFIC AND INDUSTRIAL RESEARCH. *Simplified daylight tables.* London, 1958. *National building studies. Special report,* no. 26.

(8) HOPKINSON, R. G., LONGMORE, J., and PETHERBRIDGE, P. 'An empirical formula for the computation of the indirect component of daylight factor.' *Trans. Illum. Engng Soc.* **19,** 1954, pp. 201–19.

(9) HOPKINSON, R. G. 'Reflected daylight.' *Archit. J.* **120,** 1954, pp. 173–7.

(10) HOPKINSON, R. G., and LONGMORE, J. 'The permanent supplementary artificial lighting of interiors.' *Trans. Illum. Engng Soc.* **24,** 1959, pp. 121–42.

(11) PETHERBRIDGE, P., and HOPKINSON, R. G. 'Discomfort glare and the lighting of buildings.' *Trans. Illum. Engng Soc.* **15,** 1950, pp. 39–71.

(12) McDERMOT, L. H., and GORDON-SMITH, G. W. *Daylight illumination recorded at Teddington.* BUILDING RESEARCH CONGRESS. *Papers presented in Division 3.* London, 1951, pp. 156–61.

(13) NUFFIELD PROVINCIAL HOSPITALS TRUST. *Studies in the functions and design of hospitals.* London, 1955.

(14) MINISTRY OF EDUCATION. *Colour in school buildings.* 2nd edition. London, 1956. *Building bulletin,* no. 9.

(15) GLOAG, H. L., and KEYTE, M. J. 'Rational aspects of colouring in building interiors.' *Archit. J.* **125,** 1957, pp. 399–402, 443–8.

(16) PLEIJEL, G. 'The heat balance of the window.' *Byggmästeren,* **1,** 1951, pp. 14–19.

Chapter 5

SPECIAL PLANNING PROBLEMS

NOISE

NOISE reduction and the prevention of structural vibration are related subjects, many of the measures taken for one being effective for the other. Reduction of structural vibration is necessary for the protection of sensitive pieces of apparatus and instruments. It may be impossible to read a sensitive measuring instrument with the required degree of accuracy unless it is isolated from structure-borne vibration. Generally, however, unless the site of the building is near a troublesome outside source of vibration, such measures are needed in only comparatively small areas of the laboratory building such as special instrument or balance rooms. Noise nuisance, on the other hand, both from outside and inside sources of noise is an important environmental problem in laboratories. All parts of laboratories in which people work should be protected from irritating noise.

The principles of noise control in buildings are well documented (1) (2) (3) (4) (14) and apply to laboratories as to other buildings. They are briefly summarized in general terms under the appropriate headings below. Noise problems which are peculiar to, or occur frequently in, laboratories are treated more fully.

Measures against structural vibration and for the protection of sensitive apparatus are treated separately.

Noise control

Much of the work carried out in research laboratories requires a high degree of concentration, and recent investigations suggest that noise nuisance will seriously impair efficiency in this respect (6) (7). A quiet environment is desirable for most conventional laboratory work, and for some workers may be essential. Heavy engineering and mechanical test laboratories are not considered here; they present special noise problems similar to those occurring in factories and are adequately dealt with in this connexion.[1]

The degrees of quietness to be aimed at for different kinds of work are difficult to assess owing to a number of subjective factors which cannot be easily resolved; reactions of individuals to the same noise environment vary widely, and the dominant pitch or frequency of the intruding noise may be just as critical as its loudness. Although attempts have been made to prescribe permissible noise levels (3), it is more practical from the point of view of the designer to determine suitable values of insulation between rooms or groups of rooms used for given purposes, and to relate these to the sound insulation values of typical wall and floor constructions over the relevant frequency range. This has been done by the Building Research Station for houses and flats (5), on the basis of a subjective survey conducted in buildings with a representative range of wall and floor structures. No such survey has been carried out for laboratories, but it is possible to give some guidance on these lines by evaluating laboratory noise and suggesting insulation values for walls and floors between various adjacent rooms which will minimize noise nuisance.

Structural sound insulation between rooms and against outside noise, although important, is not the only means of reducing noise nuisance. There are three stages in the prevention of noise: reduction by planning, reduction at source, and structural measures. These are discussed separately below.

Planning against noise

Planning against noise begins with the choice of site—it is obviously better to place the building as far as possible from troublesome sources of outside noise than to take expensive structural measures to keep noise out. Noise is reduced by distance from source, but disposition on the site with a view to noise reduction may have to be weighed against other vital aspects of site planning such as availability of main services, access, orientation, &c. The unique features of each site should be used to advantage if possible. For example, it may be possible to use the acoustic shadow of other buildings to screen sensitive areas against outside noise.

[1] Some guidance on these applications is available in (3) and most acoustics textbooks deal with machine noise.

The most important aspect of planning against noise, however, is in the disposition of the parts of the building in relation to each other, and the internal arrangement of the rooms themselves. Much can be done in this way to ensure that quiet areas of the building are not so placed that it becomes impossible to prevent noise reaching them except by resorting to expensive structural measures. Unless there are overriding functional reasons against it, parts of the building in which noise is generated should be grouped together and placed as far as possible from those parts where a quiet environment is needed. Often rooms which are occupied for only short periods and are themselves quiet (stores, darkrooms, &c.), can be placed between the two extremes as buffers. Ideally, very noisy rooms (unloading bays, boiler rooms, motor or compressor rooms, &c.) should be in separate buildings, but it is unlikely that such an arrangement will be an economic possibility in any but large research organizations. In multi-story laboratories, if sources of structure-borne noise have to be contained within the laboratory building, they should, if possible, be placed at basement or ground-floor level. Often, however, even this is not practicable, especially in the case of fume-extraction fans which usually discharge at high level.

Planning against noise, both on the site and in the building itself, costs nothing and may make other more expensive measures unnecessary, or at least easier and cheaper to apply.

Noise reduction at source

Reduction of noise at source is also an inexpensive method of noise control, and is often neglected. Noise in a building is usually made up of many minor noises which can be eliminated or reduced by good design and choice of materials and equipment. Some of the noises which laboratories have in common with other buildings, e.g. footsteps and door bangs, are comparatively easy to deal with by means of resilient floor finishes (see Appendix II, Materials and Finishes) and silent door closers. Wheeled equipment such as trolleys, movable cupboards, &c., should have resilient tyres.[1] Wash-up areas can be designed with noise reduction in mind, using resilient linings or edgings wherever possible. Chairs and stools, the cause of much noise in offices and laboratories can also be rubber-shod. If typing or computing is done centrally in a laboratory building the rooms used for these purposes must be regarded as major noise sources, and structural measures to reduce the spread of air-borne noise from them will almost certainly be essential.

Constable (1) devotes a whole chapter to the choice of quiet equipment for buildings, including

[1] Ordinary rubber may be unsuitable if chemical attack is likely, but synthetic rubbers and plastics can be used which would be equally effective (see Appendix II, Materials and Finishes).

lifts, electric motors, &c., and gives useful and practical information. Mechanical and electrical equipment, water and steam pipe-line and valves may all be chosen or designed with a view to reducing the noise they produce. These are dealt with separately below, together with brief notes on resilient machinery mountings for the purpose of reducing structure-borne noise (this aspect is dealt with more fully under the section on Vibration below). Insulation of ducts is discussed in the section on Sound Insulation and Absorption.

Electric fans

The amount of noise produced by rotating fan blades depends upon their peripheral speed. From the point of view of noise reduction, large slowly rotating blades are better than smaller faster ones. (Doubling the r.p.m. for a given fan increases its noise output by about 17 db.) There should be a good clearance between the blade tips and the fan casing, and the inner surface of the latter should be smooth and unbroken.

Fan design against noise has been studied in detail (McMahan established the relationship between fan noise and blade speed in 1936 (8) and the work of Goldman and Maling (9) is an example of the detailed studies at present being carried out) and manufacturers can usually specify fan speeds for quiet operation if asked to do so. Where large numbers of fans are used in a single building, e.g. in fume-extraction systems, selection of the right equipment can do much to limit the build-up of noise.

Electric motors

Electric motors of all sizes are used in laboratories either in motor rooms or for various purposes at the bench. As in the case of fans, noise control is largely a matter of selecting the equipment for quiet running. Such motors usually have specially designed frames, sleeve-bearings, restraining devices to prevent lateral movement of the spindle and casings which completely enclose the moving parts.

Resilient mountings are needed to prevent amplification of noise by resonance where motors are fixed to the structure. This is especially true for large motors such as those used in ventilating and refrigerating plant, and for small motors fixed to benches in the laboratory.

Compressors

Compressors are frequently used in laboratories for refrigeration plant, and compressed-air lines. Together with oil-fired boilers, emergency generators, &c., compressors come into the category of equipment which should be placed in a separate room, or insulated from working areas (see section on Insulation and Absorption below). Resilient mountings are essential to prevent structure-borne noise.

Noise in water systems

Water system noises are caused by badly designed equipment, by movement of water, or by vibration within the piping system. Steps similar to those described above can be taken to reduce noise from equipment at source. Silent-running pumps (usually less than 1,000 r.p.m.) are available, taps and valves designed for quiet operation and silencing devices on inlet valves to storage tanks and W.C.'s are in common use and help to reduce the levels of air-borne noise. Nevertheless, rooms used for housing central-heating equipment, water-purification plant, &c., must be considered noisy, and if possible placed away from quiet areas of the building (see section on planning against noise above), or insulated from such areas by structural means. Motors are usually coupled directly to circulating pumps and vibration from the motor is therefore transmitted directly to the pipe system. It has been suggested (1) that this may be prevented at source by using a belt-drive from motor to pump, but provided motor and pump are isolated from the building structure, other simple measures can be taken to reduce transmission of noise through the pipes (see below).

Water-hammer is caused by a sudden change in water pressure in a pipe system. In practice it is usually the result of a sudden rise in pressure when a tap or valve is shut off quickly. Measures against water-hammer are aimed at reducing the speed of flow of water or the rate of closing the tap or valve; the former by ensuring that pipes are of the correct size for the volume of water carried, the latter by selecting equipment (tap washers, valve seatings, &c.) which do not cut off the flow instantaneously. Another measure sometimes taken against water-hammer is the inclusion of a specially designed air chamber in the supply pipe to compensate for sudden changes in pressure.

In steam systems (apart from hammer noises which can be dealt with in similar ways to those described above) other loud noises sometimes occur unless flow limits are imposed in the risers (10). Steam taps and valves are also troublesome noise sources and although improvements have recently been made in their design, it is advisable to place main valves and traps away from quiet areas of the building.

Noise caused by the flow of water in pipes is usually due to turbulence in the water flow. It rarely occurs in smooth pipes, but usually at the fittings (taps, valves, &c.). Well-designed fittings (in which sharp changes of direction of flow are avoided, or which reduce speed of water flow) with throttling devices placed immediately before outlets, help to limit the build-up of noise in the pipes. In laboratory buildings water tap pressures are usually fairly high for functional reasons, and taps should be selected with the above points in mind.

Noise due to falling water (wastes, W.C. flushing, and filling of storage cisterns) has been fully dealt with elsewhere (4) (11). In laboratories there may be unusually large cold-water storage tanks either for normal or emergency use and consequently there are long periods of filling. Tanks should be placed on resilient pads above rooms where quiet conditions are not essential. Otherwise, the insulation value of the floor supporting the tanks must be high enough to prevent the noise reaching the rooms below (see section on Insulation and Absorption below).

After taking as many precautions as possible to limit noise produced by equipment, measures will probably still be necessary to eliminate or reduce the transmission of residual noise along pipe-lines, to prevent transmission of noise from pipes to the structure and to prevent radiation of noise into rooms through which they pass. Both metal and water are good conductors of sound, and noise induced in metal-pipe systems at one end of a building can be heard with almost equal clarity at the other. The usual method of reducing the spread of noise through pipework is to insert a short length of flexible tube (plain or reinforced rubber) into the pipe near the source of noise. Experimental work has been carried out at the National Physical Laboratory (12) which shows the efficacy of this measure. The value of the rubber insert increases with its length, up to a length of 6–8 in.; greater length than this does not increase noise reduction proportionately. Insulation also increases with the frequency of the noise; reinforced rubber is less effective than plain soft rubber (although in practice the former is extensively used for reasons of durability). High-frequency noises, such as water hiss, can be effectively reduced with short lengths of rubber (4–6 in.), but for a low-frequency hum (e.g. circulating pump noise) longer lengths (18 in. or more) are needed.

Some noise reduction is effected (mainly of high-frequency noises) when pipes are solidly embedded in a wall, e.g. where a pipe passes through a brick wall, but in effect the noise passes from the pipe to the structure which will itself re-radiate the sound. It is better to isolate the pipe from the wall in a more positive way with resilient material (see below).

Heavy main-service pipes carried on solid walls or floors, and even smaller distribution pipes if carried on light partitions, may produce disturbing noises either by transmitting noise to the structure, or in the case of light partitions, by drumming or resonance. Large diameter main pipes can be carried on proprietary spring isolaters supported by concrete blocks: less expensive flexible pads may be used in a similar way where there is a danger of pipe noise being transferred to the building structure. For smaller pipes, insulated clips or hangers are the most effective method. It has already been mentioned above that metal is an excellent conductor of sound and in steel-framed buildings it is especially important that pipework is not connected rigidly to the structural frame.

Air-borne noise radiated into the rooms through which pipes pass, or generated by fittings, is strictly a sound-insulation problem and is discussed under the appropriate heading below.

Noise in ventilating and air-conditioning systems

The reduction of noise generated by ventilating and air-conditioning plant (motors, fans, compressors, &c.) has been dealt with above. As in water systems, however, some noise from mechanical or electrical equipment invariably reaches the trunking or ducts, the shape and construction of which are such that they conduct the noise to every part of the building to which and through which they run. Outside noise can enter the trunking through main intake or outlet grilles: noise generated in rooms in the building will enter through room extract or input grilles or through the duct walls themselves, and noise is also produced by the flow of air in the ducts.

Hard-surfaced trunking (e.g. metal piping) will convey noise for long distances with almost no reduction in loudness, and pass on the noise through openings into every room it serves. Some reduction (10–20 db) occurs at the outlet grilles provided the room is not itself a reverberant one. Also, the duct system itself will resonate at certain fan or motor speeds, unless steps are taken to isolate the equipment (usually a leather or reinforced fabric insert between the fan and the duct serves this purpose) or to reduce the resonance of the ducting itself. Circular metal ducting is less liable to drumming effects than the rectangular type, but the latter can be stiffened with metal angles fixed outside the duct or by means of grooves pressed in the metal during manufacture.

Wind noise in ducts depends upon the speed of airflow and the amount of resistance to it. Irregularities on the inner surface of the trunking or sudden changes in direction cause eddying of the air stream and increase the noise level.

If the necessary steps are taken against equipment noise and resonance in the ducting, the problem becomes one of (a) impeding the transmission of noise along the ducting and preventing its spilling into the rooms it serves, and (b) the improvement of the insulation properties of the duct walls (for normal sheet-metal trunking this may be only about 20 db) so that duct noise is not radiated into the air of all rooms, corridors, &c., through which the ducting passes.

The lining of ducts to reduce transmission of noise within the building is fully described in the *British standard code of practice* on mechanical ventilation (13), which gives a simple formula[1] and sets out the procedure for calculating the area of absorbent required for a given reduction. In laboratories the choice of suitable lining material may be difficult and the placing of the absorbent must be considered carefully. In ducts from fume cupboards the lining may be subject to severe chemical attack, and even normal extract ducts (from mechanically ventilated or air-conditioned rooms) may carry fairly heavy concentrations of active gases or vapours. Absorbent linings must be placed in the duct between the source of noise and the point where the duct opens into a quiet room, preferably as near the noise source as possible. In some cases (e.g. short fume-extraction ducts from fume cupboards or hoods) this may mean placing the absorbent in the part of the duct most liable to chemical attack. The usual criterion in the choice of lining materials for a noise of known frequency (the sound-absorption coefficient) must, therefore, be considered in relation to the placing of the material and its liability to chemical attack. Tables of sound-absorption coefficients for duct-lining materials are given in the code of practice referred to above (13), and for laboratory applications it is essential to choose inert materials which also have high resistance to moisture absorption. In addition, it is better to use materials of low surface coefficient of friction in order to minimize loss of efficiency in the system.[2] The loose fibre materials which are the most inert (glass wool, for example) are usually covered with a thin sheet of perforated metal when used in normal ventilation ducts, but for laboratory use this is not possible, because of the liability of metals to acid attack. Recent developments in absorbent materials, however, are promising: thin plastic sheet (such as P.V.C.) over a plastics foam absorbent base[3] seems to be a future possibility for use in ducts where chemical attack is likely. At present, since the cell structure of foamed plastics needs further study, it is possible to use the inert fibre materials such as glass wool with an inner lining of continuous perforated plastic material.

Reduction of noise occurs at outlet grilles, and can be increased by using a baffle box immediately before the outlet, or by baffling the outlet itself. Quite substantial reductions (of the order of 20 db) of duct noise can be obtained in this way (Constable (1) quotes the work of Lindner in Germany and illustrates

---

[1] Noise reduction or attenuation in phons per ft. run of lining is given as follows:

$$R = 12 \cdot 6 \left(\frac{P}{A}\right) a^{1 \cdot 4},$$

where R = reduction per foot run,
P = duct perimeter in inches,
A = duct cross-sectional area in square inches,
a = absorption coefficient of the lining material.

[2] Power losses due to duct linings may be considerable with normal absorbent materials. The losses are negligible, so far as

surface resistance is concerned, when hard perforated surfaces are used, but whatever the material, reduced effective cross-sectional area of duct will necessitate either increased overall duct size or increased power for the same airflow.

[1] Such materials, consisting of a thin sheet of smooth-surfaced material over a cellular base, fixed to the rigid wall of a duct, are really 'panel' type absorbers. The facing sheet transmits sound to the cellular backing, and if the depth of cells is properly related to the rigidity of the covering sheet, absorption coefficients of up to 0·5 are obtainable over a given frequency range (1).

two effective baffle-box designs, as well as a simple outlet baffle for use with existing grilles). Ducts running between rooms should be treated to give a noise reduction between the rooms at least equal to that afforded by the partition itself. For example, if the dividing wall between adjacent rooms has an average insulation value of 40 db, the noise reduction via a duct connecting the two rooms should also be at least 40 db; supposing the room outlets to be 10 ft. apart and each outlet to give a reduction of 5 db, the remaining 30 db would have to be achieved by absorption in the duct, viz. 3 db per ft. over the whole length, or more over some shorter length. Noise can also pass from one room into an adjacent room through the duct walls. It will be obvious that with noises occurring and being received immediately adjacent to the partition on either side (with a 40 db partition), the duct wall should have an insulation value not less than 20 db, if it is not to form an alternative noise path between the rooms.

Sound insulation and absorption

The principles of sound insulation and absorption have been well documented in the last few years (2) (3) (4) (5) (14) (15) and need no elaboration here, except perhaps to stress the dependence of insulation upon the weight of a partition or wall, the importance of floating floors to reduce impact noise between the stories of a building, and to reiterate the fact that absorbent treatments are effective only in reducing the noise level in the room in which they are applied (they will not generally improve insulation between rooms) or in helping to reduce the spread of noise by reflection from hard surfaces, e.g. along a corridor or in a ventilation duct.

Parkin and Stacy (5) have shown that it is advisable to consider the insulation value of a material over the range of frequencies likely to be encountered. Most recommendations, however, are still framed in terms of the insulation value, averaged over the frequency range normally encountered in inhabited rooms.[1] When a partition is said to have an insulation value of 45 db, it means that it gives an average value of 45 db reduction of noises between 100 and 3,200 cycles per second. The actual reduction given by a wall or partition will depend upon the dominant frequency of the incident noise. In laboratories, therefore, if it is known that certain rooms will contain disturbing noise sources (e.g. electric motors, mixers, &c.), and the frequency of the sound is known, partitions can be designed to give good insulation at the relevant frequencies. For most con-

Table 74. Recommended values of sound insulation between three classes of rooms found in research laboratory buildings.

		1	2	3
1.	If sound absorbents are used in rooms themselves 35 db; otherwise no special precautions are necessary .		50 db	Special construction
2.	50 db		35 db	50 db
3.	Special construction . .		50 db	35 db

1. Noisy rooms; typing or computing rooms, boiler rooms, workshops, rooms housing ventilation plant, &c.
2. Conventional laboratories; writing rooms, offices, &c.
3. Quiet rooms; libraries, reading rooms, rest rooms, or special laboratory rooms where silence is essential.

ventional laboratories, however, insulation between rooms would be needed to prevent transmission of normal office noises, such as conversation, moving of chairs, footsteps, &c. Table 74 has been compiled to give guidance on the average insulation values between three general classes of laboratory room, and is based on values given for other types of building in authoritative post-war publications.[2] In arriving at the values in the table, it was assumed that the level of outside noise was fairly low, that is, not high enough to produce noise nuisance in the rooms irrespective of indoor noise. It should be remembered that the quieter the site, the more attention must be paid to sound insulation between rooms, as the audibility of noise from adjacent rooms is greater.

The sound insulation of a partition is considerably reduced if an ordinary door is placed in it, and if good insulation is essential, such openings should have a baffle lobby or a heavy door with a good seal between door and frame. Partitions should be continuous, that is, should go through suspended ceilings to the structural floor above and behind benches, &c., to the floor. Where it is necessary to pierce partitions for laboratory service pipes or ducts above a suspended ceiling, the holes should be sealed around the pipes as closely as possible. For good sound insulation it is better to run services in a separate duct (e.g. over the corridor) and to take single-service branches into the laboratories from it, keeping partitions between rooms continuous from floor to floor. Noise may also be transmitted from room to room through openings in corridor walls or external walls. This is known as flanking noise, and may pass through adjacent windows, doors, or badly sealed joints between partitions and flanking walls. Corridor doors should therefore be spaced well apart from each other

---

[1] Lists of the average insulation values of most common building materials are available, for example in (2) (3) (4) and (5). It should be noted that cavity construction does not necessarily give improvement in insulation value in the relevant frequency range over a solid wall of equal weight. It will only do so if the cavity is of large area (i.e. without rigid ties), and if it is of sufficient width. Cavities should not be less than 2 in. and will give added insulation at low frequencies if made wider than this, up to a maximum of 12 in. Lining cavities with sound absor-

bents will only improve insulation when the inner surfaces of the cavity are hard and smooth and liable to reflect incident noise.

[2] Insulation values given in the table should be regarded as minima; noise levels of common noises were taken from Parkin's recent table (16) and recommended levels to which noise should be reduced for various room uses, from *Post-war building studies*, no. 14 (3).

and if possible opening windows should not be placed too near to partitions between rooms in which quiet conditions are essential.

The stress laid on the need for flexibility in research laboratories has turned attention to the possibilities of movable partitions. Poor sound insulation is one of the major reasons why such partitions have not been more widely used. Of necessity, if a partition is to be easily demountable it must be light in weight. Broadly, sound insulation varies with weight, and, therefore, high insulation values are difficult if not impossible to achieve with lightweight, movable partitions. Most available sliding, folding partitions, for example, have insulation values in the range 10 to 18 db. Apart from weight, insulation depends upon the tightness of the sealing between joints, and therefore requires very close tolerances in manufacture. Joints between these partitions and structural floors and ceilings are particularly difficult to seal. One type of movable partition has been developed for use in schools which is claimed to have an insulation value of 28–30 db for single-leaf and 40–42 db for double-leaf walls. To double the partition is to double the cost and at least to double the floor area taken up by the internal walls.

Where noise is generated by service lines, trunking, &c., the latter should be insulated from rooms through which they pass, preferably in ducts made of structural materials such as bricks or blocks, with access panels of lighter materials placed in areas where noise reduction is less important (e.g. corridors, storage rooms, &c.).

In Table 74 special construction is suggested for positions where it is not possible to plan noisy rooms away from the essentially quiet ones. Completely isolated rooms are difficult and expensive to construct, but may be essential in some laboratory buildings, not only on account of noise but for ultra-sensitive apparatus which must be protected from vibration (see also section on Vibration). The detailed design of such rooms, which are in the form of a box built inside the normal room structure but completely isolated from it, should be undertaken by specialists, but care should be taken to ensure that the outer shell is continuous, providing a shield to the inner shell at every point. Ducts for ventilation, door or window frames, service pipes, &c., must not form a rigid bridge between the two shells. Special precautions must be taken in ducts to ensure that air-borne noise from outside sources is not conveyed into the room through the grilles.

An example of this kind of construction occurs in the extension to the Animal Research Unit at Cambridge, designed by the team. Here a special room is provided to house three large and several small centrifuges. The problem of insulation is not so critical in a single-story building as in a multi-story building, but lateral noise protection is given to the adjacent laboratories by providing an extra 9-in. brick wall inside the normal $4\frac{1}{2}$-in. brick partition, with a 2-in. cavity between the two brick skins. The double wall gives an average insulation value of over 55 db and the cavity construction gives added protection against the high-frequency noise from the centrifuges in use.

The use of sound-absorbent linings as a means of reducing the reverberation and thus the apparent loudness of noise in a room in which it is generated, is described in *Building Research Station digest*, no. 36 (15) and has been discussed above in relation to duct linings. In noise-producing rooms where people must work for long periods, the environment can be greatly improved by means of sound-absorbent treatments.

The problem of providing chemical resistant sound-absorbing materials has been mentioned above in relation to duct linings. A similar problem exists in finding suitable absorbents for use in the laboratory, although to a lesser degree. The surface of perforated boards and similar products can be given chemical-resistant coatings, but it is impossible to prevent fumes or corrosive gases penetrating into the perforations or other irregularities. Many of the proprietary boards are, however, made from inert materials (wood pulp, mineral fibres, &c.), and should give good service where they are not subject to splashing, e.g. on ceilings. Fire resistance must also be borne in mind, however, and sound-absorbing materials are amongst those dealt with in the sections on Safety and Fire Precautions later in this chapter. Perforated metal (backed with an insulating quilt of fibrous material) sound-absorbing systems, used as suspended ceilings, require careful treatment for laboratory use, if there is any likelihood of corrosive fumes reaching the material. Both sides of the metal must be given resistant coatings, and edges and angles are difficult to cover satisfactorily. There is usually little scope for applying absorbents to laboratory walls, but they can often be applied to ceilings and can be used to good effect in corridors to prevent the spread of reverberant noise throughout the building.

REFERENCES

(1) CONSTABLE, J. E. R., and K. M. *The principles and practice of sound insulation.* London, 1949.

(2) LLEWELYN DAVIES, R., and PETTY, D. J. *Building elements.* London, 1956.

(3) DEPARTMENT OF SCIENTIFIC AND INDUSTRIAL RESEARCH. *Sound insulation and acoustics.* London, 1944. *Post-war building studies,* no. 14.

(4) BRITISH STANDARDS INSTITUTION. *Sound insulation (houses, flats and schools).* London, 1948. *British standard code of practice,* CP 3—Chapter III.

(5) PARKIN, P. H., and STACY, E. F. 'Recent research on sound insulation in houses and flats.' *J.R. Inst. Brit. Archit.* **61,** 1954, p. 9.

(6) LEHMANN, G. 'Noise and its effect on humans.' *Z. Ver. dtsch. Ing.* **97,** 1955, pp. 1012–14.

(7) BROADBENT, D. E. 'Noise: Its effect on behaviour.' *J. Soc. Promot. Hlth.* **75,** 1955, p. 543.

(8) MCMAHAN, K. D. 'The noise problem in the application of fans.' *J. acoust. Soc. Amer.* **7,** 1936, p. 205.

(9) GOLDMAN, R. B., and MALING, G. C. 'Noise from small centrifugal fans.' *Noise Control,* **1,** no. 6, 1955, pp. 26–29, 50.

(10) FABER, O., and KELL, J. R. *Heating and air conditioning of buildings.* 3rd and revised edition. London, 1957, p. 349.

(11) NUFFIELD PROVINCIAL HOSPITALS TRUST. *Studies in the functions and design of hospitals.* London, 1955.

(12) CONSTABLE, J. E. R. 'The prevention of the transmission of sound along water pipes.' *Proc. phys. Soc. Lond.* **50,** 1938, p. 360.

(13) BRITISH STANDARDS INSTITUTION. *Mechanical ventilation and air conditioning.* London, 1958, p. 84. *British standard code of practice,* CP 352.

(14) PARKIN, P. H., and HUMPHREYS, H. R. *Acoustics, noise and buildings.* London, 1958.

(15) DEPARTMENT OF SCIENTIFIC AND INDUSTRIAL RESEARCH. 'Sound absorbent treatments.' London, 1954. *Building Research Station digest,* no. 36.

(16) PARKIN, P. H. 'Loudness of common noises.' *Acustica,* **7,** 1957, pp. 57–58.

THE REDUCTION OF VIBRATION

By R. J. STEFFENS, B.Sc. (Eng. Hons.), Senior Experimental Officer at the Building Research Station.

When the team began to investigate the protection of sensitive apparatus against structural vibration, it was found that Mr. R. J. Steffens of the Building Research Station had made a special study along these lines. The following section of the report has been prepared by Mr. Steffens with the kind permission of the Director of the Building Research Station.

Introduction

IN the design of laboratories it is important that the question of interference from vibration should be considered at the planning stage. Although much has been written on the general subject of machinery and building vibrations (see selected bibliography below), the reduction of vibration in laboratories has received little attention.

Research work usually involves a wide range of apparatus and equipment, of which many items are likely to be affected by vibration. These include sensitive balances of various kinds, galvanometers, mirror extensometers, optical and photographic apparatus, and electronic equipment. Although balances are always included in this list it will usually be found that only the ultra-sensitive instrument used for precise work is disturbed by 'normal' levels of vibration. Optical work and the observation of liquid surfaces, however, can be seriously upset by comparatively small vibrations. In the case of mercury surfaces, for example, experience shows that severe disturbance may be caused by vibrations that are imperceptible to human beings; vibration amplitudes of only a few millionths of an inch may be sufficient to impair accurate observation.

There are many sources of vibration, amongst which are road and rail traffic, nearby electrical or mechanical machinery, door slamming, or heavy foot traffic within the building. The measures taken to limit the incidence or to prevent the transmission of vibrations can be roughly classified as follows:

(*a*) An area in which sensitive apparatus is housed should be given the most suitable position so that it suffers the least possible interference from sources of vibration within the building.

(*b*) Known sources of mechanical vibration on the

premises should be adequately isolated by means of anti-vibration mountings, mats, or foundations. For laboratory use it may be advisable to use more efficient isolating systems than those commonly used in industrial practice. If the out-of-balance forces produced by a machine are large, attention should be given to rebalancing. Slight alteration in the running speed may also help to reduce severe vibration.

(*c*) Floor slabs, or, in the case of a small room, the complete floor, can be spring-mounted. In existing buildings timber floors may have to be stiffened, especially where large spans are involved, and in some cases it may be necessary to replace them with concrete structural floors.

(*d*) Apparatus may be supported on isolated piers or heavy blocks.

(*e*) Anti-vibration mountings will often be needed for individual items such as balances, galvanometers, temperature recorders, electronic equipment, &c. Commercially available mountings will often be found suitable, but in a few cases, e.g. where a high degree of isolation is required or where a very-low-frequency mounting is necessary, specially designed systems may have to be provided—possibly with some kind of damping arrangement.

(*f*) If the apparatus consists of several related components, it may be advisable to mount them on a common base to prevent differential movement between the components. This applies, for example, to mirror galvanometers and their scales; flimsy scale stands are susceptible to vibration and should be stiffened.

(*g*) Precautions should be taken against door slamming which can cause extremely severe local vibration, affecting walls for some considerable distance away from the source. Door springs or closers should be fitted where possible, and in some cases it may be necessary to use swing doors or rubber doors in positions where traffic is heavy.

The various measures listed above are discussed more fully in the paragraphs which follow.

Planning against vibration

Possible external sources of vibration should be fully considered in choosing the site for a laboratory building. To place such a building adjacent to a known source of heavy vibration may involve additional expenditure on structural isolation. When buildings are to house a wide range of activities it is wise to consider which of these activities is most likely to be affected by vibrations and to locate them accordingly. The buildings should be kept as far away as possible from known external sources of vibration, such as road and rail traffic or other buildings containing heavy machinery.

Within the building, heavy plant such as gas or diesel engines, heavy duty compressors, or reciprocating machinery should be sited with their potential nuisance value in mind. Heavy-engineering laboratories and research buildings which house industrial scale apparatus are excluded from this report. It must be remembered, however, that heavy machines are common in some types of research laboratories, and sometimes it may be essential to place rooms in which sensitive equipment is used very considerable distances away from vibration sources of this kind.

Wherever possible the most sensitive work should be carried out at ground-floor or basement level. On suspended floors, apparatus should be kept away from the middle of rooms where the amplitude of the vibration is greater. The spread of vibration through a building is complex and in the siting of sensitive areas care must be taken to ensure that by removing them from more obvious sources of vibration they are not brought nearer to other less-obvious sources which are more difficult to control.

In an existing building it may be found convenient to determine the best position for sensitive equipment by fairly simple means, such as exploring the building with a small dish of mercury. In some cases, however, it may be necessary to make a complete vibration survey, using vibrographs or other recording instruments.

As a general rule it is desirable to avoid contact between walls and the benches which support sensitive apparatus. This prevents the transmission of vibration from the shell of the building to the apparatus. In order to avoid local floor and bench vibrations, however, it is by no means uncommon to find that balances and galvanometers are mounted on brackets cantilevered from walls and this practice is satisfactory if the building structure as a whole is not subject to severe vibration. Door slamming will affect such mountings and the brackets themselves should be made as robust as possible to prevent the amplification of such vibrations.

Isolation of machinery

Having taken all possible planning precautions, consideration should next be given to reducing the vibration at its source. This can be done by providing anti-vibration mountings for machinery which is to operate in the vicinity of the laboratory. Sometimes slight variation in the running speeds of the machines will considerably reduce vibration intensity.

The general principles of vibration isolation are well known and are outlined briefly at the end of this section of the report. It is sufficient to state here that the correct value of natural frequency of the mounting system must be chosen and that this frequency must be made very much lower than that of the troublesome vibration. Therefore, the lowest possible vibration frequency from the machine must be considered, and this can usually be deduced from the machine rating in revolutions per minute. For example, the worst vibration produced by a machine running at 3,000 r.p.m. is likely to be at a frequency of 50 cycles per second, and to isolate this satisfactorily a mounting frequency of 10 c.p.s. might be needed. If this machine also produces vibration of a frequency higher than 50 c.p.s. (i.e. the frequency determined from the machine rating in r.p.m.), the mounting designed to reduce the 50 c.p.s. vibrations will be even more effective against the higher frequency. It may be found necessary to measure the frequency of vibration produced by a machine if such information is not directly available. It may be assumed that the vibration produced by vehicular traffic is at a frequency of about 15 c.p.s.

Very-low-frequency vibrations (e.g. less than 5 c.p.s.) are more difficult to suppress because a greater static deflexion is required in the mounting system. The natural frequency of the mounting system depends upon the static deflexion of the springs or flexible mountings, i.e. upon the amount by which the springs are compressed (or extended in some cases) by the supported load. It will be appreciated that design of the spring system becomes more difficult as the static deflexion increases. To achieve a mounting frequency of 2 c.p.s., for example, a static deflexion of about $2\frac{1}{2}$ in. is required, but for a 10 c.p.s. mounting only about 0·1 in.

For light machines, especially those with high r.p.m. ratings, the simple rubber-in-shear mounting will often be effective and a suitable type can be selected from the wide variety now available. In this type of mounting the rubber is deformed by shear rather than by compression or extension, and a more compact and efficient unit is obtained. They are easy to install and often make it possible to eliminate the traditional foundation block and pit. Information on load-bearing capacity and the stiffness of mountings can be found in the makers' catalogues.

For heavier machinery, heavy-duty rubber or steel-spring mountings may be needed, and units, each capable of supporting several tons, are available for this purpose. Alternatively a foundation block and pit can be used. The block is then rested on an anti-vibration 'mat', and not on 'unit' mountings. Various materials can be used for the mat, e.g. ribbed or studded rubber, cork, and proprietary materials consisting of cork and felt. Where special systems are used it is necessary to make detailed calculations to ensure that the best spring system or material is used and that the material is correctly loaded. The isolation of fatigue-testing machines and vibrator units may present special problems, particularly if the reversals per minute are low. The usual spring mounting may not be practicable here if large static deflexions are required in order to obtain suitable low-frequency mountings. In cases of this kind a heavy base block may be the only solution.

General information concerning suppliers of anti-vibration mountings and materials may be obtained from the Building Centre, Store Street, London, W.C. 1., and useful data sheets have been issued by the technical press (1).

Spring-supported floor slabs

This kind of structural treatment may be suitable for protecting limited areas from external vibration. The procedure is to mount the floor slab on a suitable elastic support, direct contact between the slab concerned and other adjacent floor slabs being avoided. The floor slab itself should be as rigid as possible and the spring system should be carried on a firm foundation. It should be noted that since a comparatively low value of natural frequency is needed in such floors, the conventional floating floor used in sound-insulation practice is rarely satisfactory.

The spring system may consist of commercially available rubber or steel spring mountings, or materials such as rubber or cork. Where the latter is used it should be remembered that normal floor loadings are likely to give very low stresses (of the order 1 lb. per sq. in.) on the mounting material if it is laid as a complete mat. It will often be necessary to cut away a good deal of the mounting material, therefore, in order to give the requisite stressing and deformation under load. Thus, a series of pads rather than a complete mat will normally be needed.

Specially designed steel-spring mountings may be required for very-low-frequency isolating systems. Special damping arrangements can be incorporated to prevent the persistence of vibration produced by impacts. It is advisable when choosing the natural frequency of the system to avoid a frequency of about 2 c.p.s. as this coincides with normal footstep frequency (2 paces per second) and may produce resonance.

Spring-supported floor beams have also been used successfully against vibration from an external source (2).

Isolated piers

This technique gives protection against vibration produced in the room in which the sensitive apparatus is housed. It is particularly suitable for balances and galvanometers and many examples can be found in existing buildings.

A brick or concrete pier is built with its own foundation separate from that of the foundations of the building and passes through the floor of the room but makes no structural connexion with it. The method is only applicable to ground-floor or basement rooms. Isolated blocks of larger area are sometimes used in the same way. It is not recommended that anti-vibration material be built into either blocks or piers.

It may sometimes be an advantage, however, in the case of very large blocks to mount the block as a whole on anti-vibration pads. The mounting material for this purpose should be selected on the basis of calculations made for the particular case under consideration. It is essential that isolated piers should not make contact with the floor of the room; an air gap should be left around the edges between the floor and the pier. The gap may be covered by a flexible strip if necessary. For convenience the piers may also pass through the laboratory bench, direct contact with the latter being avoided.

Whilst isolated piers or blocks eliminate local vibration, it should be remembered that they are still subject to external vibrations transmitted through the ground. This is of some importance in laboratory buildings where compressors, workshop machinery, &c., may be housed in the basement. It is desirable in such cases and may be a wise precaution in others to fit anti-vibration mountings between the top of the pier or block and the apparatus itself.

Anti-vibration mountings for laboratory apparatus

In the past many ingenious devices have been used to protect apparatus from vibration. Many of these earlier systems are still used, although their effectiveness is often open to question. The elastic supports took many forms; air-bags, sponge rubber, felt, cork, and even pyramids of tennis balls. Sometimes a heavy slab of marble or slate resting on a bed of sand was used, and spring suspension from the ceiling was fairly common. Such methods were sometimes effective but were arrived at by trial and error. It did not follow that a given system could be used with success elsewhere.

The principles involved in the selection of anti-vibration mountings for apparatus are the same as for machinery mountings, and the necessary calculations should be made if the correct form of mounting is to be determined. Most vibration problems can now be solved by the use of commercially available mountings specially developed for the purpose. The modern tendency is to use unit mountings, generally made of rubber, that can be fitted directly underneath the apparatus. Such mountings are very compact and resemble the engine mountings used in present-day cars. They are usually easy to fit, and are available from most of the firms which make machinery mountings. There is a wide range of mountings designed for loads of from a few ounces to several pounds per unit. Most of them will give mounting frequencies of 5 c.p.s. and upwards. Mountings for wall fixing are also available, for use with racks of electronic equipment, temperature recorders, &c.

A specially designed isolating system may sometimes be required for experimental equipment, and may require multi-mass spring systems as distinct from the commonly used single-mass system. The mechanics of such a system is a little more complicated but is dealt with by the majority of textbooks on mechanical vibration.

Some special systems have been described by Macinante (3); these include vibration-isolating supports for galvanometers, a vibration-isolated base for optical work, and an anti-vibration table with damped auxiliary mass. Self-contained supporting units, and special anti-vibration tables for balances have been marketed in this country in recent years, and a new form of balance table incorporating rubber mountings has recently become available to Government laboratories. A steel-spring system for electronic equipment has recently been used (4), the natural frequency obtained being 3 c.p.s. In this case steel springs were used because commercially available rubber mountings were found to be unsuitable.

When an experimental set-up consists of several related components, as will often apply in optical work, it is preferable that they should be placed on a common base or block isolated as a whole. Unless this is done, vibration may result in differential movement between the components, making observation difficult and definition poor. Scale stands may be particularly susceptible to vibration and require a more robust construction.

Where laboratory space is being rearranged in an existing building, particularly when a suspended wood floor on an upper story is involved, it may be necessary to consider stiffening the floor to reduce local vibration. If the floor is stiffened by supporting it from underneath at several places, it should be possible to arrange for instrument positions to be near or over the supports so as to be subjected to the least vibration.

General principles of vibration isolation

This summary is based on the behaviour of a weight on a spring when it is subjected to vibration, and applies equally to the isolation of machinery vibration and to the protection of apparatus.

If F is the frequency of vibration produced by a machine or is the frequency of vibration affecting the apparatus ('forcing frequency'),

F_n is the natural frequency of the spring-weight system used for isolation ('mounting frequency'),

then Frequency Ratio $(R) = \dfrac{F}{F_n}$,

Transmissibility $= \dfrac{1}{R^2 - 1}$ (See Table 75.)

Damping has been neglected in the expression for transmissibility; also it is implied that R is to be greater than unity.

Transmissibility may be defined as:

for machinery isolation:

$$\frac{\text{Vibratory force actually transmitted}}{\substack{\text{Vibratory force applied by machine} \\ \text{(e.g. out of balance force developed)}}}$$

for isolation of apparatus:

$$\frac{\text{Force transmitted to apparatus}}{\text{Force transmitted were there no mounting}}$$

or, $\dfrac{\text{Amplitude of vibration of apparatus}}{\text{Amplitude if there were no mounting}}$.

The greater the value of frequency ratio (R) is made, the less will be the transmissibility and the greater the degree of isolation. Damping has the effect of increasing the transmissibility, and, since some degree of damping is always present in practice, transmissibility will always be somewhat greater than that given by the simplified result above.

The natural frequency of the spring-weight system ('mounting frequency') depends purely on the extension or compression of the spring system under the supported load ('static deflexion, Δ'), the simple relationship being:

Natural ('Mounting') Frequency (F_n) =

$$\frac{3 \cdot 13}{\sqrt{\Delta}} \text{ c.p.s. or } \frac{188}{\sqrt{\Delta}} \text{ cycles/min.} \quad \text{(See Table 76.)}$$

The great majority of practical cases concern the isolation of vertical vibration. For isolation of horizontal vibration, the same relationships for transmissibility and natural frequency hold, as given. In this case, however, the static deflexion may be regarded as the lateral displacement of the spring system for a horizontal force equal to the supported weight. From Table 75 it is apparent that there is little practical advantage gained by using values of R greater than 5, unless a very high degree of isolation is required. Higher values are certainly worth using, however, if the frequency is high, e.g. over 50 c.p.s.

Example

If F were 20 c.p.s., a mounting frequency of 4 c.p.s. (giving $R = 5$) would theoretically reduce vibration from machine, or at apparatus, by about 96 per cent. (Table 75), and the stiffness of the mounting(s) would have to be such that there was a static deflexion of 0·61 in. under the supported load (Table 76). For the same value of F a mounting frequency of 2 c.p.s. ($R = 10$) would give 99 per cent. reduction, but the static deflexion required would be 2·45 in. If F were 50 c.p.s., however, a 10 c.p.s. mounting frequency ($R = 5$) gives 96 per cent. reduction and a 5 c.p.s. mounting frequency ($R = 10$) gives 99 per cent. reduction. The static deflexion for these two cases is 0·10 in. and 0·39 in. respectively.

Suggested procedure for selection of 'instrument mountings'

For the selection of the correct type of anti-vibration mounting for apparatus, it is suggested that the process be as follows:

1. The frequency of vibration affecting the instrument should be known.

2. The amplitude of existing vibration at instrument position should be known.

3. The amplitude of vibration permissible at the instrument position should be specified.

Table 75. Transmissibility and frequency ratio.

Frequency ratio (R)	2	3	4	5	6	8	10
Transmissibility .	0·333	0·125	0·067	0·042	0·029	0·016	0·010
Reduction in vibration (per cent.) .	67	87	93	96	97	98	99

Table 76. Natural ('Mounting') frequency and static deflexion.

Natural frequency (F_n) c.p.s. .	1	2	4	6	8	10	15	20
Static deflexion (Δ) in. .	9·80	2·45	0·61	0·27	0·15	0·10	0·044	0·025

(*Note:* In the absence of this specified amplitude, experience elsewhere may have to be relied upon, or some general value assumed. Little information is available on the latter point, but it would usually be safe to specify that the amplitude was not to exceed 0·0001 in.)

If the above three quantities can be specified, the following can be determined:

4. The required transmissibility.

5. The frequency ratio required to give this transmissibility (e.g. from Table 75).

6. The natural frequency of the mounting system.

7. The static deflexion of the 'springs' (e.g. from Table 76).

8. The spring stiffness (from 7, taking into account the weight to be supported).

Example

An instrument weighing 6 lb. is being affected by vibration from a motor running at 1,800 r.p.m., producing vibration of frequency 30 c.p.s. The amplitude of vibration existing at the instrument position is 0·003 in. and it is required to reduce this to 0·0001 in. by fitting anti-vibration mountings directly under the instrument. (It is assumed here that the problem is simply one of anti-vibration mounting of the instrument, although efforts should first be made to reduce the vibration at its source.)

The vibration amplitude is to be reduced from 0·003 in. to 0·0001 in. The transmissibility is therefore 0·0001/0·003, i.e. 1/30. Thus $R^2 - 1$ is to be made equal to 30. For convenience a value of $R = 6$ would be selected, giving $R^2 - 1 = 35$ which is greater than that actually required—this being recommended procedure. If $R = 6$ and $F = 30$ c.p.s. then the mounting frequency (F_n) would have to be 5 c.p.s., for which the static deflexion would be 0·39 in.

If three mountings were used, each would support 2 lb. and would have to compress 0·39 in. under this load, the stiffness of each mounting would thus be about 5 lb. per inch. For four mountings, each would need to have a stiffness about 4 lb. per inch.

REFERENCES

(1) 'Sound control: Anti-vibration mountings—rubber.' *Archit. J.*, **120**, 1954, Information Sheet 494; **125**, 1957, Information Sheet 617.

(2) 'Vibration isolators steady plant's walls.' *Engng News Rec.* **159**, 1957, pp. 38–39.

(3) COMMONWEALTH SCIENTIFIC AND INDUSTRIAL RESEARCH ORGANISATION. *Vibration and shock isolation.* Melbourne, 1958. *National Standards Laboratory technical paper*, no. 10.

(4) 'Anti-vibration mounting for low frequencies.' *Engineering, Lond.* **187**, 1959, pp. 372–3.

BIBLIOGRAPHY

CHURCH, A. H. *Elementary mechanical vibrations.* London, Pitman, 1949.

COLE, E. B. *The theory of vibration for engineers.* London, Crosby Lockwood, 1951.

CREDE, C. E. *Vibration and shock isolation.* London, Chapman & Hall, 1951.

DEN HARTOG, J. P. *Mechanical vibrations.* London, McGraw-Hill, 1956.

DEPARTMENT OF SCIENTIFIC AND INDUSTRIAL RESEARCH. *The assessment of vibration intensity and its application to the study of building vibrations.* London, H.M. Stationery Office, 1952. *National building studies. Special report*, no. 19.

JACOBSEN, L. S., and AYRE, R. *Engineering vibrations.* London. McGraw-Hill, 1958.

MANLEY, R. G. *Fundamentals of vibration study.* London, Chapman & Hall, 1948.

THOMSON, W. T. *Mechanical vibrations.* London, Allen & Unwin, 1950.

TIMOSHENKO, S. *Vibration problems in engineering.* London, Constable, 1955.

TUPLIN, W. A. *Vibrations in machinery.* London, Pitman, 1946.

VAN SANTEN, G. W. *Introduction to a study of mechanical vibration.* London, Cleaver Hume Press, 1953.

WOOD, R. H. 'Some notes on vibrations in structures.' *J.R. Inst. Brit. Archit.* **55**, 1948, pp. 553–5.

FIRE PRECAUTIONS

THE degree of fire hazard inherent in the work carried on in a building affects the arrangement of rooms, the dimensions and layout of vertical and horizontal circulation, and the choice of structural and finishing materials. For laboratories, as for other buildings, an estimate of the fire hazard must be made, and used as a controlling factor in assessing the relative merits of structural and finishing materials.

It is essential to differentiate between the precautionary measures built into the building and *fire-prevention*, which, like the prevention of accidents (see section on Safety Precautions), is largely a matter of staff discipline and training. Simple precautions such as the use of asbestos mats under heat sources and the responsible control of improvised electrical wiring are taken to prevent fires: elaborate fire-resisting construction is designed to minimize their effect. This is not to say that the designer's contribution to fire precautions is unimportant. It is aimed at providing amply for passive and active defence of the building and its contents against serious damage, and at limiting personal hazard to the occupants.

The occurrence of laboratory fires

Records of fires in laboratories were kept on a national scale in 1947 (1). In this period there were 32 fires. The number of laboratories 'at risk' is not known, and it is not possible to estimate the average risk. Table 77 gives an indication of where fires occurred and their causes. Out of the 32 fires, 16 began on floors, 14 on benches or in fume cupboards, and 2 in the structure. About two-thirds were directly

Table 77. Causes of fires in laboratories, 1947.

Cause	No. of fires	Percentage (approx.)	
Naked flame .	13	40·65	
Electric heat source .	5	15·65	
Chemical Reaction .	4	12·50	68·80
Electrical defects . .	8	25·00	
Unknown . . .	2	6·20	31·20
	32	100·00	

connected with the work carried on in the laboratories, the remainder being mainly electrical in origin.

Fire hazard

In this country, fire hazard is assessed in accordance with two authoritative documents, namely the report of the Joint Committee on Fire Grading of Buildings (2) and British Standard 476 (3). The former recommends a method of grading buildings according to fire risk and in relation to their function, the latter lays down standards for measuring the fire-resisting characteristics of building materials.

The Fire Grading of Buildings Committee divided fire hazard into three categories:

(a) Damage hazard to the structure and its contents.

(b) Personal hazard to the occupants.

(c) Exposure hazard to fire spread from surrounding buildings.

Exposure hazard is the same for laboratories as for other kinds of building and does not need special treatment in this report. Personal and damage hazard are interrelated, because the length of time materials resist ignition and prevent flame-spread determines the time in which the occupants may safely use escape routes. These classifications are, however, useful when placing laboratories on the fire-grading scale and have been used below in this way.

Fire grading of laboratory buildings

Fire grading of buildings according to occupancy on the basis of the report of the Fire Grading of Buildings Committee (2) is carried out in two parts:

(a) according to damage and exposure hazard;

(b) according to personal hazard.

The former mainly affects structure in relation to building size and combustible content, the latter affects planning (travel distances, corridor and staircase arrangements), the prevention of flame spread, &c., although, of course, all aspects of design are affected by both to some extent.

(a) Damage hazard

(i) Fire load

Damage hazard depends on the amount of combustible material in the building. The weight of each material is multiplied by its calorific value.[1] The total for all materials in the building is its calorific content which, divided by floor area, gives the fire load in B.t.u. per square foot. Three categories of fire load are given by the Fire Grading of Buildings Committee (4).

[1] Appendix III of Pt. 1 of *Fire grading of buildings* (2) gives a list of calorific values of many materials.

Low Fire Load does not exceed an average of 100,000 B.t.u. per square foot of net floor area of any compartment, nor an average of 200,000 B.t.u. per square foot on limited isolated areas, provided that storage of combustible material necessary to the occupancy may be allowed to a limited extent if separated from the remainder and enclosed by fire-resisting construction of an appropriate grade.

Moderate Fire Load exceeds an average of 100,000 B.t.u. per square foot of net floor area of any compartment but does not exceed an average of 200,000 B.t.u. per square foot, nor an average of 400,000 B.t.u. per square foot on limited isolated areas, provided that storage of combustible material necessary to the occupancy may be allowed to a limited extent if separated from the remainder and enclosed by fire-resisting construction of an appropriate grade.

High Fire Load exceeds an average of 200,000 B.t.u. per square foot of net floor area of any compartment but does not exceed an average of 400,000 B.t.u. per square foot of net floor area, nor an average of 800,000 B.t.u. per square foot on limited isolated areas.

Factories and workshops are normally placed in the moderate fire-load category, and it seems reasonable to place laboratories which house only moderate amounts of inflammable or explosive materials in the same grade. Laboratories in which only negligible amounts of such materials are used may have only a low fire-load grading. The Radio Research Station at Datchet (Fig. 98), for example, which houses mainly conventional physics techniques would have a low fire-load grading. The building contains only a few under-bench cupboards and the benches themselves do not, as a rule, support combustible apparatus or substances. There are a number of loose tables, but it is reasonable to estimate that the combustibility of the furniture would not exceed 50,000 B.t.u. per square foot of laboratory area. On the other hand, the Isotope Building at the Slough Pest Infestation Station is tightly planned with a high bench/floor ratio and is equipped with under-bench cupboards, fume cupboards, desks, &c. The total calorific value of the furniture is about 120,000 B.t.u.'s per square foot. In addition, biochemical laboratories of this kind would usually contain moderate quantities of combustible materials such as organic solvents, and the Slough building would be given a moderate fire-load grading.

Small areas of the building in which appreciable quantities of inflammable substances are kept must be given full consideration in the assessment. For example, the experimental laboratory designed by the team for the Animal Research Unit at Cambridge has a calorific content of about 105,000 B.t.u. in the normal laboratory units, barely over the average figure for low fire load. Being a small building (40,000 cu. ft. approx.) it could probably be given a low grading (5). There are, however, two rooms in the building where large quantities of inflammable solvents will be used regularly (for lipid work, and

Table 78. Grading of occupancies by fire load.

	Normal		Abnormal
Examples of occupancies of *low* fire load	Flats Offices Restaurants Hotels Hospitals	Schools Museums Public Libraries Institutional and Administrative Buildings	Factories and workshops in which special risks arise through the presence or use of limited quantities of recognized hazardous materials and processes but which would otherwise be graded as 'Low Fire Load—Normal.'
	Factories and workshops in which the materials and processes used are of a recognized non-hazardous nature, i.e. the materials involved are in general incombustible.		
Examples of occupancies of *moderate* fire load	Retail shops, e.g. footwear, clothing, furniture, groceries. Factories and workshops generally.		Retail shops and factories and workshops in which special risks arise through the presence of large quantities of recognized hazardous materials or of recognized hazardous processes.
Examples of occupancies of *high* fire load	Warehouses and other buildings used for the storage in bulk of commodities of a recognized non-hazardous nature.		Warehouses and other buildings used for the storage in bulk of commodities of a recognized hazardous nature.

for chromatography), and the fire load is high in these areas. Therefore the building must be placed in the moderate fire-load category.

Table 78 (6) gives guidance in arriving at an estimate of whether the occupancy is a normal or an abnormal one, and thus in the final placing of the building on the three-point scale. Laboratories are not specifically mentioned in the table, and, of course, must be placed according to the assessed fire load. Precautions against personal as opposed to damage hazard in abnormal occupancies are discussed below.

(ii) *Fire resistance*

When the expected intensity of an outbreak of fire in the laboratory has been assessed in terms of calculated fire load, a suitable form of construction must be chosen to give fire resistance which will limit damage short of actual collapse for a given length of time. The occupants may then escape to safety without danger from structural collapse, and the building and its contents may be saved by fire-fighting.

Standard methods of determining the fire resistance of building materials have been recommended (3), and have been used experimentally to find the relationship between fire load and fire-resistance time. The results of this work have been used (7) to prepare a table of equivalent severities (Table 79). It was concluded that where a structure would withstand a 'complete burn-out without collapse' for the

Table 79. Assumed equivalent severities of building fires.

Fire load B.t.u./sq. ft.	Equivalent severity of fire in hours of standard test
Less than 100,000, i.e. low fire load	1
100,000–200,000, i.e. moderate fire load	2
200,000–400,000, i.e. high fire load	4

number of hours given in the second column of the table, it could be regarded as 'fully protected'.

All buildings, however, need not be of 'fully protected' construction. The required degree of protection depends upon the size of the building and the density of its population as well as the fire load it carries. Three grades of construction related to the three 'fully protected' categories in Table 79 were recommended (Types 1, 2, and 3), and four further grades of less protected construction, related to building function and size, were added (Types 4, 5, 6, and 7). Definitions of the seven types of construction and fire resistance times for the various elements of structure are given in Table 80. Tables 81, 82, 83, and 84 give the limits of size for buildings of low, moderate, and high fire grades. Single-story buildings are dealt with separately in Table 84 on a less stringent grading basis, because of the ease of escape for occupants and of access for fire-fighting appliances. The only comprehensive published data relating fire resistance times to common structural systems are the tables given in the Ministry of Education *Building bulletin*, no. 7 (8). These are reproduced here as Tables 85, 86, 87, and 88.

The division of buildings into compartments by means of fire-resisting walls has an important bearing on fire grading, and can usefully be applied to the design of large laboratories. Dividing walls are used to limit or contain fire hazard within a given area. Restrictions (Tables 81, 82, 83, and 84) then apply to fire-containing compartments instead of total building size. The use of compartments is strongly recommended by the fire authorities for large buildings, where loss and damage by fire would be extensive if allowed to spread throughout the whole building before fire-fighting equipment could be brought into play. The Fire Grading of Buildings Committee recommend that such walls should have not less than 2-hour resistance in moderate or low-fire-load buildings and not less than 4-hour resistance in high-

Table 80. Proposed minimum fire-resistance requirements for graded types of construction, with examples of construction conforming to type.

Grading of Construction	Minimum fire resistance (in hours) of main elements of structure					Examples of construction conforming to type‡
	Walls, and columns and beams supporting walls				Floors and roofs and columns and beams supporting floors and roofs	
	External	Separating	Division	Other F.R. or load-bearing		
Type 1. Incombustible, fire-resisting construction. To be considered fully protected in relation to high fire loads, e.g. large warehouses.	4	4	4	4	4	Steel frame with 2½-in. concrete protection. Walls of brickwork 9 in. thick. Filler joist or reinforced concrete floors 6 in. thick or hollow tile floor of equivalent fire resistance.
Type 2. Incombustible fire-resisting construction. To be considered fully protected in relation to moderate fire loads, e.g. shops and factories.	2	4	2 4†	2	2	As above but 2-in. protection to steel, filler joist or reinforced concrete floors 5 in. thick or hollow tile or other floors of equivalent fire resistance.
Type 3. Incombustible fire-resisting construction. To be considered fully protected in relation to low fire loads only, e.g. office and residential buildings.	2*	4	2 4†	1	1	As above but 1-in. protection to steel or 1 in. cement mortar on expanded metal. Concrete floors 3½ in. thick, or equivalent.
Type 4. Fire-resisting construction but not necessarily incombustible and may therefore include timber floors and timber roof construction. Partially protected only in relation to all fire loads.	2*	4	2 4†	1	½	Load-bearing brick walls. Timber floors and roof, protected by plaster ceilings on expanded metal. Fire-retardant roof covering.
Type 5. Externally protected construction. Fire-resisting incombustible external walls, non-fire-resisting internal construction.	2	4	2 4†	1	..	Load-bearing brick walls. Timber floors and roofs. Fire retardant roof covering.
Type 6. Non-fire-resisting construction. Incombustible.	..	4	2 4†	..	..	Unprotected steel frame and roof trusses, clad externally with corrugated sheeting.
Type 7. Non-fire-resisting construction. Combustible.	..	4	2 4†	..	..	Timber framed and/or clad external walls. Timber floors and roof with fire-retardant covering.

* 1 hour for low fire load occupancies in framed buildings not exceeding 50 ft. in height.
† If occupancy is of high fire load.
‡ It should be appreciated that these are intended as examples only, and any other form of construction which complies with the recommended grades could be used.

fire-load buildings (9). Resistance characteristics for doors through such walls are also specified.

On the basis of damage hazard, a number of worked examples indicate that most laboratories will fall in the moderate fire load grade, although, as shown above, there will be exceptional cases, in which the fire load for all or part of the laboratory will result in a higher or lower grading. Fully protected construction will not be essential for many small laboratories with moderate or low fire loads, but the team concluded that no permanent laboratory building should have a structure less fire-resisting than Type 5. For example, although the experimental laboratory building at Cambridge (moderate fire-load rating) has so small a cubic capacity (approx. 40,000 cu. ft.) that, on the basis of Table 84, it could be built in any type of construction, Type 5 construction was chosen. Precautions will be taken in rooms with exceptionally high fire load to ensure that personal hazard in these rooms is not higher than in other parts of the building (see under (b) Personal Hazard below).

Where laboratories adjoin office accommodation, workshops, &c., the mixed occupancy requires special fire-grading assessment. Offices and workshops are normally given a moderate fire-load rating, and may fall in the same class as the laboratory. If, however, there are exceptional fire-loading conditions in the laboratories, it may be more economical to compartment the office buildings as a separate unit with a lower fire grading than the laboratories, giving consequent economies in structure and finish.

It is not uncommon for laboratories to contain equipment the value of which far exceeds the value of the building itself, and records of work in progress may be irreplaceable. Expensive, heavy equipment cannot be moved quickly in case of fire and there is, therefore, a good case for placing laboratories in a higher rather than a lower fire-load grade for reasons which are not directly connected with the fire hazard inherent in the work. It is suggested that whilst the grading of structure according to fire load forms a sound basis for specifying minimum standards, the unique nature of much research work may warrant

133

Table 81. Maximum heights, floor areas, and cubic capacities of compartments of buildings of Types 1, 2, or 3 construction containing *Low Fire Loads* (e.g. flats, offices, &c.).

Type of construction	Height (feet)	Minimum accessibility of building or division	Floor area of compartment (sq. ft.)		Cubic capacity of compartment (c. ft.)		Notes
			Normal occupancy	Abnormal occupancy	Normal occupancy	Abnormal occupancy	
1. (4 hours)	No limit (normal) 100 ft.★ (abnormal)	Three-quarters of perimeter	No limit	60,000	No limit	500,000	1. Cubic capacity to be measured on maximum story height of 12 ft. 6 in. 2. It is recommended that buildings containing abnormal occupancies should be sprinklered throughout where compartment floor area exceeds 10,000 sq. ft. Where for some reason sprinklers cannot be installed the floor area should not exceed half the area quoted. 3. Special precautions are required when building exceeds 100 ft. in height or 10,000 sq. ft. floor area.
2. (2 hours) or 3. (1 hour)		8 ft. per 1,000 sq. ft. of floor area	No limit	40,000	No limit	750,000	

Maximum heights and cubic capacities of buildings or divisions of Types 4, 5, and 7 construction containing *Low Fire Loads*.

Type of construction	Height (feet★)	Minimum accessibility	Cubic capacity of building or division (c. ft.)		
			Normal occupancy	Abnormal occupancy	
				Sprinklered	Not sprinklered
4. (¼ hour) . .	50	8 ft. per 1,000 sq. ft. of floor area of division	500,000†	250,000	125,000
5. . . .	50	,,	250,000†	200,000	100,000
7. . . .	30	,,	36,000 (2 stories only)	See Table 84	

★ Subject to tolerance of +5 ft.   † If in one occupation.

Table 82. Maximum heights, floor areas and cubic capacities of compartments of buildings of Types 1 or 2 construction containing *Moderate Fire Loads* (e.g. shops, factories, &c.). Normal and abnormal occupancies.

Type of construction	Height (feet)	Minimum accessibility of building or division	Floor area of compartment (sq. ft.)	Cubic capacity of compartment (c. ft.)	Notes
1. (4 hours) or 2. (2 hours)	No limit (normal) 100 ft.★ (abnormal)	Three-quarters of perimeter	60,000	750,000	1. Cubic capacity to be measured on maximum story height of 12 ft. 6 in. 2. It is recommended that buildings should be sprinklered throughout where compartment floor area exceeds 10,000 sq. ft. Where for some reason sprinklers cannot be installed the floor area should not exceed half the floor areas quoted. 3. Special precautions are required when building exceeds 100 ft. in height or 10,000 sq. ft. floor area.
		8 ft. per 1,000 sq. ft. of floor area	40,000	500,000	

Maximum heights and cubic capacities of buildings or divisions of Types 3, 4, and 5 construction containing *Moderate Fire Loads*.

Type of construction	Height (feet★)	Minimum accessibility	Cubic capacity of building or division (c. ft.)			
			Normal occupancy		Abnormal occupancy	
			Sprinklered	Not sprinklered	Sprinklered	Not sprinklered
3. (1 hour) .	75	8 ft. per 1,000 sq. ft. of floor area of division	500,000	250,000†	250,000	125,000
4. (¼ hour) .	50	,,	250,000	125,000	150,000	75,000
5. . .	40	,,	100,000	50,000	100,000	50,000

★ Subject to tolerance of +5 ft.   † Maximum area on any one floor not to exceed 7,500 sq. ft.

Table 83. Maximum heights, floor areas, and cubic capacities of compartments of buildings of Type 1 construction containing *High Fire Loads* (e.g. warehouses, &c.). Normal and abnormal occupancies.

Type of construction	Height (feet)	Minimum accessibility of building or division	Floor area of compartment (sq. ft.)	Cubic capacity of compartment (c. ft.)	Notes
1. (4 hours)	No limit (normal) 100 ft.★ (abnormal)	Three-quarters of perimeter	60,000	750,000	1. Cubic capacity to be measured on full story height. 2. It is recommended that buildings should be sprinklered throughout when compartment floor area exceeds 10,000 sq. ft. Where for some reason sprinklers cannot be installed the floor areas should not exceed half the values quoted. 3. Special precautions are required when building exceeds 100 ft. in height or 10,000 sq. ft. floor area.
		8 ft. per 1,000 sq. ft. of floor area	40,000	500,000	

Maximum heights and cubic capacities of buildings and divisions of Types 2, 3, 4, and 5 construction containing *High Fire Loads*.

Type of construction	Height (feet)★	Minimum accessibility	Cubic capacity of building or division (c. ft.)			
			Normal occupancy		Abnormal occupancy	
			Sprinklered	Not sprinklered	Sprinklered	Not sprinklered
2. (2 hours)	75	8 ft. per 1,000 sq. ft. of floor area of division	500,000	250,000†	250,000	125,000
3. (1 hour)	50	,,	250,000	125,000	150,000	75,000
4. (½ hour)	50	,,	100,000	50,000	100,000	50,000
5. ..	25	,,	50,000	25,000	50,000	25,000

★ Heights subject to tolerance of +5 ft.　　　　† Maximum area on any one floor not to exceed 7,500 sq. ft.

Table 84. Single-story buildings (in one occupation and without basements). Maximum cubic capacities of buildings, divisions, and compartments of buildings. *Types of construction lying above the thick line are regarded as fully protected in relation to the particular occupancies.*

Type of construction	Maximum cubic capacity of building or division★ (c. ft.)					
	Low fire load occupancies		Moderate fire load occupancies		High fire load occupancies	
	Normal	Abnormal	Normal	Abnormal	Normal	Abnormal
1	No limit	1,000,000 (no limit if sprinklered)	1,000,000		1,000,000	
2					1,000,000	
3			500,000		500,000	
4	500,000	250,000	250,000		250,000	
5						
6	500,000	250,000	250,000		250,000†	
7	75,000	50,000	75,000†	50,000†	50,000†	40,000†

★ Cubic capacity to be based on height of 12 ft. 6 in., excepting occupancies of high fire load, and buildings of Type 7 construction.

† Height of building not to exceed 25 ft.

Cubic capacities may be doubled if buildings are 'sprinklered', except as indicated.

additional structural protection in limited areas of laboratory buildings.

The need for flexibility of use in new laboratories also has a bearing on fire grading. Techniques within a single discipline may develop and change rapidly. Some allowance in the fire grading may be necessary in order to give freedom in this respect, without increasing the damage hazard.

(b) Personal hazard

Except in so far as the calculation of fire load and the choice of fire-resistant structure provides a margin of structural safety, sections (*a*) (i) (ii) above are principally concerned with the preservation of the building for a period long enough to allow active fire-fighting measures to be taken, and thus to

Table 85. Fire resistance achieved by various types of wall and partition.

Construction and materials		Minimum thickness in inches exclusive of plastering to attain indicated fire resistance		
		2 hours	1 hour	½ hour
Solid bricks of clay, concrete or sand-lime	Solid wall. No plaster	$8\frac{1}{2}$	$4\frac{1}{4}$	$4\frac{1}{4}$
	Solid wall plastered on both sides	$4\frac{1}{4}$	$4\frac{1}{4}$	$4\frac{1}{4}$
	Cavity wall. No plaster	$10\frac{1}{2}$	$10\frac{1}{2}$	$10\frac{1}{2}$
Solid concrete blocks (conforming to B.S. 492)	Class 1 (a) aggregates:			
	Solid wall. No plaster	4	3	$2\frac{1}{2}$
	Solid wall plastered on both sides	3	2	2
	Class 1 (b) aggregates:			
	Solid wall. No plaster	4	3	$2\frac{1}{2}$
	Solid wall plastered on both sides	4	$2\frac{1}{2}$	2
	Class 2 aggregates:			
	Solid wall. No plaster	..	4	3
	Solid wall plastered on both sides	4	3	2
Reinforced concrete*	Class 1 aggregates	4	3	3
	Class 2 aggregates	4	3	3
Hollow clay blocks Thickness of material on each side of cell not less than $\frac{3}{4}$ in.	All plastered $\frac{1}{2}$ in. thick on each side, except where otherwise stated:			
	1 cell in thickness; not less than 50 per cent. solid	..	4	3
	1 cell in thickness; not less than 30 per cent. solid	..	6	6
	2 cells in thickness; not less than 50 per cent. solid	$8\frac{1}{2}$	4	4 (without plaster not less than 60 per cent. solid)
	2 cells in thickness; not less than 45 per cent. solid	..	6	6 (without plaster)
Hollow concrete blocks (conforming to B.S. 728 or 834)	Plastered $\frac{1}{2}$ in. thick on each side except where otherwise stated. 1 cell in wall thickness:			
	Class 1 (a) aggregates	4	$2\frac{1}{2}$ (4 without plaster)	$2\frac{1}{2}$
	Class 1 (b) aggregates	$4\frac{1}{2}$	3 ($4\frac{1}{2}$ without plaster)	$2\frac{1}{2}$
	Class 2 aggregates	..	$8\frac{3}{4}$	3
Solid blocks of gypsum	No plaster	4	3	2
	$\frac{1}{2}$ in. plaster on each side	3	2	2
Hollow blocks of gypsum not less than 70 per cent. solid	No plaster	4	3	2
	$\frac{1}{2}$ in. plaster on each side	3	2	2
Solid woodwool slabs	$\frac{1}{2}$ in. plaster on each side	2	2	2
Solid plaster	Central reinforcement of metal lath on steel rods or studs	..	2	2
Plasterboard supported top and bottom edges in steel channels	$\frac{5}{8}$ in. gypsum plaster on both sides	..	$\frac{3}{4}$	$\frac{3}{4}$
Glass blocks	Not exceeding 8 ft. × 8 ft. built to makers' specification	..	4	4
Compressed straw slabs	3 in. × $\frac{1}{2}$ in. wood cover strips over joints:			
	No plaster	..	..	2

Hollow partitions†		Fire resistance in hours
$\frac{3}{8}$ in. plasterboard on each side	$\frac{3}{16}$ in. plaster on each side of partition	$\frac{1}{2}$
$\frac{1}{2}$ in. plasterboard on each side	No plaster	$\frac{1}{2}$
	$\frac{3}{8}$ in. plaster on each side of partition	1
	No plaster. Mineral wool infilling	1
$\frac{3}{4}$ in. plasterboard on each side	No plaster	1
Gypsum, Portland cement or cement lime plaster‡ on expanded metal on each side (steel or timber studding)	$\frac{1}{2}$ in. thick on each side	$\frac{1}{2}$
	$\frac{3}{4}$ in. thick on each side	1
1 in. woodwool slabs on each side	$\frac{1}{2}$ in. plaster on each side of partition	$\frac{1}{2}$
$1\frac{1}{2}$ in. woodwool slabs on each side	$\frac{1}{2}$ in. plaster on each side	1
$\frac{1}{2}$ in. insulating board on each side	$\frac{1}{2}$ in. plaster on each side	$\frac{1}{2}$
$\frac{1}{4}$ in. plywood on each side	No plaster. Glass or mineral wool infilling nailed between studs	$\frac{1}{2}$

* † ‡ For notes see foot of opposite page.

Table 86. Fire resistance achieved by various types of floor.

Construction and materials	Minimum thickness in inches to attain indicated fire resistance: 2 hours	1 hour	$\frac{1}{2}$ hour
Filler joist concrete; maximum spacing of joists as allowed for structural requirements. Any aggregate:			
Minimum slab thickness . .	5	4	$3\frac{1}{2}$
Minimum cover on flanges of joists:			
Top	1	Nil	Nil
Bottom	1	$\frac{1}{2}$	$\frac{1}{2}$
Solid reinforced concrete slab (not prestressed). Any aggregate:			
Minimum slab thickness . .	5	4	$3\frac{1}{2}$
Minimum cover to reinforcement	$\frac{1}{2}$	$\frac{1}{2}$	$\frac{1}{2}$
Hollow tile:			
Minimum thickness of incombustible material, i.e. thickness of concrete slab and of solid material in tiles	$3\frac{1}{2}$	3	$2\frac{1}{2}$
Minimum cover to reinforcement	$\frac{3}{4}$	$\frac{3}{4}$	$\frac{1}{2}$
	Minimum thickness of plaster in inches to attain indicated fire resistance		
Timber joist; $\frac{7}{8}$ in. T. and G. boards on joists not less than 6 in. × 2 in.:			
$\frac{1}{2}$ in. plasterboard and plaster ceiling	..	..	$\frac{3}{16}$
Ceiling of two layers of $\frac{3}{8}$ in. plasterboard	..	..	Nil
$\frac{1}{2}$ in. insulating board and gypsum plaster ceiling	..	..	$\frac{1}{2}$
$\frac{3}{8}$ in. plaster board and plaster ceiling	..	..	$\frac{5}{8}$
$\frac{1}{4}$ in. asbestos insulation board ceiling fixed direct to joists .	..	..	Nil
Timber joist; irrespective of thickness of floorboards or size of joist. T. and G. or plain edge boards:			
1 in. woodwool slab and plaster ceiling	..	..	$\frac{3}{16}$
Ceiling of plaster on expanded metal lathing	..	..	$\frac{1}{2}$
Ceiling of vermiculite/gypsum plaster on expanded metal lathing	..	..	$\frac{1}{2}$

Table 87. Protection afforded to floors by various types of suspended ceiling.*

Construction and materials	Minimum thickness in inches to attain indicated protection*: 2 hours	1 hour	$\frac{1}{2}$ hour
Plaster on expanded metal (cement/lime/sand or sanded gypsum mix)	..	$\frac{7}{8}$	$\frac{5}{8}$
Vermiculite/gypsum plaster on expanded metal (1:$1\frac{1}{2}$ mix) . .	$\frac{3}{4}$	$\frac{1}{2}$	$\frac{1}{2}$
Vermiculite/gypsum plaster on $\frac{3}{8}$-in. plaster lath	..	$\frac{1}{2}$	..
Precast vermiculite slabs . .	$1\frac{1}{2}$†	1	1

* Where the above ceilings are used in conjunction with metal floor beams which are otherwise unprotected the times stated give the fire resistance to be expected from the floor as a whole.

† To achieve this protection careful attention to the mix and the type of vermiculite used are necessary.

Table 88. Fire resistance achieved by various types of protected steel columns and beams.*

	Construction and materials	Minimum thickness in inches of protection outside steel to attain indicated fire resistance†: 2 hours	1 hour	$\frac{1}{2}$ hour
Solid protection†	Brickwork with filling of brick and mortar, all properly bonded	2	2	2
	Concrete, not leaner than 1:2:4 mix. Reinforced centrally with steel mesh or wire:			
	Class 1 aggregates . .	$1\frac{1}{2}$	1	1
	Class 2 aggregates . .	2	1	1
	Gypsum concrete (7 parts gypsum/1 part wood chips, poured *in situ*) . .	$1\frac{1}{2}$	1	1
	Hollow clay tile with concrete filling-thickness of solid material	..	..	$1\frac{1}{2}$
	Foamed slag blocks with concrete or block filling. Wire reinforcement in every horizontal joint . . .	2	2	2
	Gypsum blocks with interior filling. Wire reinforcement in every horizontal joint .	2	2	2
	Sprayed asbestos . . .	1	$\frac{1}{2}$	$\frac{1}{4}$
Hollow protection†	Brickwork or solid clay blocks. Wire reinforcement in every horizontal joint . .	3	2	2
	Foamed slag blocks. Wire reinforcement in every horizontal joint	2	2	2
	Gypsum blocks. Wire reinforcement in every horizontal joint	2	2	2
	Moulded asbestos held in position with nichrome wire .	$1\frac{1}{2}$	1	1
	Plaster on expanded metal lathing	..	$\frac{3}{4}$	$\frac{1}{2}$
	Asbestos insulation board on non-combustible battens .	$\frac{3}{4}$	$\frac{3}{8}$	$\frac{1}{4}$
	Vermiculite/cement spray following profile of section .	$1\frac{1}{2}$	$\frac{3}{4}$	$\frac{1}{2}$
	Plaster on plasterboard .	$\frac{1}{2}$ in. plaster on $\frac{3}{4}$ in. plasterboard bound with 14 s.w.g. wire at 4 in. pitch	$\frac{1}{2}$ in. plaster on $\frac{3}{8}$ in. plasterboard bound with 14 s.w.g. wire at 4 in. pitch	$\frac{3}{16}$ in. plaster on $\frac{3}{8}$ in. plasterboard bound with 14 s.w.g. wire at 4 in. pitch
	Precast vermiculite cement slabs with skim coat of plaster. Thickness of slab .	2 with wire reinforcement in every horizontal joint	1 with mesh reinforcement in slabs	1 with mesh reinforcement in slabs

* Not all methods are necessarily suitable for beams.

† See also qualifications given in the original publication (8).

Notes to Table 85.

* Walls to be reinforced vertically and horizontally at not more than 6 in. centres, and reinforcement to be not less than 0·2 per cent. of volume. Walls less than 5 in. thick to have a single layer of reinforcement in the middle of the wall.

† These partitions are of various types of cladding on timber framing unless otherwise stated. Similar results could be expected from the same claddings on lightly reinforced concrete framing; light-gauge metal frames generally would not perform so well.

‡ Thickness of plaster measured from outer face of lathing.

prevent total loss of the building and its contents. In effect, fire grading of buildings for human occupancy in these terms gives a sound framework on which to apply other precautions designed for the personal safety of the occupants.

Local authorities have powers to require adequate means of escape from buildings in case of fire, but there is not a uniform set of fire regulations (except in Scotland), and it is common practice for building schemes to be submitted individually to the local fire service. Some authorities (e.g. London and Liverpool) give guidance to architects in the form of notes or recommendations. As in the case of damage hazard, the report of the Fire Grading of Buildings Committee (2) provides an authoritative common basis for recommendations on precautions against personal hazard.

The fire risk to a person using a building depends principally on two aspects of the occupancy, the population characteristics and the building function.

(i) *Population*

Population density affects panic risk in case of fire. The number of people using public buildings is restricted in order to reduce danger in panic conditions.

Buildings are grouped in three categories in relation to population characteristics (10) as follows:

Group A: Assembly buildings.
Group B: Trade, commercial and industrial buildings.
Group C: Residential and institutional buildings.

Population densities recommended by a number of authorities for buildings in Group B are shown in Table 89.[1]

In research laboratories, estimates of space necessary for each worker vary widely with the type of work. For example, where the work is large-scale, as opposed to bench-scale, density would be low. Hiscocks (11) examines estimates of space requirements and quotes figures ranging from 150 to 350 sq. ft. per research worker. In the National Physical Laboratory, which Hiscocks uses as an example, laboratory floor area varies between 240 and 370 sq. ft. per person. These figures may be com-

Table 89. Range of population densities in existing recommendations.

Building type	Range of recommended densities in square feet per person
Shops, Department stores . .	20–75
Offices	50–100
Warehouses	100–300
Factories	25–100

[1] Table 89 has been prepared from the data in *Fire grading of buildings*, Pt. 3, Table I, p. 28, and the summary of recommended densities on p. 31

pared with those in Table 89. It will be seen that laboratories have a low population density and panic hazard may be regarded as low. In addition, the laboratory population will generally be able-bodied and it may be expected that research workers will have some knowledge and training in safety matters.

There seems little need to limit laboratory population density, since functional space requirements will normally keep this well within safe limits.

(ii) *Building function*

Fire hazard is directly related to the nature of the apparatus and substances used in the laboratory processes. The following occupancy groups are suggested by the team. These follow closely the kind of grouping used by the Fire Grading of Buildings Committee:

Group 1. Laboratories in which negligible quantities of inflammable or explosive substances and few heat sources are found, i.e. laboratories in which the work is largely microscopical, mathematical, physical, or physiological.

Group 2. Laboratories in which appreciable quantities of inflammable or explosive substances and/or considerable numbers of heat sources or pieces of electrical apparatus are found, i.e. most chemical, some biochemical and physics laboratories.

Group 3. Laboratories in which large amounts of inflammable or explosive substances are found.

The grouping purposely eliminates scientific discipline as a means of definition, as there is much overlapping of techniques between disciplines, and because flexibility of use may require complete changes in room function.

Laboratories, generally, fall in the broad population Group B, which also covers offices, warehouses, factories, &c. This category includes both normally and abnormally hazardous uses (12), so that all three occupancy groups (1, 2, and 3 above) would be covered by the general Group B. In particularly hazardous areas, precautions aimed at reducing personal hazard would be made more stringent (see below).

Planning and construction in relation to personal fire hazard

Structural elements, the design of which is affected by fire-load rating, also play an important part in personal safety in an outbreak of fire. Structural walls and floors must remain intact and safe while the occupants of the building escape. It is believed that the recommended fire-resistance times for specified fire loading are adequate in this aspect. A number of other factors are of equal importance from the point of view of personal safety, however, and are discussed below.

(a) Restricting spread of flame

When a fire begins in an occupied room, danger to the occupants depends upon the speed at which the fire spreads in the contents of the room and on the wall, floor, and ceiling surfaces. In the laboratory the working apparatus varies with the technique or process and it is assumed that staff would be trained and disciplined in the uses of their equipment, thus restricting hazard from this source to a minimum. Surface linings, however, are built-in hazards, and must be chosen with their flame-spreading properties in mind.

Four classes of lining materials are defined in B.S. 476 (1953) as follows:

Class 1. Surfaces of very low flame spread.
Class 2.   ,,   ,, low   ,,   ,,
Class 3.   ,,   ,, medium   ,,   ,,
Class 4.   ,,   ,, rapid   ,,   ,,

Table 90 gives the classification of a number of common lining materials. All the materials in this table are classed as combustible (5). Asbestos cement, various asbestos wallboards, plaster, and wall tiles are classed as incombustible finishes.

The Fire Grading of Buildings Committee recommends that for buildings in Group B (see p. 138 above), only linings in Classes 1 to 3 be used (13). Although Class 3 linings may cause fairly rapid fire spread, it is thought that the alertness of people in this class of building would reduce the risk of personal injury.

The categories of laboratory use (Groups 1, 2, and 3, p. 138, above) make possible a further classification. It is suggested that laboratories in Groups 2 and 3 should have linings in Classes 1 and 2 only. There are

Table 90. Spread-of-flame classification of combustible wall and ceiling linings.*

Plasterboard Woodwool slabs Metal-faced plywood Asbestos-paper-faced fibre insulation board	Class 1
Synthetic-resin bonded paper and fabric sheets Compressed-straw slabs (uncovered)	Class 2
Timber weighing more than 25 lb./cu. ft. Plywood weighing more than 25 lb./cu. ft. Wood-particle board Hardboard Compressed-straw slabs (paper covered) Glass-reinforced polyester-resin sheets (with fire-retardant additives)	Class 3
Timber weighing less than 25 lb./cu. ft. Plywood weighing less than 25 lb./cu. ft. Fibre insulation board Acrylic sheets (polymethyl methacrylate) Glass-reinforced polyester-resin sheets (without fire-retardant additives)	Class 4

*Fire-retardant treatment may improve the classification of some surfacing materials. It will not make the material more or less combustible.

also many special situations in laboratories which may be separately considered, for example, the areas of wall surface immediately behind benches on which heat may be generated should be lined with Class 1 materials; protection of the same kind is normally given to the tops and immediate surroundings of glass-blowing benches, benches carrying furnaces, fume cupboard floors, &c.

Circulation spaces (corridors, staircases, &c.) outside the working areas may be used as escape routes, and it has been recommended that only incombustible linings are suitable in these positions (14).

Table 90 shows mainly wall and ceiling materials. For floors, no serious hazard is likely from the materials commonly used in laboratories, i.e. hardwoods, rubber, linoleum, or plastics (15).

(b) Restricting the spread of smoke and hot gases

When a fire begins to spread the danger to other occupants is in direct relation to the ease with which smoke and hot gases can spread through the building, especially in the circulation areas. Smoke can cause panic when there is little danger of fire-spread; the majority of fire fatalities are due to asphyxiation and not to burning.

Primarily, escape routes should be protected, and smoke and gases confined as far as possible to the area in which the fire originates. Smoke-stopping alone for corridors and stairs is, of course, not enough, and the recommendations for fire resistance of walls bounding escape routes (16) should be strictly applied to laboratories. Partitions bounding corridors should provide a smoke stop, and at the same time give at least half an hour's resistance to flame penetration. This excludes the use of very light partitions of combustible materials, and requires the use of heat-resistant glazing in doors and borrowed lights (17). Smoke-stop doors have been specified as of solid timber at least $1\frac{3}{4}$ in. thick or any other material of equal fire resistance; any glazing to be fire resisting (e.g. wired glass). In multi-story buildings, similar recommendations on fire resistance and smoke-stopping apply to staircases (18) and should be followed in the design of laboratories, as in other buildings where personal safety is a governing factor.

(c) Limitation of building size

The Fire Grading of Buildings Committee suggested limits of cubic capacity on the grounds of damage hazard. These have already been referred to and are embodied in Tables 81, 82, 83, and 84. Further restrictions were recommended for buildings where personal hazard was to be considered. As they are detailed and complicated, reference should be made direct to the Committee's report (19).

(d) Planning against personal hazard

Most of the matters discussed above have been concerned with the structure and finishes of the building. Personal safety, however, demands that fire risk should also be considered as a major factor in the planning of the building. The following items affect laboratory planning:

    i. The provision of sufficient exits, suitably located.

    ii. Limitation of travel distance to exits or to some point protected by compartmenting.

    iii. The provision of corridors and staircases of adequate width.

    iv. The provision of adequate escape routes from working positions.

The local-authority requirements governing these factors may vary, and of course, would have to be satisfied for any proposed building. References here are again mainly to the report of the Fire Grading of Buildings Committee, in the absence of a single mandatory code.

i. *The provision of exits*

For most Group B buildings it has been recommended that floor area should not exceed 4,000 sq. ft., unless an alternative exit is provided. In single-story laboratories, however, it is suggested that at least two exits, remote from each other, should always be provided, no matter what the floor area.

The provision of alternative escape routes in small multi-story buildings is more difficult. It is usually uneconomic to provide more than one staircase in such buildings. The Fire Grading of Buildings Committee suggested restricting the number of occupants, and the floor area and height of such buildings. These restrictions should be strictly applied to all laboratories. Height is restricted to 42 ft. (to the highest floor level). Floor area and number of occupants are restricted for different grades of construction (Table 91). Provisos and exceptions to these proposed restrictions are given fully in Part III of the report of the Fire Grading of Buildings Committee (2).

In multi-story buildings with more than one staircase the floor areas and the distribution of exits is usually governed by limitations imposed on the maximum distance of travel from the work point to an exit or a staircase (see below).

ii. *Limitation of travel distance*

The aim of limiting travel distance to an exit or staircase is to allow the occupants of the building to escape before there is an appreciable accumulation of smoke and hot gases in corridors and circulation areas generally. In laboratories, where the smoke and fume concentrations may be high and at the same time toxic, or at least noxious, limitation of travel distance is of major importance. The Fire Grading of Buildings Committee recommends one standard for all occupancies (20). The maximum recommended distance for fully protected buildings (Types 1, 2, and 3[1]) is 150 ft. of which not more than 100 ft. is along a corridor, or if escape is from a dead-end area, a maximum of 100 ft. of which not more than 60 ft. is along a corridor: 150 ft. is recommended for single-story buildings of incombustible materials: 60 ft. where these conditions are not met.

iii. *Widths of corridors and staircases*

A great many variables affect the choice of suitable dimensions for corridors and staircases. These were discussed in great detail by the Fire Grading of Buildings Committee (21), and tables relating stair width to population were published. It is suggested that these, reproduced as Tables 92, 93, and 94 below, give suitable minimum dimensions for laboratory staircases.

No recommendations are made on corridor width, but in multi-story buildings, corridors should not be made narrower than staircases. The team has visited many laboratories where corridors are used for storage of equipment, and in which the floor area was considerably restricted in consequence. Unless special provision is made for it, the storage of apparatus, &c., in corridors is to be deprecated on grounds of personal fire hazard. With this proviso, it is reasonable to assume that corridor widths derived from functional requirements would also be adequate for escape purposes.

iv. *Escape routes from working positions*

In assessing the need for alternative means of escape from the working position, laboratories must be regarded as unique. There are usually naked bunsen flames or other sources of heat in every room, and at least minute quantities of inflammable liquids in use. These constitute local fire risks, precautions against them normally being taken by the scientist himself. Small outbreaks of fire, which can be controlled with the fire-fighting equipment provided in the laboratory may, however, make it necessary for other occupants of the room to leave if only to seek help. It is desirable, therefore, to have alternative means of exit from such rooms—even though the

Table 91.★ Limits of floor area and number of occupants in small multi-story buildings.

	Maximum floor area in sq. ft.	Maximum number of occupants
Fully protected (Types 1, 2, and 3)	4,000	250
Partially protected (Type 4) .	2,500	150
Other types† (Types 5, 6, and 7)	1,000	50

★ Table prepared from data in *Fire grading of buildings*, Pt. 3, pp. 47–62.

† The team considers Types 6 and 7 unsuitable for laboratory buildings.

[1] Types of construction are given in Table 80.

Table 92. Staircase width in relation to population: *Single-staircase buildings.*

Staircase width	Calculated number of people in building						
	2' 6"	3' 0"	3' 6"	4' 0"	4' 6"	5' 0"	5' 6"
Where population is mainly concentrated on one or two floors	50	100	150	175	200	225	250
Where population is distributed over more than two floors	75	125	175	225	250	..	..

Table 93. Minimum width of each staircase (population distributed over all floors): *Two-staircase buildings.*

No. of stories above ground story	Calculated number of people in building above ground story											
	Shops, dept. stores, and abnormal risk factories—not sprinklered; any building of Type 4 or 5 construction*				Shops, dept. stores, and abnormal risk factories—if sprinklered; residential buildings				Normal risk factories; offices			
2	300	340	380	430	350	400	450	510	410	470	540	600
3	340	390	440	500	400	460	530	600	470	550	630	710
4	390	450	510	580	450	520	600	680	530	620	710	810
5	430	500	570	650	500	590	680	770	590	700	800	910
6	470	550	630	720	560	660	760	860	650	770	890	1,010
7	510	600	690	790	610	720	830	950	710	850	980	1,110
8	550	650	750	860	660	780	910	1,040	770	920	1,070	1,210
9	600	710	820	940	710	840	980	1,120	830	1,000	1,160	1,320
10	640	760	880	1,010	760	910	1,060	1,210	890	1,070	1,240	1,420
Minimum width of each staircase	3' 6"	4' 0"	4' 6"	5' 0"	3' 6"	4' 0"	4' 6"	5' 0"	3' 6"	4' 0"	4' 6"	5' 0"

* Buildings of Type 4 or 5 construction should be limited in height—see text.

Table 94. Minimum width of each staircase (population distributed over all floors): *Three-staircase buildings*

No. of stories above ground story	Calculated number of people in buildings above ground floor											
	Shops, dept. stores, and abnormal risk factories—not sprinklered; any building of Type 4 or 5 construction*				Shops, dept. stores, and abnormal risk factories—if sprinklered; residential buildings				Normal risk factories; offices			
2	540	610	690	770	590	670	760	850	650	740	840	940
3	610	700	800	900	680	780	890	1,000	740	860	980	1,100
4	690	800	910	1,030	760	880	1,010	1,140	830	970	1,110	1,260
5	760	890	1,020	1,160	850	990	1,140	1,290	930	1,090	1,250	1,420
6	840	990	1,140	1,300	930	1,100	1,270	1,440	1,020	1,200	1,390	1,580
7	920	1,090	1,260	1,430	1,020	1,210	1,400	1,590	1,120	1,320	1,530	1,740
8	1,000	1,180	1,370	1,560	1,100	1,310	1,520	1,730	1,210	1,440	1,670	1,910
9	1,070	1,270	1,480	1,690	1,190	1,420	1,650	1,880	1,310	1,560	1,810	2,070
10	1,150	1,370	1,590	1,820	1,270	1,520	1,770	2,020	1,400	1,670	1,950	2,230
Minimum width of each staircase	3' 6"	4' 0"	4' 6"	5' 0"	3' 6"	4' 0"	4' 6"	5' 0"	3' 6"	4' 0"	4' 6"	5' 0"

* Buildings of Type 4 or 5 construction should be limited in height—see text.

alternative door or opening only leads to another room or office. Where laboratories open off a corridor, it is obviously better to have the alternative exit remote from the door to the corridor. This arrangement has been adopted by the team in planning the extension to the Animal Research Unit at Cambridge (see Fig. 42), and is becoming usual in America; it is used in some parts of Courtaulds Ltd. new Acetate and Synthetic Fibres building at Coventry. An alternative method was used in the Bell Telephone Laboratories, Murray Hill, New Jersey; a hatch with a sliding panel remote from the door was provided between chemical laboratories. Even though this arrangement means climbing over the bench, it is preferable to being completely isolated if the door is blocked.

It seems, therefore, that planning for alternative access is simplified if free space is available along the window wall. This consideration adds further weight to the arguments for keeping the window wall free of benches and services (see Part II, Chapter 1).

Services distribution and fire hazard

The team has been told of a number of laboratory fires which began in service ducts and spread through the ducts and damaged other parts of the building.

To some extent continuous ducts act like flues, and if small in cross-section will spread fire rapidly. Ducts should be of incombustible construction and as large in section as is economically possible. To limit fire-spread, it is important that fire-stops should be placed at intervals in the length of ducts. The space around service pipes which pass through walls (particularly if these are compartment walls) should be filled with incombustible material.

Ventilation systems should be arranged so that they can be turned off easily in the event of fire.

Fume cupboards

Materials for the construction of fume cupboards are dealt with in Appendix II, Materials and Finishes. Fume-cupboard floors should be of incombustible materials. Glazing should be of heat-resisting glass if high-temperature work is involved, or if highly inflammable substances are to be used.

Fire-alarm systems

The Factories Act, 1937, specifies that 'where in any factory more than 20 persons are employed in the same building, or explosive or highly inflammable materials are stored or used in any building in which persons are employed, effective provision shall be made for giving warning in case of fire, which shall be clearly audible throughout the building'.

Fire-alarm systems can be either manually or automatically operated. They should be operated from an independent electrical circuit. The supply of electricity should be from batteries, and an indicator board, connected to the alarm system and giving a visual indication of the location of the fire, should be placed in a central position where it is under constant observation. In laboratories which are unoccupied at night it may be necessary to place a second indicator board in the caretaker's or night-porter's room. Systems are available which combine manually operated call points with automatic heat detectors fitted to the ceilings in those parts of the building not frequently visited and in such places as boiler rooms, storage areas, &c.

A manually operated system should have push buttons for the operation of the alarm placed so that everyone in the building is within 100 ft. of a push button. Each push button should be in a prominent position, clearly marked to show the method of operation.

There are two types of automatic fire-alarm systems: one is activated by heat and the other by smoke. The former operates when a predetermined temperature is reached (usually 150° F.) and should also function when there is an excessive *rate* of temperature rise. Alarm systems operated by smoke may give the alarm when smoke interrupts a beam of light focused on a photo-electric cell. Another type utilizes the property of smoke which enables it to absorb certain products of radioactivity. The emission of particles from a radium source in an ionization chamber renders the atmosphere in the chamber electrically conductive and a voltage applied across the chamber thus results in a flow of current. When smoke enters the chamber it absorbs the particles, thereby lowering the conductivity in the chamber and consequently reducing the current flow. A relay is operated by the reduction in current and the alarm is set off. It is important to note that a smoke-operated system may be affected by fumes or dust and by smoke entering from sources outside the building.

Further information is contained in the *British standard code of practice* (22). Automatic alarms should be installed in accordance with the rules of the Fire Offices Committee, Fire Protection Association.

Fire-fighting equipment

The training of laboratory staff in elementary precautions to be taken to prevent the outbreak of fires has already been mentioned above. Such training should include detailed instructions to staff on calling the Fire Service and the use of hand extinguishers, hose reels, &c. The Fire Service should be called to any fire, however trivial, if there is the slightest doubt of the completeness of its extinction. In large research establishments a responsible senior member of staff should be put in charge of fire instruction.

Local fire authorities will usually stipulate the kind of hand equipment to be provided, and this should be placed preferably in the same position on each floor. The following equipment may have to be provided in each laboratory room: buckets filled with sand or earth, carbon dioxide extinguishers, blankets, and showers at or near the entrance and exit.

Most chemical laboratories handle many different types of highly inflammable liquids and substances—oils, spirits, alcohols, and solvents—each of which is in itself an extremely potent fire hazard. Where there are volatile liquids of this nature, the use of any cooling agent such as water for fire-fighting is not only useless but can be dangerous, since its application may lead to the spreading of the blazing liquid. Many of the chemicals used in laboratories generate their own oxygen, therefore specialized fire-extinguishing agents must be used. Carbon dioxide, the most generally recommended fire-extinguishing medium for laboratories, is quick-acting, potent, clean, non-injurious, and has the advantages of being non-toxic and a non-conductor of electricity. It is suggested by Schramm (23) that the amount of inflammable substances stored in the laboratory should be limited to the amount which can be dealt with by the staff with hand extinguishers.

Asbestos blankets of several kinds are available which can be used for smothering small bench fires. These must be kept in conspicuous positions in laboratories where fire risk is high.

The provision of emergency shower fittings is mentioned in the section of this report dealing with

Safety Precautions. These showers are also a worthwhile precaution against personal fire hazard. A person's clothing catching fire may be the beginning of a serious laboratory fire. It can be rapidly and easily extinguished without alarming other workers by means of a shower in the laboratory.

Hoses should be installed in buildings which are not easily accessible to the fire brigade, or in research establishments situated in the country some distance from a fire service, as well as in the normal manner (with dry or wet risers, depending on building height) in multi-story buildings.

REFERENCES

(1) DEPARTMENT OF SCIENTIFIC AND INDUSTRIAL RESEARCH AND FIRE OFFICES' COMMITTEE JOINT FIRE RESEARCH ORGANISATION. *Fires in laboratories, 1947.*

(2) MINISTRY OF WORKS. *Fire grading of buildings.* London, 1946, pt. 1; 1952, pts. 2, 3, 4. *Post-war building studies,* nos. 20 and 29.

(3) BRITISH STANDARDS INSTITUTION. *Fire tests on building materials and structures.* London, 1953. *British standard,* no. 476.

(4) MINISTRY OF WORKS. *Fire grading of buildings.* London, 1946, pt. 1, pp. 15–16. *Post-war building studies,* no. 20.

(5) DEPARTMENT OF SCIENTIFIC AND INDUSTRIAL RESEARCH. *Fire: materials and structures.* London, 1958. *Building Research Station digest,* no. 106.

(6) MINISTRY OF WORKS. *Fire grading of buildings.* London, 1946, pt. 1, p. 17. *Post-war building studies,* no. 20.

(7) Ibid., p. 20.

(8) MINISTRY OF EDUCATION. *Fire and the design of schools.* London, 1955. *Building bulletin,* no. 7.

(9) MINISTRY OF WORKS. *Fire grading of buildings.* London, 1946, pt. 1, p. 21. *Post-war building studies,* no. 20.

(10) MINISTRY OF WORKS. *Fire grading of buildings.* London, 1952, pt. 3, pp. 23–4. *Post-war building studies,* no. 29.

(11) HISCOCKS, E. S. *Laboratory administration.* London, 1952, p. 266.

(12) MINISTRY OF WORKS. *Fire grading of buildings.* London, 1952, pt. 3, p. 26. *Post-war building studies,* no. 29.

(13) Ibid., pp. 34–35.

(14) Ibid., p. 93.

(15) DEPARTMENT OF SCIENTIFIC AND INDUSTRIAL RESEARCH. *Fire: materials and structures.* London, 1958, p. 2. *Building Research Station digest,* no. 106.

(16) MINISTRY OF WORKS. *Fire grading of buildings.* London, 1952, pt. 3, pp. 87–94. *Post-war building studies,* no. 29.

(17) Ibid., p. 92.

(18) Ibid., pp. 87 et seq.

(19) Ibid., pp. 32–42.

(20) Ibid., p. 54.

(21) Ibid., pp. 71–91.

(22) BRITISH STANDARDS INSTITUTION. *Installation of electrical fire alarms.* London, 1951. *British standard code of practice,* CP 327. 404/402. 501.

(23) SCHRAMM, W. *Chemische und biologische Laboratorien. Planung, Bau und Einrichtung.* Leipzig, 1957, pp. 66–67.

Further detailed treatment of all aspects of fire prevention can be found in the publications of the Fire Protection Association, 31–45 Gresham Street, London, E.C.2., and readers are also referred to the papers of a recent Symposium, *Practical Fire Protection* (January 1960), published by the Royal Institute of British Architects.

SAFETY PRECAUTIONS

SAFETY precautions are taken against hazards of two kinds, accidents and long term cumulative effects on health. Although the elimination of hazards is primarily a matter of internal organization and discipline on the part of the people using the building, the designer can make safety precautions easier, and ensure that hazards are not built into the scientist's environment. More can be done than merely complying with statutory regulations, where they apply: measures may be taken to help and encourage the

scientist to reduce the hazards and to mitigate their effects. Nevertheless, responsibility for evaluating the risk rests upon the scientist himself, and the effectiveness of the precautions depends upon the care exercised in carrying them out. It is not possible to legislate for variability in the human factor, particularly in relation to the occurrence of accidents, and the importance of training in safety procedures and laboratory discipline cannot be over-emphasized.

There is a great deal of variation in the degrees of

hazard between the disciplines studied by the team. It must be remembered, however, that even within a single discipline, techniques and processes change or develop over comparatively short periods of time, introducing hazards where none previously existed. Therefore, as the building may change rapidly and frequently in function, it is better to assume that all laboratories are potentially dangerous.

Accident and long term hazards in relation to laboratory processes can be closely defined for most known techniques. There are many publications (see Bibliography, p. 153) which describe these hazards in detail and prescribe safety measures to be taken by the scientist in handling and setting up equipment and the routines to be followed in the practice of given processes. It is not proposed to deal with these in any detail here, but to give guidance in general terms on those measures which affect the design of the building and which will encourage and facilitate the scientist's task of protecting himself against possible hazards.

In many techniques the risk largely depends on the scale of the work. In the conventional type of laboratory with serviced benches, with which this report is chiefly concerned, the scale of the work is usually small enough to limit the hazard. Nevertheless, most chemical laboratories house moderate quantities of dangerous substances, and all make use of sources of heat, often in the form of a naked flame.[1] In biological disciplines there are dangers in the handling of malignant organisms, and in physical laboratories electrical and mechanical hazards. There are, of course, a few laboratories in which exceptional hazards are encountered, e.g. those dealing with explosives or large quantities of petroleum products, and these present special design problems (see below). With the exception of the latter it is reasonable to assume that research laboratories of the kind covered in this report should be classified as having a moderate degree of accident hazard.

Laboratories as such are not a recognized category of accommodation in the Model By-laws, and there is no specific legislation which applies to their design and construction. Where laboratories are connected to factories or where development work is on a pilot scale, the Factory Acts may be applicable. In such cases laboratories are likely to be included in the 'Warehouse Class' as defined in the Model By-laws. Most research laboratories, however, cannot reasonably be described as factories or warehouses, nor can they be included in the category of 'Public Buildings' in the sense in which this description is used in the Model By-laws. For design purposes, therefore, the types of laboratory with which this report is concerned may be regarded as 'Domestic Buildings' with an additional moderate degree of accident hazard. Where quantities of inflammable liquids are stored or

used, the Petroleum (Consolidation) Act, 1928, may apply, and the Explosives Act, 1875, is relevant to the design of laboratories where quantities of explosive material are in use. The Public Health Act, 1936, as it affects the provision of amenities in work places, also applies to laboratories.

The incidence of hazard is directly related to the efficiency and convenience of the laboratory. For example, working in overcrowded conditions is conducive to accidents, especially if the normal equipment and materials in use are potentially dangerous. Safety is considered below in terms of a number of design factors, the aim being to describe under each category the items which are relevant to working efficiency and which may contribute to the safety of the working environment.

Frequency of occurrence of laboratory accidents

Systematic records of laboratory accidents and their causes are rarely available, although many laboratories maintain records of accidents involving personal injury. Where such records exist it is difficult to determine how far they reflect the degree of hazard and how far the standards of discipline and training in safety measures of the laboratory staff. Nevertheless, accident records give some indication of the incidence and seriousness of the safety problem.

Tables 95 and 96 show, for one large research establishment, the number of accidents recorded in thirteen accident books during a period of nine years (1947–56). Each book was kept by a different department. The data are classified according to place of occurrence (Table 95) and type of accident (Table 96). Almost all the injuries were minor ones.

It will be seen from the tables that about three-quarters of the total number of accidents were cuts and abrasions, and almost half of these are recorded as having been caused by the handling of glassware. About one-sixth of all the accidents were burns, about a quarter of them being caused by acids. There were no fatal accidents during the period covered by the records, and none, so far as could be ascertained, with serious or lasting consequences. Out of a total of 264 injuries, 186 occurred in laboratories proper, as opposed to workshops, service rooms, &c.

These records give no precise evidence about the causes of the accidents resulting in injuries. There is no means of determining the proportion which might have been prevented by more efficient working conditions. Inquiries at other research establishments practising similar disciplines showed that the figures in Tables 95 and 96 are fairly typical.

The total number of staff covered by the records was just over 200; the accident rate being about 30 per year. Considering the minor nature of most of the injuries recorded, these figures seem to confirm that for the disciplines covered by the records only a

---

[1] Fire Precautions are dealt with separately in the previous section of this chapter.

Table 95. Injuries recorded 1947–56 in a large Agricultural Research Station.

Book no.	Department	Lab. and service rooms	Greenhouse, potting shed, animal house, field sample house, &c.	Office, workshop, store, library, boiler room	Not recorded	Accident totals
			Sites of accidents			
1	Chemistry	12	3	..	..	15
2	Botany	3	2	3	1	9
4	Apiary	..	7	2	..	9
5	Biochemistry and chemistry	12	3	4	..	19
7	Soil Microbiology	67	1	5	4	77
8	Pedology	58	..	1	..	59
9	Statistics	..	3	4	..	7
10	Plant Pathology	2	..	..	..	2
12	Insecticides	..	..	..	23	23
13	Nematology	2	2	..	..	4
14	Biochemistry	30	1	6	..	37
15		..	2	..	..	2
16		..	..	..	..	..
17		..	..	..	..	..
18	Electronic Computer (Stats.)	..	..	1	..	1
Totals		186	24	26	28	264
			50			

N.B. Only accidents which occurred in workplaces have been included in the table.

Table 96. Injuries recorded 1947–56 in a large Agricultural Research Station.

Book no.	Department	(a) Recorded as caused by glassware	(b) Other causes or unspecified	(a) From acids	(b) Other causes	Other injuries	Accident totals
		Cuts and abrasions		Burns			
1	Chemistry	5	6	3	1	..	15
2	Botany	4	5	..	..	..	9
4	Apiary	..	7	..	..	2	9
5	Biochemistry and chemistry	7	9	1	2	..	19
7	Soil Microbiology	35	28	1	9	4	77
8	Pedology	19	26	2	10	2	59
9	Statistics	..	6	..	..	1	7
10	Plant Pathology	1	..	..	..	1	2
12	Insecticides	9	14	..	..	..	23
13	Nematology	2	..	..	2	..	4
14	Biochemistry	12	11	7	5	2	37
15		..	2	..	..	..	2
16		..	..	..	..	..	..
17		..	..	..	..	..	..
18	Electronic Computor	..	..	..	1	..	1
Totals		94	114	14	30	12	264
		208		44			

Note: Cuts attributable to glassware at least 35·6 per cent. of total.
(The true proportion is almost certainly much greater as the cause of many cuts is not recorded.)
Burns account for 16·6 per cent. of total.

Only accidents which occurred in workplaces have been included in the table.

moderate degree of hazard need be assumed for the conventional type of laboratory.

General considerations affecting laboratory safety

The provision of the right amount of space for the work in hand is one of the most important factors governing safety. Crowded conditions which limit movement and reduce clear floor space increase the degree of hazard. On the other hand, excessive space may increase the distances over which the scientist has to walk, possibly carrying pieces of apparatus or containers, and may be almost as undesirable as the lack of it.

Wherever the scale of the work permits, potentially dangerous or noxious processes should be carried out in special rooms expressly designed for the purpose.

Natural and artificial lighting are vital factors in determining visual efficiency and therefore in the prevention of accidents caused by the mishandling or faulty observation of apparatus. Quantity and quality of illumination are dealt with fully in Part II, Chapter 4. Their importance in working efficiency and thus in the reduction of working hazard cannot be over emphasized.

The design and layout of laboratory furniture also have a direct bearing on safety. Uncomfortable stretching and leaning which throw the body off balance are known to be contributing factors in accidents in other types of building. Bench width and spacing are discussed below in relation to safety and also in Part II, Chapter 1.

Heating, ventilation, the effective and rapid disposal of noxious fumes, and the control and suppression of noise all affect the comfort of the working environment. They are related to safety in that they may seriously impair the mental awareness and efficiency of the laboratory worker. Ventilation, drainage, and fume disposal systems play a vital part in reducing long-term hazards consequent upon exposure to airborne agents with cumulative toxic effects.

Design factors affecting safety

1. Overall planning

The local authority regulations governing overall planning requirements in relation to fire precautions will normally be adequate in allowing free movement of staff in case of other emergencies.

2. Layout of laboratory rooms

(a) ESCAPE ROUTES

In the 'traditional' chemistry laboratory with island benches in large rooms, alternative ways of escape (around either end of the benches) were automatically provided. The island bench is difficult and expensive to service and the peninsular bench has become more common in post-war buildings. Peninsular bench layouts are discussed in Part II, Chapter 3, in relation to laboratory planning and economy in servicing.

The area between peninsular benches should be amply proportioned if no alternative escape route is available. No gangway between benches should be less than 4 ft. wide and this is only sufficient for peninsulars up to 5 ft. or 6 ft. long. Longer peninsular benches should have wider gangways (up to 6 ft. wide), related to the position of working areas and traffic between them, as described in the section on bench width and spacing (Part II, Chapter 1). In considering the widths necessary in an emergency, the room must be visualized as it is likely to be when in use. The gangway may, for instance, be partly blocked by stools, chairs, open cupboard doors, or pieces of mobile apparatus (Fig. 83).

Bench spacing in relation to safety is particularly relevant in modern laboratory planning, as the need for economy in building may require rooms of greater depths than have been common hitherto. This results in longer benches at right angles to the windows and longer cul-de-sacs between the benches.

It has been recommended that small laboratories should be designed for a minimum of two workers if the work involves accident hazard (1). This, however, does not ensure that there will always be two people in the room when an accident occurs. Small rooms housing two- or three-man research teams have become more common in the last few years and in these it may be necessary to allow alternative means of escape at the end of the bench remote from the door, even at the expense of reduced bench length. The provision of communicating doors allows a worker to seek immediate help in case of accident, without going out into the corridor, as well as giving an alternative escape route, should the door to the corridor become inaccessible. There is a distinct advantage in having the communicating doors remote from the corridor, so that both doors cannot easily be cut off simultaneously by the same accident.

(b) FURNITURE, CUPBOARDS, ETC.

The spacing of furniture has been discussed in (a) above, and bench width and spacing are dealt with in detail in Part II, Chapter 1, above. Bench width is a critical factor in accident hazard. Benches which are too deep will encourage undue leaning forward and stretching to reach taps or articles stored at the back of the bench. The clear working width of the bench should be limited to *useful working* width, and permanent bench storage should be reduced to an absolute minimum. The 2 ft. width suggested in Chapter 1 takes account of safety and functional efficiency. Benches should be placed so that sufficient light is available for the task involved, and so that heavy overshadowing does not occur. At the other end of the scale, to place a work bench in a position where the scientist may suffer acute discomfort from glare (from the sky, or from lighting fittings) is to increase accident hazard, even though the work-

Fig. 83. Gangway blocked by open cupboard doors, mobile equipment, &c.

bench, for example under a south-facing window, is extremely well-lit.

Benches, tables, and cupboards should be stable, so that they cannot be overturned by pushing or leaning. Chairs and stools correctly related to benches with adequate kneehole space reduce fatigue and facilitate movement in emergency.

3. Storage

(a) IN THE LABORATORY

Inflammable liquids, reagents, &c., should not be stored at the back of benches because of the danger of spilling when reaching forward, possibly over or through assembled apparatus.

An adequate and easily accessible chemical store is essential to safety in laboratory rooms (see (b) below). The latter are often far more dangerous than they need be because materials are kept in one laboratory in excess of actual requirements. If any large bottles or other heavy or bulky objects have to be kept in the laboratory, they should be stored below bench-top level. Only small bottles should be kept above the bench top and whatever their size, the shelf or rack on which they are kept should have a lip or trays to contain spilled liquids and prevent accidental knocking or dripping.

When cupboards are placed below benches, especially if used for storage of liquids or fragile objects, it should be remembered that it is difficult to see the contents of such cupboards precisely and to manipulate equipment accurately at low level. A cupboard depth of 1 ft. 9 in. is about the maximum at which safe handling is possible. When a cupboard is used for bottle storage the risk of spilling or breaking is reduced if only the floor is used. Bottles not exceeding 1 litre in size, containing corrosive or inflammable liquids, may be placed on impervious trays large enough to hold their contents. It is inadvisable to store volatile substances in any quantity in the laboratory, but wherever they are kept, good ventilation is essential to prevent the build-up of high concentrations of inflammable vapours.

From the point of view of safety, bottle storage is of major importance. The bottle trolley, developed at the Medical Research Council Laboratory at Harwell, is safer as well as more convenient than cupboards for this purpose. Bottles are kept on small trolleys with a number of shelves open on both sides, which, when not in use, are stored endwise under the bench. To obtain a bottle, the trolley is pulled out and all the bottles are then visible from either side and easily accessible (Fig. 84).

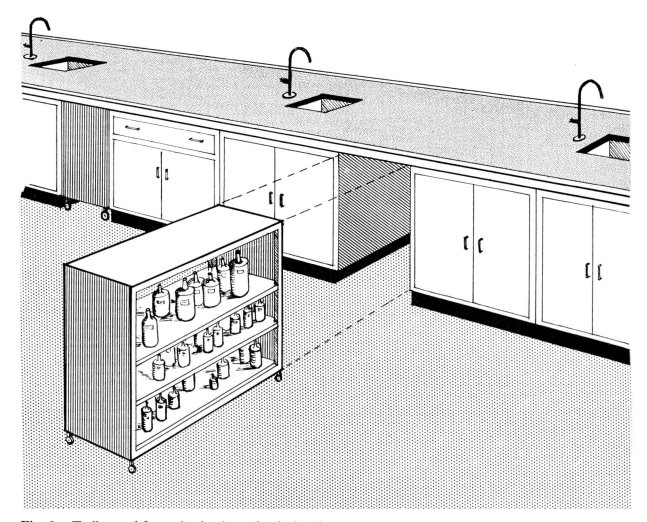

Fig. 84. Trolley used for storing bottles under the bench.

(b) BULK STORAGE

(i) *Poisons*

Poisonous chemicals should be kept in a separate lockable room or cabinet.

(ii) *Inflammable and explosive materials*

Under the Petroleum (Consolidation) Act, 1928, permission must be obtained to store more than three gallons of petroleum products, compressed gases, calcium carbide, and calcium disulphide, and under the Explosives Act, 1875, to store scheduled explosives. Detailed guidance on the storage of such materials is available in official publications (2). In general, most local authorities require explosive or inflammable materials to be stored in detached and fireproof buildings, or, at least, in a fireproof room with access to the open air only. Good natural or artificial ventilation is essential.

(iii) *General storage*

To avoid excessive carrying distances and to discourage storage of materials in excess of actual requirements in the laboratory, space for storage should be provided near the laboratory room.

Racks and shelves which are difficult to reach present accident hazards. The normal method of storing heavy objects near the floor is sensible from the point of view of safety as well as convenience. Harmful liquids and large glass containers should also be stored at low level to avoid the hazards inherent in handling above head height. Adequate trolley access, good lighting, and ventilation are all essential to the safe handling of bulk materials.

4. Service outlets and controls

Service controls should be placed so that the user does not have to run the risk of accidentally coming in contact with apparatus on the bench. This does not necessarily mean that all service controls should be placed at the front of the bench, nor is this position entirely foolproof—controls may be operated accidentally by becoming entangled in clothing. One alternative is to mount controls and outlets at a convenient distance above the bench top in positions where they can be manipulated and seen easily. Control knobs or switches should be of distinctive shape and where there is a multiplicity of supplies, controls should be colour coded (B.S. 1710: 1951. *Colour identification of pipe lines*). It should be evident when the control is switched on. Wherever possible, electrical outlets should be placed well away from and at higher level than water taps or sinks. Continuous open drainage channels are dangerous if electrical services are available on the same bench: plugs or cables may be immersed while in use.

5. Drainage and waste disposal

Dilution of liquid wastes should occur as near the sink as possible. If receivers are used it may be necessary to provide one for each room, so that substances which become dangerous in contact with each other cannot be inadvertently brought together by people in different rooms.

Inflammable liquids should not be discharged into the waste system, but deposited in metal containers provided with lids, and disposed of away from the working areas.

Waste bins should be provided for each class of solid waste, e.g. glass, chemicals, and paper.

Flooding is a frequent accident hazard. It is often caused by a break in rubber tubing where water is being run continuously for an experiment. Sink drains in floor ducts are especially difficult to inspect and may leak for some time before the fault is noticed. There is therefore great advantage in keeping waste lines above floor level, where faults are immediately evident. Electrical cables should be given adequate protection against such risks and switches should be arranged so that it is obvious to the night-watchman whether services are on or off. Floors require an impervious layer to protect the rooms below (see Appendix II, Materials and Finishes). Where risk of flooding is high, consideration should be given to laying floors to fall to a trap with adequate drainage.

6. Electrical installations

A good short account of the hazards of electrical work and some precautions which may be taken against them is given by Cornwell (3). Although voltages as low as 60 have produced fatalities, it is not customary to provide special protection, such as insulated enclosures, for apparatus using less than 600 volts. Except in certain physics laboratories high voltages are rarely economical, the most usual being the normal 240 volts A.C. A number of general points may be made about safety in relation to electrical installations at normal mains voltage.

(a) Installations should be earthed. Ring main systems with fused plugs are satisfactory and there is much to be said for systems in which rooms are separately wired and controlled. The supply can then be cut off in emergency without interfering with other parts of the building.

(b) Accidents are caused by improvised wiring, the need for which can be reduced by the provision of outlets on a generous scale.

(c) Outlets and switches (see 5 above).

(d) An insulating floor finish such as rubber or linoleum and non-conducting materials for bench tops may help to prevent injury.

(e) Sparking from electrical apparatus frequently causes fires and explosions in laboratories in which solvent vapours are present. Electrical equipment should be chosen with this in mind. In some cases, it may be necessary to install spark-proof switches, and to take similar precautions with other items of equipment such as fans, compressors, &c.

7. Fume disposal

Fume cupboards are provided primarily as a means of giving protection to the laboratory worker both from accident hazards and long-term effects. An efficient fume-disposal installation is usually a safe one, but ventilation alone may not always afford sufficient protection in hoods where highly inflammable liquids are employed. For such operations a CO_2 extinguishing system may be advisable. Fans must be stopped and doors closed automatically to prevent escape of the CO_2 gas.

Where processes involving noxious gases and vapours are carried out regularly on a large scale, it is advisable to provide special rooms so that only a few workers are exposed to the hazards for comparatively short periods, and return to the laboratory while the process is being completed (see Part II, Chapter 2).

Handling of radioactive materials

Laboratories designed specifically for the handling of radioactive materials are outside the scope of this report. However, as the use of radioactive substances in laboratory work is now widespread, a brief reference to them is necessary. Precautions must be taken against external radiation, accidental ingestion by swallowing, inhalation of radioactive gases or vapours, dust, or powder, and contamination of the skin, clothing, or hair.

The *Code of Practice* (4) for the protection of persons exposed to such hazards classifies laboratories, according to the level of radioactivity involved, into three grades C, B, and A, shown in Table 97, and makes the following broad recommendations:

Grade C. For manipulation of small amounts of radioactivity few modifications are needed in a modern chemical laboratory having floors covered with linoleum.[1] Work benches should be provided with non-absorbent tops or with disposable covers. There should be at least one good fume hood with a high rate of extraction. The exhaust air should be carried outside the building but need not be filtered.

[1] Floors should have smooth, continuous, and non-absorbent surfaces, and should be made of materials which can easily be cleaned and which, preferably, possess a surface which is easily removable. Polished linoleum is a satisfactory floor covering, except where floors have to be hosed, for example, in animal rooms. Floors should be cleaned by wet mopping or by the use of moist cleaning compounds. Dry sweeping should be avoided.

Table 97. Grade of laboratory required for various quantities of isotopes of various radio-toxicities.*

Relative radio-toxicity of isotope	Classification	Grade of laboratory required for unsealed isotopes at rough levels of activity specified below		
		C	B	A
Very high	1	$< 10 \mu c$	$100 \mu c$–1 mc	> 10 mc
High	2	$< 100 \mu c$	1 mc–10 mc	> 100 mc
Moderate	3	< 1 mc	10 mc–100 mc	> 1 c
Slight	4	< 10 mc	100 mc–1 c	> 10 c

Modifying factors to be applied to the above quantities, according to the complexity of the procedures to be followed.

Procedure	Modifying factor
Storage (stock solutions)	$\times 100$
Very simple wet operations	$\times 10$
Normal chemical operations	$\times 1$
Complex wet operations with risk of spills }	
Simple dry operations }	$\times 0.1$
Dry and dusty operations	$\times 0.01$

Millicurie (mc): $1/1,000$ curie.
Microcurie (μc): $1/1,000,000$ curie.

* The *Code of Practice for the protection of persons exposed to ionizing radiations* is at present in course of revision, and this table will be changed. When the revised Code is published, reference should be made to the new table.

Grade B. Care in design is necessary to facilitate the control of contamination. In addition to fume hoods, it may be necessary to use glove boxes which considerably reduce the hazards from inhalation or ingestion of radioactive materials. In some circumstances, however, the valuable gain from using glove boxes is offset partly by increased exposure to external radiation resulting from longer handling times, and partly by the tendency for workers to exercise less care in maintaining cleanliness.

Grade A. For this category of work a specially designed laboratory is essential and specialist advice should be sought.

Most radioisotope laboratories fall in Grade B, and recommendations on layout, materials, fume hoods, glove boxes, &c., particularly applicable to this grade, and on the storage and movement of radioactive materials are given in the Code.

Solid waste materials which are radioactive may be placed in a refuse bin fitted with a foot-operated lid and lined with a stiff paper or polythene bag. For radioactive materials with half-lives less than 100 days, the bags can be stored until it is safe to dispose of them by normal methods. For solid waste containing radioactive material with a half-life greater than 100 days, it may become necessary to store the waste for long periods before disposal is possible and screened and isolated storage space is needed.

Long half-life liquid wastes should not be poured down normal drains. They should be collected in special vessels and stored until sufficiently inactive for disposal. With the exception of the United Kingdom Atomic Energy Authority, the disposal of radioactive wastes in this country is at present subject only to the same control as applies to ordinary domestic and industrial waste. In many cases small quantities of short half-life liquid wastes are passed directly into normal drainage systems. In a recent White Paper (5), however, recommendations are made which suggest that a more stringent control is required. It is recommended in the White Paper that the present temporary power vested in the Minister of Housing and Local Government and the Minister of Agriculture, Fisheries and Food and, in Scotland, the Secretary of State, should be made permanent and that all users of radioactive materials should be required to register their premises with the appropriate Minister and that no disposal of radioactive waste should be allowed without his authorization. It is also suggested that a disposal service for long half-life materials should be set up on a national basis and that more active and continuous control should be exercised over the amounts of radioactive material discharged into sewage systems.

Until legislation is introduced, however, no regulations exist which apply specifically to the disposal of radioactive waste (by organizations other than the Atomic Energy Authority), but advice on individual disposal systems may be obtained from the appropriate Ministry.

High-pressure equipment

The design of laboratories in which high-pressure equipment is to be used presents several specialized problems. Ideally, such equipment should be housed in a separate building, well removed from other occupied buildings and circulation routes. The pressures involved may range from a few thousand up to about 60,000 lb. per square inch and the principal danger is from projectile action, if equipment bursts. Buildings to house such equipment should be provided with large windows or light panelled walls, which will blow out and afford pressure relief in case of accidents. In addition, protective barricades should be provided inside the building behind which all laboratory staff must stay when the equipment is under pressure. Laboratory discipline is of the greatest importance in high-pressure work and staff must be trained to take full advantage of the protection provided. Temporary protection can be given by using sandbags but usually the protective barrier is made of reinforced concrete or steel. Further detailed information on the design of high-pressure laboratories is given by R. L. Savage (6), but every installation must be treated on its merits, and with due reference to the siting of other occupied buildings.

Gas cylinders containing corrosive or explosive gases under pressure are a much more common laboratory problem than the special high-pressure equipment discussed above. Such cylinders are often brought into the laboratory or used just outside it, the gas being piped to the laboratory bench from the cylinder. It is most important that the cylinders should be properly supported and securely fastened, so that they cannot be dislodged or tipped. In laboratories where gas cylinders are used continuously, special provision should be made for them, so that they can be clamped firmly in a safe position, if possible well removed from sources of heat.

Again, strict laboratory discipline should be exercised in the use and handling of cylinders, i.e. proper checks for leakage and for correct labelling should be made before bringing the cylinders into the laboratory and the necessary precautions taken with gauges, regulators, and traps in the outlet lines.

Protective and first-aid equipment

There are a number of items of equipment which are either essential to or conducive to safe working and accident prevention. Provision may have to be made for placing these in the laboratory in conspicuous positions to encourage their use.

1. Protective clothing

Gloves, eye-shields, overalls, gas and dust masks are provided where work requires their use for personal safety. Asbestos clothing is available for protection against heat and flame, and leather and rubber clothing and shields for mechanical protection. Provision should be made for its storage in the laboratory in a convenient position, so as to encourage its use as a matter of routine. Useful detailed information on protective clothing is given in the papers of a recent symposium (7).

Fig. 85. Portable protective screening vented at the top, used rather than personal protective clothing. Imperial Chemical Industries Limited, Billingham Division.

Fig. 86. Overhead shower fitting in a door recess. Esso Research Centre, Linden, New Jersey.

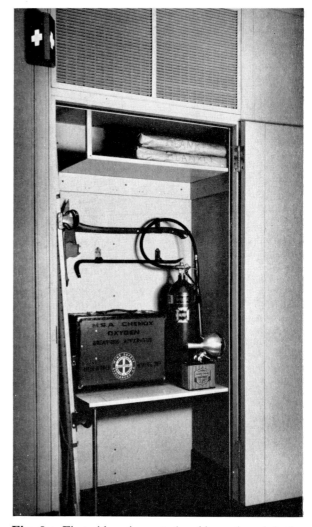

Fig. 87. First-aid equipment placed in cupboards in the corridor.

2. Protective equipment

Protection against spilling and splashing of dangerous or unpleasant liquids, &c., is given by plastic or steel shields placed between the worker and his apparatus. An example of a plastic shield is given in Fig. 85. Measures of this kind are essential if the experiment does not warrant the use of a fume cupboard or cannot be housed in an enclosed space for one reason or another.

Remote handling equipment, even of the simplest kind, e.g. tongs, is necessary in almost every laboratory.

3. Emergency showers

Wide-spray fittings are usually placed near to a door and should be easily operated. One of the earliest examples of their use was in the Imperial Chemical Industries Ltd. Dyestuffs Laboratory at Blackley, where they are placed near to fume cupboards. The position of showers can also be clearly marked on the floor as, for example, in the Acetate

and Synthetic Fibres Laboratory of Courtaulds Ltd. at Coventry, where a large yellow disk is set into the floor below the shower fittings. Fig. 86 shows a shower fitting in a door recess in the American Esso Research Centre. It is also quite common in American laboratories to find eye-spray fittings. These are built into the wall at convenient positions, usually near to fume cupboards.

If no emergency showers or sprays are provided, it is essential that each room should have at least one sink large enough to allow the worker to immerse head and arms at the same time.

4. First-aid boxes

The Factory Act of 1937 requires that a first-aid box with prescribed contents be provided where more than 150 people are employed.

Another box must be provided for every additional 150 employees. It is reasonable even for laboratories with only slight degrees of hazard to be equipped with a first-aid box, which is kept by a member of staff trained in first-aid. All members of the laboratory staff should be made aware of its whereabouts, and know which person to go to for immediate aid. Fig. 87 shows first-aid equipment placed in a corridor cupboard. Although the practice is not common in this country, a first-aid room is needed in large establishments; in many American laboratories first-aid rooms and staff rest rooms are combined.

5. Resuscitation apparatus

Where there is a high degree of electrical hazard it may be necessary to provide accommodation for a rocking stretcher and a cylinder trolley for carbon dioxide and oxygen.

6. Fire-fighting apparatus

(See section on Fire Precautions.)

REFERENCES

(1) THE GENERAL SAFETY COMMITTEE OF THE MANUFACTURING CHEMISTS' ASSOCIATION, INC. *Guide for safety in the chemical laboratory.* New York, 1954, p. 11.

(2) MINISTRY OF TRANSPORT. *The carriage of dangerous goods and explosives in ships.* London, 1952.

(3) CORNWELL, J. C. 'Prevention of accidents arising from electrical work.' ROYAL INSTITUTE OF CHEMISTRY. *Report of a conference on the origins and prevention of laboratory accidents.* London, 1948, pp. 24–34.

(4) MINISTRY OF HEALTH. *Code of practice for the protection of persons exposed to ionizing radiations.* London, 1957.

(5) MINISTRY OF HOUSING AND LOCAL GOVERNMENT. *The control of radioactive wastes.* London, 1959. *Cmnd. 884.*

(6) COLEMAN, H. S. *Laboratory design.* New York, 1951, pp. 241–9.

(7) GRAHAM, W. J. S. 'Symposium on protective clothing: Protective wear for laboratory staffs.' *Lab. Pract.* **5,** 1946, pp. 146–52.

BIBLIOGRAPHY

BLENDERMANN, L. 'Emergency devices for protection of laboratory personnel.' *Air Condit. Heat. Vent.* **54,** 1957, pp. 96–99.

BURRAGE, L. J. 'Safety in the laboratory and on the plant.' *Proceedings of 4th Conference on chemical works safety.* Buxton, 1952.

DEPARTMENT OF SCIENTIFIC AND INDUSTRIAL RESEARCH. *Safety measures in chemical laboratories.* London, H.M. Stationery Office, 1955.

FAWCETT, H. H. 'Laboratory safety.' *Chem. Engng News,* **29,** 1951, pp. 1302–5. [The article includes a selected bibliography on laboratory safety.]

FAWCETT, H. H. 'Safety and industrial hygiene in the laboratory.' *Chem. Engng News,* **30,** 1952, pp. 2588–91.

FISHER SCIENTIFIC COMPANY. *Manual of laboratory safety.* Pittsburg, 1952.

'How to prevent accidents in the laboratory.' *Laboratory,* **16,** 1946, pp. 58–66.

MINISTRY OF EDUCATION. *Safety precautions in schools.* London, H.M. Stationery Office, 1948. *Pamphlet no. 13.*

PIETERS, H. A. J., and CREYGHTON, J. W. *Safety in the chemical laboratory.* London, Butterworths Scientific Publications, 1951.

THE GENERAL SAFETY COMMITTEE OF THE MANUFACTURING CHEMISTS' ASSOCIATION, INC. *Guide for safety in the chemical laboratory.* New York, D. Van Nostrand Company, Inc., 1954.

THE ROYAL INSTITUTE OF CHEMISTRY. *Report of a conference on the origins and prevention of laboratory accidents, 6th November 1948.* London, 1949.

WEBSTER, A. 'Safety in the laboratory.' *Lab. Pract.* **2,** 1953, pp. 552–5, 601–4, 655–7.

J. C. BOURSNELL's recent book *Safety techniques for radioactive tracers,* Cambridge, 1958, gives a useful bibliography on protection from radioactive hazards.

Chapter 6

THE GENERAL PLANNING OF LABORATORY BUILDINGS

The development of laboratory sites

THE main problem when considering the master plan for a laboratory site is to provide effectively for growth. Most research institutions have grown enormously in the last twenty years, and there is very little indication that this growth has ceased, or is likely to cease. Therefore, the principal object in planning is to provide for growth to take place without disruption. On restricted city sites this problem may be insoluble because of height restrictions or the cost and inconvenience of extending a building vertically. It is for this reason that very many new institutions have been established on the outskirts of towns where fairly large sites, giving room for growth, can be found. Even for industrial firms, to whom moving into the country means moving away from the factory, this approach has become necessary. Bernhard (1) points out, 'recent thinking has led to serious consideration of the idea that the aesthetic and long term economic advantages of a laboratory ideally situated in its own surroundings may well outweigh the less permanent gain of the location near a factory'.

In drawing up a development plan the methods of town planning must be used: traffic routes must be established, and the site zoned for development. Areas must be set aside for each of the departments of the institution, large enough to provide for anticipated growth, and so grouped that development will not interfere with the basic circulation routes on the site.

Dr. Lea (2) has discussed the problem of laboratory site development. He calls attention to the importance of the central focus composed of buildings such as the library and the canteen, which may serve all other departments. He points out that if one such focus is established in the obvious place, i.e. the centre of the site, then the first departments built will be conveniently close to it, but others will be progressively farther away. The Johns-Manville Research Centre, Manville, N.J., for example, is planned with its central facilities towards the western boundary of the site (Fig. 88). This is fairly convenient for staff in the two products development buildings, which form the bulk of the present accommodation, but will be less so for staff occupying the proposed future buildings which continue the development eastwards. It is suggested by Dr. Lea that it might be better to provide more than one focal point from the start, when planning an institution likely to grow to a considerable size. In this way development of the site would proceed from two or three centres instead of one. In developing such a plan, however, the distribution of main services would probably determine the extent of the decentralization. Long service lines are expensive and difficult to maintain and it seems doubtful that decentralization of boiler plant, for example, would be an economic possibility. The nearest approach to this kind of planning is the Danish Atomic Energy Research Establishment at Risø (Fig. 89) in which the first group of buildings at the eastern end of the site has been provided with its own canteen and library facilities. These will serve only one further group of laboratories of equal size to those already existing. Future groups will have their own central amenities. Administration is, however, to be centralized.

It is perhaps relevant to look at the opposite end of the scale, namely the compact arrangement of laboratories, offices, and central amenities in one building. In the Wyeth Laboratories at Radnor, Pennsylvania (Fig. 90), this method of planning was adopted even though the site is a large suburban one. All the main accommodation is provided in an immensely thick (over 120 ft.) three-story block. Future expansion will be westwards from the main block and on similar compact lines, maintaining short lines of communication with offices and central amenities.

An alternative possibility would be to plan the central facilities in linear form, placing libraries, canteens, workshops, stores, &c., along a 'street' running down the centre of the site. Laboratories would be arranged on either side of the street. One advantage of such a plan is that the centre itself is open-ended, and can be extended as the need arises.

Except in the case of very large establishments, it seems unlikely that the cost of servicing a horizontal development will be higher than for a vertical one, but this must be considered in choosing the site and

Fig. 88. Site plan.
The Johns-Manville
Research Centre,
Manville, New Jersey,
U.S.A

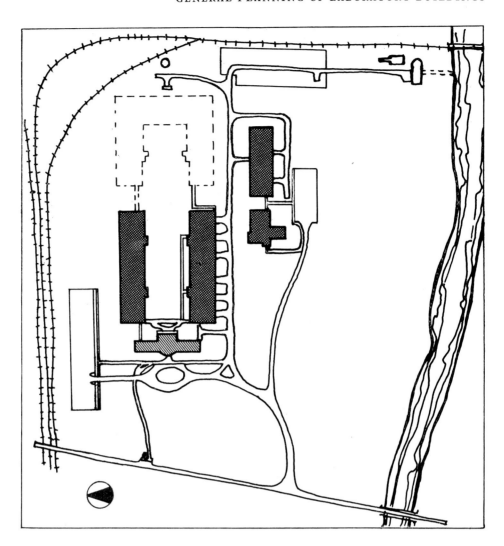

in arranging the buildings. Compact arrangement of the serviced areas of the establishment will result in an economical overall building cost.

Overall space requirements

In Chapter 1 of Part II an approach to the space requirements within the laboratory room was established. It was shown that considerations of functional efficiency pointed towards the establishment of a unit of space with an area of approximately 300 sq. ft., and that this space could be expected to accommodate three workers in a great majority of scientific disciplines. From this it was deduced that about 100 sq. ft. of laboratory space would be required per worker. This, however, only gives the size of the laboratory proper; in addition, the laboratory buildings will have to provide many other facilities. Certain areas are closely associated with the laboratory room and are normally planned to adjoin it: these include special rooms for various purposes and rooms with controlled environment, instrument rooms, &c. As a rule these rooms require a similar provision for gas, water, drainage, and other services as is needed in the general laboratory. In addition, some establishments require space for large-scale laboratory work, and these areas are normally well provided with mechanical services. In the discussion which follows the foregoing areas are all referred to under the general heading of 'primary space'.

Laboratory buildings include other spaces of a rather different kind: offices, stores, staff rooms, boiler rooms, &c., have to be provided, and space is needed for corridors, stairs, and lifts. In the following discussion such spaces are referred to generally under the heading of 'secondary space'. In general these areas do not require any special provision of mechanical services as is necessary in the laboratory areas.

The building owner and his architect often wish to make an approximate estimate of the building area required for a projected laboratory at an early stage in the development of the scheme. It would therefore be useful if some relation could be shown between the number of staff which the laboratory is to house and the total area of building likely to be needed. The relationship between the laboratory area proper and the number of staff has been discussed in Part II, Chapter 1, and it would be possible to make an estimate of total area if the area of the laboratories could be related to the remaining space required in the building. In order to throw some light on this question the plans of a number of laboratory buildings were subjected to analysis. (These

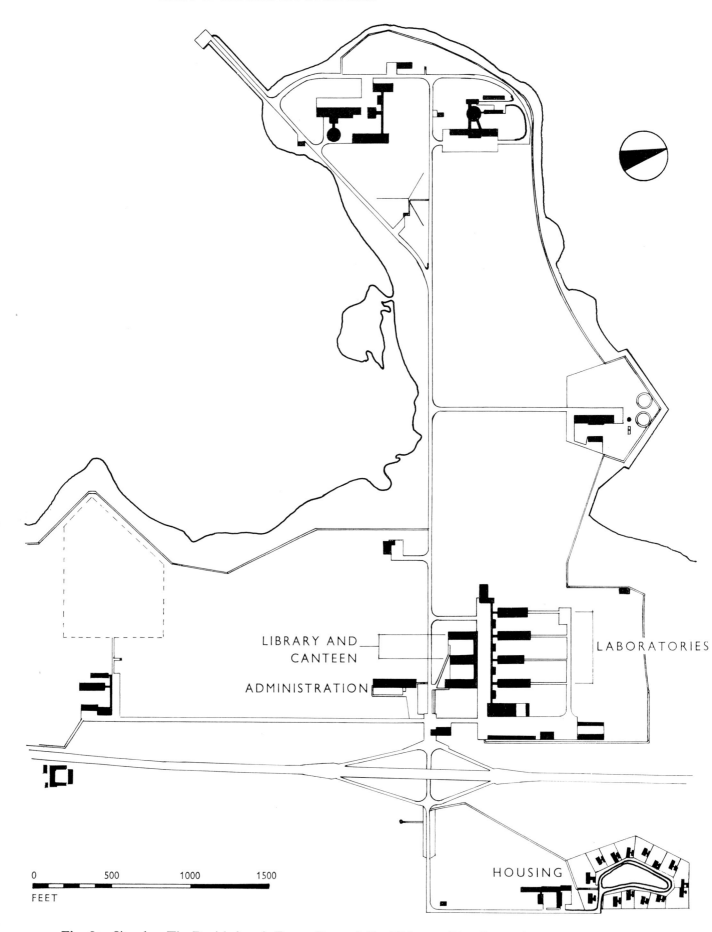

LIBRARY AND
CANTEEN

ADMINISTRATION

LABORATORIES

HOUSING

0   500   1000   1500

FEET

Fig. 89. Site plan. The Danish Atomic Energy Research Establishment, Risø, Denmark.

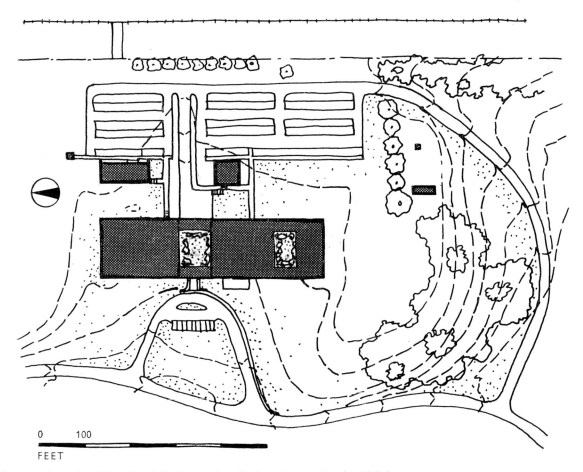

0   100

FEET

Fig. 90. Site plan. The Wyeth Laboratories, Radnor, Pennsylvania, U.S.A.

laboratories are in most cases those for which cost analyses were made: plans and descriptions of the latter buildings will be found in Appendix I.)

While the analysis was being made, all the laboratories were visited and care was taken to allot each room correctly. Wherever there was some doubt about the use of an individual room or area, the laboratory staff were consulted. Measurements were made to the inside face of all external walls and the centre lines of all internal walls. Where circulation routes passed through a room an appropriate proportion of the floor area was allotted to circulation.

The laboratories examined ranged in size from 3,000 sq. ft. to 83,000 sq. ft. in total area; all were engaged in research and none was concerned with teaching. Some of the laboratories examined were self-contained and included the full range of secondary space needed by the establishment, others were individual buildings or departments erected on a site where certain administrative and other facilities were already available. This difference is reflected in varying ratios between primary space and secondary space. In four cases a proportion of the primary space was devoted to large-scale laboratories.

Tables 98 and 99 show the results of the analysis. It will be seen from Table 98, which refers to complete laboratories, that there is considerable variation in the proportion of space devoted to the different

categories of accommodation, but that the overall proportion as between primary space and secondary space is rather more uniform. The approximate average proportion of primary space is 40 per cent. of the whole area of the building. Therefore, if an assessment can be made of the primary space on the basis of the work to be carried out, an approximate figure for the total size of the building can be found.

If the only data available are the number of scientific staff and technical assistants for whom provision is needed, a forecast for total area can still be made, but it will be somewhat less accurate. Laboratory space proper is needed at the rate of about 100 sq. ft. per worker. If this space is taken as 20 per cent. of the whole laboratory (on the basis of Table 98), then the total area needed is about 500 sq. ft. per worker. It should be remembered that this calculation is based on the *number of scientific workers to be housed in the building*: it should include only scientific staff, their technicians and laboratory assistants; it should not include secretarial, administrative, or other staff connected with the establishment. The resulting total area will, of course, include the area needed to house the non-scientific staff.

It is of some interest to compare this result with a previous study made by the National Research Council of Canada (3). This study was based on a large number of laboratories in Canada and resulted

Table 98. Laboratory area analysis: *complete blocks.*

Laboratories	Purpose/techniques	Primary space				Secondary space						Total	
		General labs.	Special rooms	Controlled environment	Large-scale labs. or workshops	Offices	Stores	Service space	Staff acc.	Circulation	Miscellaneous	Primary space	Secondary space
DATCHET Radio Research Station Total area: 54,295 sq. ft.	Physics	19·7	2·3	..	7·9	26·1	9·5	8·2	9·0	14·2	3·1	29·9	70·1
STEVENAGE Water Pollution Research Station Total area: 47,527 sq. ft.	Physics Microbiology Zoology Chemistry Biochemistry	17·2	7·1	1·0	11·2	12·7	12·5	13·8	6·7	13·8	4·0	36·5	63·5
WEYBRIDGE Therapeutic Substances Laboratory Total area: 29,750 sq. ft.	Microbiological Production	11·5	17·7	6·8	..	1·7	5·2	26·0	6·2	24·9	..	36·0	64·0
HURLEY Grasslands Research Station Total area: 40,808 sq. ft.	Chemistry Biochemistry Biology	20·9	5·3	..	15·9	12·6	5·9	7·8	10·8	20·8	..	42·1	57·9
WELLESBOURNE National Vegetable Research Station Total area: 33,766 sq. ft.	Plant Pathology Plant Physiology Entomology	30·5	12·3	4·0	..	15·3	6·7	3·5	7·1	20·6	..	46·8	53·2
COVENTRY Acetate and Synthetic Fibres Building, Courtaulds Ltd. Total area: 83,573 sq. ft.	Physics Biochemistry Chemistry	23·5	14·2	2·6	0·2	13·1	8·5	12·6	6·2	19·1	..	40·5	59·5
DERBY British Railways Laboratory Total area: 14,606 sq. ft.	Metallurgy Engineering Chemistry	26·6	5·0	1·3	18·8	18·8	4·9	2·7	2·7	19·2	..	51·7	48·3
ENFIELD Colour Television Laboratory (Sylvania Thorn) Total area: 28,372 sq. ft.	Electronics Chemistry (Development)	37·1	0·4	4·6	5·0	11·9	6·5	7·4	7·1	20·0	..	47·1	52·9
FARNHAM Forest Research Station Total area: 23,000 sq. ft.	Entomology Pathology Silviculture	14·3	11·7	10·1	..	17·9	10·2	10·0	3·8	22·0	..	36·1	63·9
WELWYN Research Building, Plastics Division, I.C.I. Ltd. Total area: 35,204 sq. ft.	Chemistry Physical Chemistry Physics	27·8	8·6	5·6	..	17·7	5·7	5·2	3·6	25·8	..	42·0	58·0
LEVINGTON Fisons Research Station Total area: 38,780 sq. ft. (Main labs. and admin. only)	Chemistry Biochemistry Plant Physiology	16·9	11·7	2·6	..	19·0	7·5	15·3	4·1	22·9	..	31·2	68·8
WELWYN T.S. and D. Building, I.C.I. Ltd. Total area: 79,366 sq. ft.	Chemistry Chemical Engineering Physics (Development)	12·1	..	..	34·8	20·0	6·6	3·7	3·8	19·0	..	46·9	53·1
Approximate average percentages		21·5	8·0	3·0	7·5	15·5	7·5	10·5	6·0	20·0	0·5	40·5	59·5

For key to this table see foot of Table 99.

Table 99. Laboratory area analysis: *new blocks within existing establishments.*

| Laboratories | Purpose/techniques | Percentage of total area | | | | | | | | | | Total | |
| | | Primary space | | | | Secondary space | | | | | | | |
		General labs.	Special rooms	Controlled environment	Large-scale labs, or workshops	Offices	Stores	Service space	Staff acc.	Circulation	Miscellaneous	Primary space	Secondary space
SLOUGH Pest Infestation Isotopes Total area: 3,392 sq. ft.	Radiobiochemistry Radiobiology	47·0	8·2	13·8	..	..	..	5·5	9·9	15·6	..	69·0	31·0
SLOUGH Pest Infestation Insecticides Total area: 8,004 sq. ft.	Chemistry Biochemistry	35·9	22·0	..	..	1·6	9·6	9·7	5·4	15·8	..	57·9	42·1
HURLEY Animal Nutrition Unit Project Total area: 3,557 sq. ft. (heating from existing boiler house)	Animal Physiology	50·7	12·6	..	..	9·5	6·4	0·5	5·0	15·3	..	63·3	36·7
ROTHAMSTED Plant Pathology Laboratory Total area: 19,382 sq. ft.	Plant Pathology Insecticides Entomology	45·0	8·7	8·1	..	3·9	3·7	3·2	1·7	25·7	..	61·8	38·2
Approximate average percentages		44·5	13·0	6·0	..	3·5	5·0	4·5	5·5	18·0	..	63·0	37·0

PRIMARY SPACE

Laboratories and special rooms normally associated closely with laboratory work. It includes the following:

General laboratories—rooms with services, benches, fume cupboards, &c., but without special facilities, such as controlled environment.

Special rooms—rooms devoted to specialized activities. For example, dark rooms, chromatography, kjeldahl analysis, balance, instrument, preparation and standards, wash-up and sterilizing, small animal rooms.

Controlled environment rooms—special rooms with closer limits of control. For example, constant-temperature and humidity rooms and rooms for which climatic control plant is provided. Air-conditioned rooms are not included unless fine controls are required.

Large-scale laboratories—experimental rooms for large animals, glasshouses, large testing rooms, engineering laboratories, pilot-plant laboratories, and laboratory workshops.

SECONDARY SPACE

Space other than laboratories, including offices, store rooms, staff rooms, and circulation areas.

Offices—administrative offices and scientists' offices, libraries, conference and lecture rooms.

Stores—store rooms in which no scientific work is done.

Service space—boiler rooms (and fuel stores), plant rooms, large ducts, transformer rooms, cleaners' rooms, &c.

Staff accommodation—common rooms, canteens, kitchens, changing rooms, rest rooms, lavatories, &c.

Circulation—corridors, stairs, and any space used for access to other rooms.

Miscellaneous—garages, implement sheds, &c.

in a recommended standard of 400 sq. ft. per person. The recommendation is based on the *total staff of the establishment*. If it is assumed that scientific staff constitute four-fifths of the total laboratory population, the two studies result in the same broad standard for floor area per person.

Table 99 shows a similar analysis for four new laboratory blocks built within existing establishments. Much laboratory building takes place in this way, as it becomes necessary to expand the work of an existing establishment. In these cases it is usual to find that the central facilities for administration, staff welfare, &c., are able to serve the new building which therefore consists principally of laboratories. In these buildings the ratio of primary to secondary space is higher. The number of examples analysed is small and the resulting figures must therefore be treated with reserve, but the proportion of primary space is fairly consistent and close to the average of 63 per cent. The average proportion of space devoted to general laboratories is nearly 45 per cent., more than double the comparable figure in Table 98. These proportions can be used to make rough estimates of the total area likely to be needed in new buildings in a manner similar to that discussed above.

Storage space

Very little has been written elsewhere in this report on the question of storage space, because the team was unable to embark upon a separate major study of the complex requirements of laboratory storage. Nevertheless, certain experience of these problems has been gained during the course of the work. The proportions of total floor area allotted to storage in a number of laboratory buildings are shown in Table 98 above: the range is from 5 to $12\frac{1}{2}$ per cent. Naturally the amount of space needed for storage varies with the nature of the work, and the chemical and biological disciplines seem to generate the greatest demands.

The figures in Table 98 include local and central storage, but take no account of storage in the laboratory (i.e. in underbench units, wall cupboards, &c.). In the course of visits to existing establishments it became evident that local storage space was rarely adequate. It is the team's view that at least 10 per cent. of total floor area is needed for storage, and of this, it is necessary to provide convenient floor space for storage outside, but near to the laboratory, if valuable serviced bench is not to be taken up with local long-term storage. Scientists are often loath to return out-of-use items to central stores if they know they will need them again, although perhaps not for a further three months. Meanwhile such items usually take up valuable laboratory bench or floor space. Locally controlled and conveniently placed stores, to the extent of about one-quarter of the total storage space provided in the building, would overcome many storage problems and release working space for its proper use.

The cost of laboratory buildings

A general description of the objectives and methods of cost study in building is given in Part I, Chapter 3. The study of laboratory building cost made by the team was essentially a pioneer effort intended to establish a technique for analysing the cost of existing laboratories and to develop means of comparison between them. The actual cost figures resulting from the study must therefore be treated with reserve until further material becomes available covering a sufficiently wide range of laboratories to enable valid conclusions to be drawn. It should also be remembered that the prices are worked out as at 31 March 1957. The data, however, are of general interest for those concerned with the provision and design of laboratory buildings.

The details of the cost analysis for each of the eight laboratories studied are given in Appendix I together with a diagrammatic plan and a short description of each building. Table 100 presents the results of the analyses in condensed form. It will be seen from Table 100 that building cost has been broken down into eight element groups which are also defined in Appendix I.

Perhaps the most striking feature of the analyses is the very high proportion of total cost going on element groups 5 and 7, services and fittings; if these two groups are added together they often account for something like half the total cost of the building. Consequently, any effort directed towards the economical and efficient design of services and fittings will be amply repaid. As these items of cost refer principally to general laboratory areas, and to the special rooms associated with them, it is clear that the provision of services in relation to primary space should receive intensive study at the planning stage and should be no more extensive than is necessary for the efficient performance of the work (see Part II, Chapter 3, pp. 74–76).

The next largest item is Group 2, which includes all the structural elements of the building and this accounts generally for something like one-third of the total cost. But this group covers most of the normal building items, and no one of them taken alone contributes very largely to the total cost of the building. In laboratory design therefore the return to be expected from the intensive study of a single item such as the structural frame, or the exterior walling, would not be very great. No discernible relation was found between the number of stories in the building and the cost per square foot.

Table 101 shows the total cost per square foot for each of the eight laboratories. The variation is considerable, and is all the more striking because the laboratories analysed were deliberately chosen as being of competent design and it was believed that all had been planned with an eye to reasonable economy. (It was felt that there would be little purpose in including in the study laboratories which

Table 100. Summary of cost analyses of eight laboratories

Analysis no.	Laboratories	Purpose/techniques	No. of stories	Primary space	Secondary space	1 Work below ground-floor level	2 Super-structure	3 Partitioning and internal doors	4 Finishes and decorations	5 Laboratory and normal plumbing	5 Mechanical	5 Electrical	5 Total	6 External works and services	7 Fittings	8 Sundries	Total
1	SLOUGH Pest Infestation Isotopes. Total area: 3,392 sq. ft.	Radiobiochemistry Radiobiology	1	69.0%	31.0%	6.67 / 5.8%	28.0 / 24.5%	2.83 / 2.5%	7.25 / 6.3%	5.33 / 4.7%	20.65 / 18%	9.52 / 8.3%	35.5 / 31.0%	4.42 / 3.8%	29.0 / 25.3%	1.0 / 0.8%	114.67
2	HURLEY Animal Nutrition Unit Project. Total area: 3,557 sq. ft.	Animal Physiology	1	63.3%	36.7%	8.86 / 5.9%	35.36 / 23.1%	..	13.52 / 8.9%	15.33 / 10%	19.13 / 12.4%	14.65 / 9.5%	49.12 / 31.9%	22.00 / 14.4%	24.33 / 15.8%	..	153.19
3	SLOUGH Pest Infestation Insecticides. Total area: 8,004 sq. ft.	Chemistry Biochemistry	1	57.9%	42.1%	9.96 / 8.1%	35.77 / 29.2%	4.69 / 3.8%	13.10 / 10.7%	3.48 / 2.9%	14.13 / 11.6%	8.10 / 6.7%	25.71 / 21.0%	10.21 / 8.3%	22.0 / 17.9%	1.19 / 1.0%	122.63
4	WEYBRIDGE Therapeutic Substances Laboratory. Total area: 29,750 sq. ft. (and 28,213 sq. ft. for items 1 and 2)	Microbiological Production	3 + b*	36.0%	64.0%	13.25 / 8.9%	38.33 / 25.9%	3.42 / 2.3%	14.46 / 9.9%	5.15 / 3.4%	42.98 / 29.2%	6.97 / 4.5%	55.10 / 37.1%	7.97 / 5.4%	13.67 / 9.3%	1.81 / 1.2%	148.01
5	WELLESBOURNE National Vegetable Research Station. Total area: 33,766 sq. ft. (and 29,940 sq. ft. for items 1 and 2)	Plant Pathology Plant Physiology Entomology	2 + b	46.8%	53.2%	9.92 / 9.1%	39.14 / 36.2%	4.64 / 4.3%	14.67 / 13.6%	4.08 / 3.8%	13.98 / 12.9%	9.42 / 8.7%	27.48 / 25.4%	3.90 / 3.6%	8.19 / 7.6%	..	107.93
6	LEVINGTON Fisons Research Station. Total area: 38,780 sq. ft.	Research connected with the manufacture of artificial fertilizers	3 + b	31.2%	68.8%	4.98 / 4.1%	23.73 / 19.5%	5.83 / 4.8%	12.02 / 9.9%	13.15 / 10.9%	30.34 / 24.8%	13.59 / 11.1%	57.10 / 46.8%	..	18.16 / 14.9%	..	121.82
7	DATCHET Radio Research Station. Total area: 54,295 sq. ft.	Physics	Mainly one story	29.9%	70.1%	8.0 / 8.2%	29.08 / 29.7%	4.25 / 4.3%	8.08 / 8.4%	1.67 / 1.7%	13.43 / 13.8%	7.15 / 7.1%	22.25 / 22.6%	10.25 / 10.5%	14.75 / 15.0%	1.25 / 1.3%	97.91
8	COVENTRY Acetate and Synthetic Fibres Building, Courtaulds Limited. Total area: 83,573 sq. ft. (and 71,313 sq. ft. for items 1 and 2)	Physics Biochemistry Chemistry	4 + b	40.5%	59.5%	12.18 / 8.9%	35.65 / 26.1%	6.36 / 4.7%	13.75 / 10.1%	5.25 / 3.8%	21.52 / 15.7%	13.87 / 10.2%	40.65 / 29.7%	11.08 / 8.1%	17.03 / 12.4%	..	136.70

Percentage of total area (see Tables 98 and 99). Costs of element groups in shillings per sq. ft. and as percentages of total cost (Prices as at 31 March 1957). 5 Services.

* Basement.

Table 101. Total cost of 8 laboratories arranged in order of cost (as at 31 March 1957).

Analysis no. (Appendix I)	Laboratory	Cost per square foot
		£ s. d.
7	Datchet	4 18 0
5	Wellesbourne	5 8 0
1	Slough (isotopes)	5 15 0
6	Levington	6 2 0
3	Slough (insecticides)	6 3 0
8	Coventry	6 17 0
4	Weybridge	7 8 0
2	Hurley	7 13 0

were exceptionally expensive, or laboratories where working efficiency had been sacrificed to achieve a very cheap building.) The figures in Table 101 suggest therefore that some factors in the design requirements must operate to cause a variation in cost, and that the crude measure of average *cost per square foot* is neither an accurate index for predicting the future cost of laboratory projects, nor a fair basis on which to establish cost ceilings or yardsticks for the control of future development.

This problem is of some general interest, as it arises in many other fields of building apart from laboratories. The difficulty is essentially due to the fact that no two laboratories are quite identical in function. The same problem is encountered with hospitals, with farm buildings, and with factories. In all these cases differences in function between individual buildings make it unsatisfactory to use cost targets based on average price per square foot. Nevertheless, some yardstick is desirable, if any effective comparison between different projects is to be made, or any control is to be exercised over cost. Up to the present the only means that has been suggested to meet the problem is the subdivision of each building into sections, each separately costed and compared. In the case of laboratories this would mean trying to separate off the cost of the primary space from the cost of the remaining parts of the building. Little progress has been made along these lines because of the immensely laborious analysis that is involved. Further, the method involves attributing many major items of cost by guess-work to different areas of the building, and is therefore of doubtful accuracy. A new approach suggested itself to the team: an attempt to identify measurable factors indicative of those functional differences between individual buildings which lead to variations in cost. Clearly if such factors can be identified, a formula for predicting cost could be developed which would allow for the variation in functional requirements.

A number of factors were selected, on general common-sense grounds as worth investigating for this purpose; these included the following:

x_1 = total floor area, in thousands of square feet;
x_2 = primary space area, in square feet;
x_3 = floor to floor height, in feet;
x_4 = total length of serviced benching, in feet;
x_5 = bench length per 100 sq. ft. of primary space, in feet.

Each of these factors was investigated in relation to the total cost of the eight laboratories, *adjusted to exclude all external works*, (y). The method of investigation was by partial regression analysis.[1] For the examples studied it was found that factors x_3 and x_5, in addition of course to x_1, appeared likely to affect the cost to a significant degree. From the study it was possible to propose an equation involving x_1, x_3, and x_5 which gives a substantially better prediction of total cost than can be obtained by the use of average price per square foot.

Where y is the estimated total cost *in thousands of pounds*, the equation is

$$y = 5.88x_1 + 15.41x_3 + 9.03x_5 - 277.12.$$

Table 102 shows a comparison between the actual cost of the eight laboratories, and the estimated

Table 102. Estimated costs for 8 laboratories, compared with actual cost.

Analysis no. (Appendix I)	Laboratory	Total cost excluding all external works, £000		
		Actual	Estimated from regression equation	Estimated at average £5·49 per sq. ft.
1	Slough (isotopes)	19	29	19
2	Hurley	23	17	20
3	Slough (insecticides)	44	37	44
4	Weybridge	193	192	163
5	Wellesbourne	167	144	185
6	Levington	236	232	212
7	Datchet	237	250	298
8	Coventry	496	478	459

[1] This method, though difficult in calculation, leads to a simple system of scoring the various factors, and gives results which are easy to interpret.

Example:
See Appendix I, Analysis no. 1. Biochemistry Laboratory, Slough.

Total floor area = 3,392 sq. ft.
∴ x_1 = 3·392
Floor to floor height = 9 ft. 10 in.
∴ x_3 = 9·83
Bench length per 100 sq. ft. of primary space = 15 ft.
∴ x_5 = 15·00
y = (5·88 × 3·39) + (15·41 × 9·83) + (9·03 × 15·0) − 277·12
= 29·7
∴ Estimated cost = 29·7 × 1,000
= £29,700

Fig. 91. Comparison of actual cost for eight laboratories with cost estimated by means of a regression equation and with average cost ($£5\cdot49$ per sq. ft.).

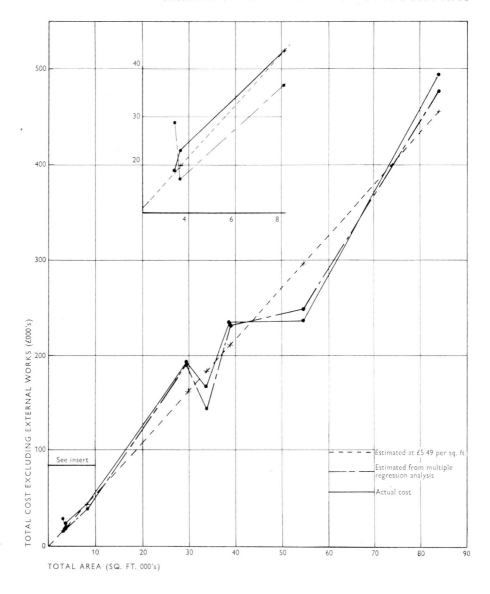

TOTAL COST EXCLUDING EXTERNAL WORKS (£000's)

TOTAL AREA (SQ. FT. 000's)

See insert

---- Estimated at £5·49 per sq. ft.
— — Estimated from multiple regression analysis
—— Actual cost

cost; (i) from the regression equation above and (ii) from the average price per square foot. It will be seen that, generally, the regression equation gives a much closer result. Fig. 91 shows the data for Table 102 in the form of a graph, and brings out clearly the superior accuracy of the regression equation.

This study suggests that the use of regression analysis in cost studies is likely to be fruitful, and might lead to the development of an acceptable yardstick for cost control. The actual equation, derived from the eight laboratories studied by the team, is not put forward for general use: the additive form of the equation was the only one which could be arrived at with the data available. A much wider range of laboratory buildings would have to be studied before any generally valid cost formula emerges. In such a formula the progressive effect of variable factors, such as ceiling height for buildings of increasing size, would take factorial rather than the additive form given here. Other variables

might be found to be significant if more data were studied.

General conclusions

Considerations advanced in this report point towards a general approach to the design of laboratories which differs in some respects from earlier practice. Most of the conclusions have been brought out elsewhere in the report, where each point has been argued in detail. However, it is convenient to bring them together and summarize them here.

During the course of the present study, the team has been able to advise building owners and architects and has influenced a number of designs. Thus most, if not all, of the ideas put forward here have already begun to pass into practice, and very soon will be subjected to the test of use. The team's own experimental building, the extension to the Animal Research Station, Cambridge, is now completed.

Laboratory space

The general laboratories and the special rooms associated with them are the heart of the laboratory building. They occupy a substantial proportion of the total space, and in them are concentrated the most expensive elements of the building. Therefore, the first step in seeking economy in design is to ensure that this area is planned with maximum efficiency. An index of this efficiency will be the available length of serviced wall or benching in proportion to the floor area; the higher this is the more efficient is the plan, so long, of course, as the necessary working clearances are maintained.

Long straight runs of benching are desirable to give maximum flexibility and convenience. In the interests of efficient servicing these runs should be at right angles to the window walls, and should abut the corridor walls. These considerations lead to laboratory buildings of considerable thickness. If the laboratory room is 25 ft. from window to rear wall, and two such spaces are provided on either side of a central corridor, 6 ft. wide, then a building about 56 ft. in width will result (Fig. 40). Where the proportion of special rooms, offices, &c., is high a layout similar to that used in the team's experimental building is an alternative; here deep laboratories are provided on one side of the corridor and a shallower area on the other (Fig. 42). Both arrangements may be usefully combined in a single building, or group of buildings.

Flexibility

Flexibility can be provided in the laboratory areas by the wise positioning of the service sub-mains. If these run in the central corridor, either vertically in ducts or horizontally beneath the ceilings, branches can be taken off freely into the laboratory space on either side. The vertical duct system is preferable on maintenance grounds and so long as the ducts are spaced at appropriate centres (see Part II, Chapter I), they will serve any possible arrangement of large or small laboratory rooms, special rooms, &c., as shown in Fig. 40. There will normally be no need for floor ducts or under-floor distribution where this system of sub-mains is employed. There are many objections to the use of floor ducts, particularly where radioactive material is used in the work. Demountable partitioning is convenient but not always essential. Normally it will not be necessary to make provision for its erection except along the major grid lines established by the service sub-mains.

The spacing and working width of laboratory benches may be determined on anthropometric principles to allow for most eventualities in normal bench-type laboratories, and this in turn should determine the spacing of the service lines to the benches from the sub-mains. Having thus arrived at a room width which will meet all requirements in the laboratory areas, the bench-length data derived from the survey may be used to design a unit of laboratory space which will give a great deal of flexibility of use. Standardization of the bench services on the basis of demand ensures that change of function may take place freely without the need for expensive and inconvenient modifications to the service lines.

Daylighting

Difficulties arise in the provision of a satisfactory light in the interior of the deep buildings described above. Single-story construction enables this problem to be solved by the use of overhead lighting. Special measures must be taken in the design of overhead lighting in laboratories in order to ensure that the quality and quantity of light are satisfactory. Suitable designs have been developed for the Cambridge laboratory and for the new Radiobiological Laboratory at Letcombe Regis. Sections of these two buildings are illustrated in Figs. 42 and 43. In the case of buildings of more than one story it has been shown that very high ceilings will be necessary to give good light in the interior if only natural light is used. Therefore, it is recommended that permanent supplementary artificial light should be installed where necessary. The design of such installations is now more fully understood, and techniques are developing which allow natural and artificial lighting to be designed as one installation (4).

Single-story versus multi-story construction

There appears to be little to choose in terms of cost between laboratory buildings of single-story or multi-story construction. The decision between them can reasonably be made on functional grounds and in relation to the site. On functional grounds there is much to be said for single-story buildings. They have the great merit of lending themselves to easy alteration and extension. In a laboratory where all the different departments are housed in single-story units it is generally possible to add to or alter any one of them without interfering with the others. The objection to single-story construction is the amount of space it covers and the length of service mains needed to reach it. On many sites this may preclude its use. In this connexion it should be noted that the highly compact, wide buildings proposed in this report occupy less space on the ground and have shorter runs of corridor, than traditional single-story laboratories. In the case of the Radiobiological Laboratory, Letcombe Regis (Fig. 43), single-story construction had been rejected at an early stage in the design because of site coverage, but when the buildings were replanned with deep laboratory rooms on either side of a central corridor, it was found possible to use single-story buildings.

Office space

Offices for the administration, and generally for

use by persons not mainly engaged on laboratory research, are best placed in a separate wing or block, which will not require the expensive mains services of the laboratory building. But the working scientist needs some privacy for reading and writing, and his room should be in intimate contact with the laboratory in which he works. These offices can be very small, and should be made as small as possible in view of the high cost of space in this part of the building. Such rooms are shown in Fig. 40.

Special purpose rooms

The most frequent cause of internal alterations in laboratories arises from the need to provide, alter, or abolish rooms intended for special purposes. These are best planned as partitioned-off areas of the main laboratory. When this is done, space devoted to special rooms can revert to general laboratory use when no longer needed for its original purpose. Such arrangements are shown in Figs. 40, 42, and 44.

REFERENCES

(1) BERNHARD, H. C. 'The analysis of several laboratory plot plans.' *Buildings for research.* New York, F. W. Dodge Corporation, 1958, p. 26.

(2) LEA, F. M. 'The direction of research: Buildings—what is required.' *Builder, Lond.* **141,** 1956, pp. 589–91.

(3) NATIONAL RESEARCH COUNCIL OF CANADA DIVISION OF BUILDING RESEARCH. *Report on space requirements for scientific laboratories.* Ottawa, 1949. *Technical report,* no. 3.

(4) HOPKINSON, R. G., and LONGMORE, J. 'The permanent supplementary artificial lighting of interiors.' *Trans. Illum. Engng Soc.* **24,** 1959, pp. 121–42.

COST ANALYSES

Introduction

Cost analyses for eight laboratory buildings are given below. The scope and methods adopted in the study are given in Part I, Chapter 3, pp. 35 to 37, and a general discussion of laboratory costs (referring to the data in this Appendix) is to be found in Part II, Chapter 6, pp. 160 to 165. Also, a number of summarized conclusions are given in this Appendix.

The following buildings were studied:	Source of data and analyses
1. Biochemistry Laboratory in the Isotope Tracer Section, Pest Infestation Laboratory, Slough, Bucks. *Department of Scientific and Industrial Research.*	Ministry of Works.
2. Project for Animal Nutrition Unit at Grasslands Research Station, Hurley. *Agricultural Research Council.*	Division for Architectural Studies, Nuffield Foundation.
3. Insecticides Laboratory and Local Stores, Pest Infestation Laboratory, Slough, Bucks. *Department of Scientific and Industrial Research.*	Ministry of Works.
4. Therapeutic Substances Laboratory at the Ministry of Agriculture, Fisheries and Food Veterinary Laboratory, Weybridge.	Ministry of Works.
5. National Vegetable Research Station, Wellesbourne. *Ministry of Agriculture, Fisheries and Food.*	Ministry of Agriculture, Fisheries and Food.
6. Laboratories and Administration Block, Fisons Limited Research Station, Levington.	Analysis previously published.
7. Radio Research Station, Datchet, Bucks. *Department of Scientific and Industrial Research.*	Ministry of Works.
8. Acetate and Synthetic Fibres Laboratory, Courtaulds Limited, Coventry	Courtaulds Limited.

The range of work carried on in the buildings (see Part II, Chapter 6, Table 100) is fairly wide, and the standards of provision are comparable. Outstanding or unusual items are noted in the descriptions of the buildings given with the analyses in this Appendix. Four of the buildings (1, 2, 3, and 7) are single-story, one is a two-story building, and the remainder are three- or four-story buildings.

The number of buildings for which cost data were available for inclusion in this study was limited. Some were excluded because work of a highly specialized character had dominated the design. All the buildings chosen contain conventional laboratories with serviced benches. Six of the buildings were designed for Government-sponsored research and two for research sponsored by industry. It is not claimed that the examples analysed are a representative sample; they are mainly bench-type research laboratories. The methods of analysis used could, however, be applied to laboratories of the open, factory-like kind used for engineering, pilot-scale development work, &c., but the scope of the laboratory study generally, as defined earlier in this report, has also been adhered to in the cost study.

Grouping of elements

In a bill of quantities, every item which forms part of the building is broken down into its component parts, each part being measured and included in the portion of the bill with the appropriate trade heading, e.g. bricklayer, glazier, plumber, &c. If, for example, it is necessary to extract the cost of a given length of wall, the various items which go to make up the wall and which may be divided between several trades in the bill of quantities, must be collected and added together. For the designer or the building user, the bill of quantities is not a satisfactory tool for calculating the cost of individual parts of the building. Building elements, to the designer, are the complete and finished elements which he brings together to enclose space and provide a working environment. It is the cost of these elements which cost analysis aims to compare. Most of the elements fall naturally into groups, but a few of the items included in overall building cost are difficult to place in the groups, and may have to be divided between them all. The grouping of elements used in this report is partly the result of consultation between the team and a number of authorities,[1] architects, engineers, and quantity surveyors who have had considerable experience in cost analysis, and partly determined by the special problems of laboratory buildings. The grouping of elements is shown below. This is followed by notes on each element group and on the items of cost which are apportioned between them.

1. ELEMENTS BELOW GROUND-FLOOR LEVEL (SUBSTRUCTURE)

   (a) Work below lowest floor level.
   (b) Frame.
   (c) External walls.
   (d) Internal load-bearing walls.
   (e) Intermediate basement floors and stairs.

---

[1] See acknowledgements, p. ix.

2. SUPERSTRUCTURE ELEMENTS

   (a) Frame.

   (b) External walls.

   (c) Internal structural walls.

   (d) Roof construction and coverings (including flashings and rainwater goods).

   (e) Upper floors.

   (f) Staircases.

   (g) Windows and external doors (including fittings and glazing).

   (h) Roof lights (including fittings and glazing).

3. INTERNAL PARTITIONING

   (a) Partitioning.

   (b) Internal doors and fittings.

4. FINISHES AND DECORATION

   (a) Wall and partition finishes.

   (b) Floor finishes (including skirtings).

   (c) Ceilings.

   (d) Decoration.

5. SERVICES AND DRAINAGE

   (a) Drainage (including settling or sampling tanks, &c.).[1]

   (b) Plumbing and fittings:
      (i) to laboratories;
      (ii) to other accommodation.

   (c) Electrical installation:
      (i) main supply;
      (ii) lighting installation;
      (iii) socket outlet installation;
      (iv) ancillary wiring;
      (v) clock system;
      (vi) fire alarm;
      (vii) emergency lighting.

   (d) Other laboratory services:
      (i) gas;
      (ii) compressed air;
      (iii) vacuum, &c., as appropriate.

   (e) Heating system.

   (f) Hot water system.

   (g) Ventilation and air-conditioning system.

   (h) Refrigeration.

   (i) Miscellaneous services, telephones, &c.

6. EXTERNAL WORKS AND GROSS COST ITEMS

   (a) Cost of associated buildings not analysed above.

   (b) Cost of services to meter or switchboard. Drainage work connected with the building but not analysed above.

   (c) Landscaping and external works and services:
      (i) roads, paths, and paving;
      (ii) street lighting, drainage, external water, or electrical services, &c.;
      (iii) planting, preparation of ground, &c., and other subdivisions that may be thought appropriate.

   (d) Foundation costs due to unusual site conditions.

---

[1] It is advisable to accept the definition suggested in Ministry of Education *Building Bulletin*, no. 4, 2nd ed., March 1957, item 30, p. 28. 'All drains from last connecting manhole up to and including connection to gullies and W.C.s.'

7. FITTINGS AND FURNISHING

   (a) Laboratory benches.

   (b) Fume cupboard carcases.

   (c) Laboratory cupboards, &c.

   (d) Built-in fittings outside laboratories.

   (e) Blinds.

   (f) Loose furniture.

   (g) Machine tools, &c.

8. SUNDRIES

Unclassified items: e.g. balustrades, &c., and minor items of day-work.

Discussion of element groups

I. WORK BELOW GROUND-FLOOR LEVEL

This heading was used in the Ministry of Education *Building Bulletin* (1) and, as schools rarely had basements, it was comparatively easy to interpret. Laboratories, however, often have basement floors, and it was felt that for such buildings the whole of the work below ground floor ought not to be assessed together, but that basement structure and finishes ought to be separated from the items originally covered by this group. This is still the team's view, but it was found impossible to make this separation with the information available. This group, therefore, includes all basement structure, damp-proofing, &c. The apportioning of cost of other groups of elements (e.g. partitioning) per sq. ft. of floor area, in relation to basements is dealt with in the analyses themselves.

2. SUPERSTRUCTURE

There are many debatable points of detail in deciding which portions of structure are attributable to the several elements in this group. For example, it is often difficult to separate the framing in a framed building from floors or walls; the frame is normally costed as a system, and cannot be broken down into horizontal and vertical components. Where this is the case, frame, floor, and roof construction are expressed as a single item in the detailed analyses.

External walls consist of those parts of the vertical structural or weather-repelling surfaces of the building not used for the admission of light or air. Interior finishes such as plaster or panelling are excluded. Internal structural walls are included in this group and are treated similarly. The item for windows, external doors, and roof lights, also in this group, includes frames, sub-frames, &c.

The cost of the roof element includes all structural work above ceiling level, and plumbing associated with water disposal from the roof.

3. PARTITIONING AND INTERNAL DOORS

Non-structural walls, doors and their frames or linings, glazed screens, &c., are included in this group. Surface finishes would only be included where integral with the structure, e.g. in some proprietary partitioning systems.

4. FINISHES AND DECORATION

This group includes decorative finishes or finishes associated with room function; plasterwork, tiles, terrazzo dadoes, panelling, splashbacks behind benches, floor finishes, skirtings, &c., would all come under this heading, but not casings or linings specifically chosen for fire-protection, insulation, &c., which would come into the structural categories. External as well as internal decoration is included. Difficulties can arise in this group; e.g. where floor finish and structure are integral, but on the whole it is easy to distinguish these items as finishes not essential to structure.

5. SERVICES

This group includes drainage from the building to the first inspection chamber. It covers the whole of the services, including artificial lighting and heating and ventilation.

6. EXTERNAL WORKS AND SERVICES

Drainage from inspection chambers nearest the building to the sewer or other disposal point and extra external works consequent upon site position or locality as well as paving, planting, &c., are covered in this group. The proportion of cost allotted to these elements will obviously vary greatly with the site, a variation which is fully reflected in the wide discrepancies in the figures shown in the analyses under this heading.

7. FITTINGS AND FURNISHING

This group covers fixed or movable furniture, fume cupboards, shelving, store cupboards, &c., but not items such as lighting fittings and sanitary ware, which are included in 5 above.

8. SUNDRIES

Only small proportions of total cost are involved in this group, and it is intended for minor items which cannot be classified.

Cost analyses

The following sections are numbered 1 to 8, a section for the analysis of each of the buildings studied. Each section contains a floor plan (a typical floor in the case of multi-story buildings), an outline isometric drawing showing the shape of the building as a whole, a brief description of the building, and a summarized cost analysis under the headings given above. The data are further summarized and collected in Table 100, Part II, Chapter 6, in the section headed 'The cost of laboratory buildings', which also contains a general discussion on laboratory costs.

Summarized conclusions

1. The cost of the laboratories surveyed ranges between 97s. and 153s. per sq. ft., with five laboratories lying between 97s. and 125s. per sq. ft. No relation is discernible between cost per square foot and the complexity of the plan shape. There is a suggestion that larger laboratories are a little cheaper per square foot than small ones but the evidence on this point is not conclusive.

2. Approximate costs (excluding external works) per cubic foot of enclosed space have been calculated for the eight buildings. They are as follows:

	Shillings per cu. ft.
Biochemistry Laboratory (Isotope Tracer Section), Slough	10·5
Animal Nutrition Unit, Hurley	12·6
Insecticides Laboratory, Slough	10·2
Therapeutic Substances Laboratory, Weybridge	10·4
National Vegetable Research Station, Wellesbourne	9·4
Fisons Limited, Research Station, Levington	9·8
Radio Research Station, Datchet	8·7
Acetate and Synthetic Fibres Laboratory, Courtaulds Limited	9·4

It will be seen that the variation in overall cost is much less than when costs are analysed in terms of area.

It may be inferred, therefore, that cost per square foot is clearly related to room height. Laboratory ceilings should be no higher than is functionally necessary (see also Part II, Chapters 3 and 4).

3. The range of total costs is partly attributable to the varying proportion of space devoted to laboratories and service rooms (primary space) or to other purposes (secondary space). Therefore in estimating the cost of a future laboratory or in making a comparison of costs, consideration should always be given to the ratio of primary space to secondary space in the plan.

4. The cost of superstructure in the examples studied varied between 19·5 per cent. and 36 per cent. The cost of structure and also of partitioning is closely related to ceiling height. The modest proportion of the total cost taken up by superstructure suggests that more economical methods of construction will yield only a small return in reducing the cost of laboratory building.

5. The provision of services and fittings in the laboratories studied accounted for 33 per cent. to 62 per cent. of total cost. It is clear that economies achieved in the design and provision of services and fittings will have a significant effect on the cost of laboratory building. The cost of providing services per foot run of bench (i.e. per worker provided for), was found to be less when the bench space was compactly planned.

6. The foregoing conclusions suggest some means whereby lower costs per square foot could be sought for in laboratory design, but it must be borne in mind that the most significant economies may be found in so planning laboratory buildings as to provide the maximum number of working spaces in a given area. Where this is done, it may be found that the cost per square foot of the resulting design is comparatively high. It follows that the cheapest building in terms of cost per square foot of total area may not always be the most economical.

REFERENCE

(1) MINISTRY OF EDUCATION. Cost study. 2nd edition, London, 1957. *Building bulletin*, no. 4.

ANALYSIS No. 1

Biochemistry Laboratory in the Isotope Tracer
Section, Pest Infestation Laboratory, Slough,
Bucks.

Department of Scientific and Industrial Research

Cost information supplied by the Ministry of
Works

Biochemistry Laboratory in the Isotope Tracer Section, Pest Infestation Laboratory, Slough

This is a small laboratory unit, simply planned with rooms on either side of an off-centre corridor. The deeper rooms (large radiochemistry and radiobiology laboratories and isotope rooms) are 19 ft. approximately from corridor wall to window wall: the rooms on the opposite side (small laboratories for biochemistry, preparation rooms, and special purpose rooms) are 13 ft. 6 in. deep. The corridor is 5 ft. wide, giving a building 41 ft. 6 in. thick overall. The building is an addition to an existing research establishment and therefore contains little administration or staff facilities, and in consequence the proportion of laboratory (primary) space is high (69 per cent.) and of circulation space low (15·6 per cent.). Other accommodation includes lavatories, showers, &c. The rooms throughout are 9 ft. 10 in. high. Planning, generally, is on a 12 ft. lateral grid.

The building is of load-bearing brick construction, in some places $13\frac{1}{2}$ in. and 18 in. thick, elsewhere 11 in. cavity walls. An internal structural wall at approximately mid-span is of 9 in. brickwork. The ground floor is of normal screeded concrete construction. The roof is of hollow tiles carried on steel joists on the grid lines and covered with asphalt. Metal windows are used and non-structural partitions between rooms are in $4\frac{1}{2}$ in. brickwork. Floors to laboratories and corridor are covered with lino and walls and ceilings are plastered and painted.

Items included under services (element group 5) are:

Heating:
Gas-fired boiler.
Convectors.

Ventilation:
Extracts to fume cupboards only.

Constant Temperature:
2 rooms.

Hot water services:
Gas-fired cylinder.

Town gas services:
Gas supply to benches and boilers.

Electrical services:
Tungsten and fluorescent lighting.
Wiring to ancillary equipment, e.g. to exhaust fans, heat balancer units, &c.

Clock installation:
Impulse clock system.

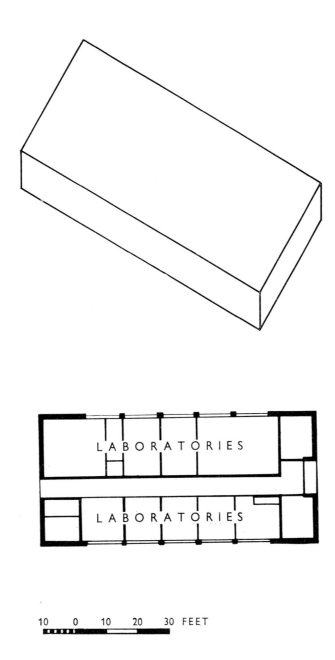

Fig. 92. Plan and block isometric of the Biochemistry Laboratory in the Isotope Tracer Section, Pest Infestation Laboratory, Slough, Bucks.

Cost Analysis

Total cost (as at 31 March 1957)

	£
Building work	9,416
Engineering services (including builders' work, &c.) . . .	5,104
Laboratory and other fittings, furniture, &c.	4,925
	£19,445

Gross floor area: 3,392 ft. sup. Cost per ft. sup. gross: £5. 14s. 8d.

Analysis by items:

	Per foot super gross		Percentage	
	£ s. d.	£ s. d.		
1. Work below ground-floor level	6 8		5·8	
Total		6 8		5·8
2. Superstructure:				
Structural frame including floors, stairs, roof, roof covering, flashings, and rain-water goods	15 3		13·3	
External walling including facings	5 7		4·9	
Windows and external doors including glazing and ironmongery	5 10		5·1	
Internal structural walls	1 4		1·2	
Total		1 8 0		24·5
3. Partitioning and internal doors:				
Internal partitions	1 4		1·2	
Internal doors and borrowed lights	1 6		1·3	
Total		2 10		2·5
4. Finishes and decorations:				
Internal finishes to walls, floors, and ceilings	5 3		4·6	
Decorations—internal and external	2 0		1·7	
Total		7 3		6·3
5. Services:				
Normal plumbing and sanitary services	2 3		2·0	
Laboratory ditto	3 1		2·7	
Engineering services:				
Mechanical:				
Boiler-house plant and associated equipment	3 2¼		2·8	
Heating services in buildings	4 10¼		4·2	
Hot-water service	1 2¾		1·0	
Gas installation	2 0¾		1·8	
Ventilation—fume cupboards	5 9		5·0	
Constant-temperature rooms—equipment	2 9½		2·4	
Fire appliances	9¼		0·8	
Electrical:				
Lighting installation	2 4		2·0	
Lighting fittings	10		0·8	
Socket outlet installation	3 9¼		3·3	
Ancillary electric wiring	1 1		0·9	
Clock installation (including clocks)	1 6		1·3	
Total		1 15 6		31·0
6. External works and services:				
External services including fencing, roads, paths, drainage, landscaping, &c.	4 5		3·8	
Total		4 5		3·8
7. Fittings and furnishing:				
Laboratory benching fixed including fume cupboards	1 1 2¾		18·5	
Laboratory furniture—apparatus racks, apparatus cupboards, wall racks, wall stools, laboratory desks, laboratory chairs	4 1¾		3·6	
Blinds	5½		0·4	
Lino	2 7¾		2·3	
Office furniture	6¼		0·5	
Canteen equipment, including cookers, refrigerators, kitchen fittings, &c.	—		—	
Total		1 9 0		25·3
8. Sundries:				
Sundries including fittings, balustrades and minor items of day work	1 0		0·8	
Total		1 0		0·8
Total cost per ft. sup. gross		£5 14 8		100·0

ANALYSIS No. 2

Project for Animal Nutrition Unit at Grasslands
Research Station, Hurley.

Agricultural Research Council

Project designed by the Nuffield Foundation
Division for Architectural Studies

Cost data based on tender prices

Proposed Animal Nutrition Unit, Hurley

The laboratory unit which is the subject of this analysis was part of a larger unit which also included a second detached building to house animal calorimetry rooms and accommodation for large animals (cows, calves, &c.). The laboratory was planned to house the investigation techniques associated with research into animal metabolism. The building was planned on a 40 in. horizontal module, internal partitions falling on the grid lines. 16 ft. 8 in. deep rooms were placed on each side of a 6 ft. 8 in. corridor, giving a total building depth of 40 ft. As a result of early lighting studies (see Part II, Chapter 4), the ceiling height was reduced to 8 ft. 6 in., with supplementary natural lighting from a roof light. Services were carried in a ceiling duct over the corridor.

The building had a large proportion of primary space (63·3 per cent.) and was economical in circulation area (15·3 per cent.). Offices and stores accounted for 15·9 per cent. of total area.

The structure was a proprietary pre-fabricated timber system specially modified to fit laboratory conditions, built up from a concrete ground-floor slab and with fire-resisting internal linings. Internal partitions were structural and also in timber. Floors were finished in lino-tiles. Only gas (at mains pressure), hot and cold water, and electricity services were laid on to benches; central heating, supplied from the parent research establishment was by convectors placed under windows. The cost of carrying main services to the unit from the parent building is included in the analysis.

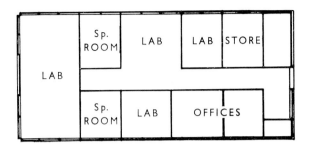

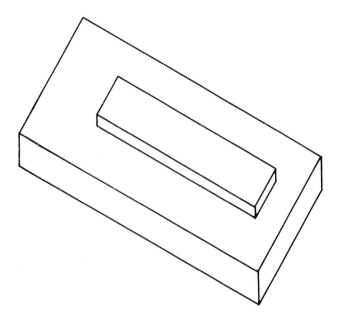

10   0   10   20   30 FEET

Fig. 93. Plan and block isometric of the Animal Nutrition Unit project at Grasslands Research Station, Hurley.

Cost Analysis

Total cost (as at 31 March 1957)

		£
Building work		16,913
Engineering services (including builders' work, &c.) . . .		6,008
Laboratory and other fittings, furniture, &c.		4,329
		£27,250

Gross floor area: 3,557 ft. sup. Cost per ft. sup. gross: £7. 13s. 2d.

Analysis by items:

	Per foot super gross		Percentage	
	s. d.	£ s. d.		
1. Work below ground-floor level:				
Work up to and including ground-floor slab	5 8½		3·8	
Proportion of sum of preliminaries, insurances, and contingencies . .	3 1¾		2·1	
Total		8 10¼		5·9
2. Superstructure:				
Structural frame including floors, stairs, roof, roof covering, flashings, and rain-water goods	13 7		8·9	
External walling and internal structural walls	11 8¼		7·6	
Windows and borrowed lights and external doors including glazing . .	6 4		4·2	
Proportion of sum of preliminaries, &c.	3 9		2·4	
Total		1 15 4¼		23·1
3. Partitioning and internal doors not included in analysis				
4. Finishes and decorations:				
Internal finishes to walls, floors, and ceilings	7 8		5·1	
Internal decorations and ironmongery	3 5½		2·2	
Proportion of preliminaries, &c.	2 4¾		1·6	
Total		13 6¼		8·9
5. Services:*				
Normal plumbing, sanitary, and laboratory services	15 4		10·0	
Engineering services:				
Mechanical	19 1½		12·4	
Electrical	14 7¾		9·5	
Total		2 9 1¼		31·9
6. External works and services:				
(including fencing, roads, paths, drainage to and beyond sampling chamber, water main, and electricity connexions)	19 4½		12·7	
Proportion of preliminaries, &c.	2 7½		1·7	
Total		1 2 0		14·4
7. Fittings and furnishing:				
Laboratory benches and fittings, other joinery fittings	19 7¾		12·8	
Kjeldahl apparatus.	1 1½		0·8	
Firefighting equipment	4¾		0·2	
Telephones	3½		0·1	
Proportion of preliminaries, &c.	2 10½		1·9	
Total		1 4 4		15·8
Total cost per ft. sup. gross		£7 13 2		100·0

* Proportion of preliminaries has been added to individual items, in the case of 5. Services, in order to maintain consistency with Table 100.

ANALYSIS No. 3

Insecticides Laboratory and Local Stores. Pest Infestation Laboratory, Slough, Bucks.

Department of Scientific and Industrial Research

Cost information supplied by the Ministry of Works

Insecticides Laboratory and Local Stores at the Pest Infestation Laboratory, Slough

Like the Isotopes Laboratory (Analysis No. 1), the insecticides building is an addition to an existing establishment. Administration and staff amenities are housed elsewhere and the proportion of laboratory (primary) space is high (57·9 per cent.). The building is the first part of a larger unit, and this has had some effect on plan shape and disposition. A 40 in. grid was used in the planning, the laboratory area being of the eccentric corridor type. Rooms on one side of the corridor are 16 ft. 2 in. deep, on the other 14 ft. The corridor width is 5 ft. The building is about 37 ft. 6 in. deep. Room widths are related to the 40 in. module, ranging from 6 ft. 8 in. to 26 ft. 8 in. Ceiling height throughout is 10 ft. 6 in.

The entrance, lavatories, and services accommodation are in a square-shaped wing at one end of the laboratory block, and a structurally separate stores and spray-chamber building (not shown in Fig. 94) is similarly placed at the opposite end. In the laboratory area, preparation rooms, offices, special rooms, and laboratory rooms are fairly evenly distributed on either side of the corridor.

The blocks at either end of the building, which house the spray-chambers and the engineering services are of load-bearing 11 in. brick cavity wall construction with light-weight slab roofs, carried on internal walls and finished with bituminous felt. The laboratory block is pre-fabricated, with cold-rolled steel columns carrying standard lattice beams, the spans across the building being 20 ft. and 16 ft. 8 in. (there are internal columns on one side of the corridor only). The external cladding takes the form of patent glazing, partly filled solid with aluminium-faced panels and partly glazed. End walls of 11 in. cavity (brick and thermolite) construction are non-structural. The laboratory roof is formed with 3 in. wood-wool slabs on patent bearers, and finished with 3-layer bituminous felt. There are no internal load-bearing walls in the laboratory area, all of which are non-structural 6 in. thermolite blocks. Window frames throughout are of galvanized steel. Floors are of screeded concrete, and covered with 6–7 mm. linoleum in the laboratory block, and with concrete tiles in the spray chamber and service blocks. Walls and ceilings in the laboratories are plastered and painted; the light-weight blocks are fair-faced and painted in service areas.

Items included under services (element group 5) are:

Heating:
    Hand-fired boilers.
    Circulating pumps.
    Self-supporting mild steel, brick-lined chimney stack.
    150-gallon indirect cylinder.
    Low pressure hot water 2-pipe accelerated system with convector elements incorporated in service ducts below laboratory benches and concealed type convectors in corridor.
    Boiler plant.

Ventilation:
    Simple extract.
    4 roof extract units.
    Inlet and outlet volume control grilles.
    Extract to fume cupboards.

Hot water:
    Indirect accelerated system, using galvanized tubes.

Town gas:
    Gas supply to benches and fume cupboards.

Compressed air:
    Supply to 14 outlets.
    Compressor—single stage, air cooled, belt driven by electric motor.

Vacuum installation:
    22 outlets.

Fire appliances:
    CO_2, S.A., and Teletetra extinguishers with asbestos cloths and sand buckets.

Electrical services:
    Tungsten and fluorescent lighting.
    Wiring to ancillary equipment, e.g. exhaust fans, circulating pump motors, &c.

Clock installation:
    Impulse clock system.

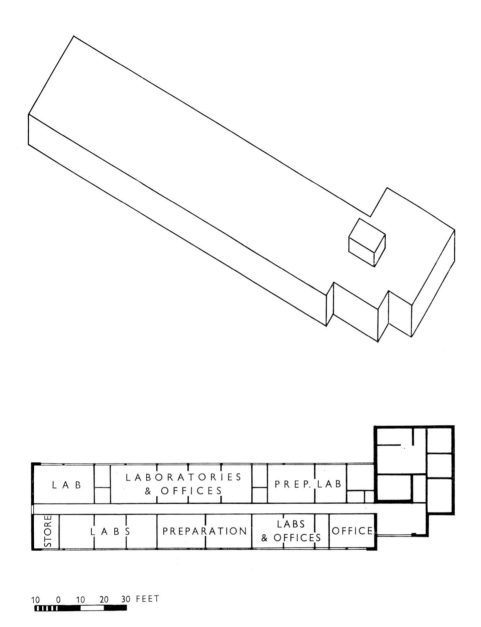

Fig. 94. Plan and block isometric of the Insecticides Laboratory and Local Stores, Pest Infestation Laboratory, Slough, Bucks.

Cost Analysis

Total cost (as at 31 March 1957)

	£
Building work	31,379
Engineering services (including builders' work, &c.) . . .	8,922
Laboratory and other fittings, furniture, &c. . . .	8,805
	£49,106

Gross floor area: 8,004 ft. sup. Cost per ft. sup. gross: £6. 2s. 7½d.

Analysis by items:

	Per foot super gross		Percentage	
	£ s. d.	£ s. d.		
1. Work below ground-floor level	9 11½		8·1	
Total		9 11½		8·1
2. Superstructure:				
Structural frame (mostly prefabricated) including floors, stairs, roof, roof covering, flashings, and rainwater goods . . .	16 8¼		13·6	
External walling including facings	9 0½		7·4	
Windows and external doors including glazing and ironmongery	9 2½		7·5	
Internal structural walls	10		0·7	
Total		1 15 9¼		29·2
3. Partitioning and internal doors:				
Internal partitions	3 1		2·5	
Internal doors and borrowed lights	1 7¼		1·3	
Total		4 8¼		3·8
4. Finishes and decorations:				
Internal finishings to walls, floors, and ceilings	9 11½		8·1	
Decorations—internal and external	3 1¾		2·6	
Total		13 1¼		10·7
5. Services:				
Normal plumbing and sanitary services	1 5½		1·2	
Laboratory ditto	2 0½		1·7	
Engineering services:				
Mechanical				
Boiler house and plant and associated equipment	3 7¾		2·9	
Heating services	3 11		3·2	
Hot-water service	1 3		1·0	
Ventilation to spray chambers and fume cupboards	2 2¾		1·8	
Gas installation	1 1		0·9	
Compressed air	11		0·7	
Vacuum installation	1 0½		0·8	
Fire appliances	0½		0·1	
Electrical				
Lighting installation	1 8		1·4	
Lighting fittings	1 4½		1·1	
Socket outlet installation	2 3½		1·9	
Ancillary electric wiring	1 11½		1·6	
Clock installation (including clocks)	9¾		0·7	
Total		1 5 8½		21·0
6. External works and services:				
External services including fencing, roads, paths, drainage, landscaping, &c. . .	10 2½		8·3	
Total		10 2½		8·3
7. Fittings and furnishing:				
Fixed laboratory benching including fume cupboards	15 10¼		12·9	
Laboratory furniture—apparatus cupboards, apparatus racks, stools, chairs, desks .	3 4½		2·7	
Lino	1 1½		0·9	
Stores racking	1¾		0·2	
Office furniture	1 6		1·2	
Canteen equipment including cookers, refrigerators, kitchen fittings, &c. . .	—		—	
Total		1 2 0		17·9
8. Sundries:				
Sundries including fittings, balustrades, and minor items of day work . .	1 2¼		1·0	1·0
Total		1 2¼		
Total cost per ft. sup. gross		£6 2 7½		100·0

ANALYSIS No. 4

Therapeutic Substances Laboratory at the Ministry of Agriculture, Fisheries and Food Veterinary Laboratory, Weybridge.

Cost information supplied by the Ministry of Works

Therapeutic Substances Laboratory, Weybridge

The laboratory building houses the production of therapeutic substances, the manufacture and control of which involves the use of a great deal of specialized accommodation such as controlled-temperature rooms, sterilizing rooms, &c. Services provision is complex, involving plenum and other artificial ventilation, piped vacuum and steam as well as the normal bench supplies. Planning is on the 'race-track' principle; temperature-controlled rooms being placed in the middle of the building, with corridors on either side and laboratories, preparation rooms, &c., between corridors and outside walls. The central core of special rooms is 20 ft. deep, corridors 6 ft. wide, and laboratories about 15 ft. deep. The total thickness, including walls and partitions is about 68 ft., and the whole building is of simple rectangular shape. In cross-section the building is complicated, the top story which houses services plant being only as wide as the central core with its floor well below finished roof level. The intermediate space allows direct access from plant room to first-floor ceiling ducts. Floor to floor height is about 14 ft.; false ceilings house the ducting system. The laboratory ceilings are partly 8 ft. 6 in. high (as it is in corridors) and slope upward to 11 ft. 6 in. high in areas nearer the windows.

There is a low proportion of general laboratory space (11·5 per cent.) and a high proportion of special rooms (17·7 per cent.+6·8 per cent.), but as a whole the proportion of primary space is low (36 per cent.). Service space is, of course, inflated by the unusually large area devoted to engineering plant. The proportion of circulation space (24·9 per cent.) is the highest of any of the buildings analysed. The structure is on a 12 ft. horizontal grid, and most internal partitions fall on the grid lines.

The building is framed in reinforced concrete, with a metal curtain-wall outer skin. The roof finish is bituminous felt carried on a hollow tile slab between the concrete beams. End walls and internal structural walls are in $13\frac{1}{2}$ in. and 9 in. brickwork respectively. Partitions are mainly $4\frac{1}{2}$ in. brickwork. Painted plaster finish is used internally. The floor finish is linoleum generally; asphalt and granolithic finishes are used in special rooms, ster8ilizing rooms, &c.

Items included under services (element group 5) are:

Heating:
> Embedded ceiling coils.
> Panel convectors and radiators.
> Plenum heating.

Ventilation:
> Input and extract fan units.
> Plenum input and extract plant, complete with filters, heater batteries and cooler coils, serves laboratories.
> Local input and extract ventilation systems are installed in dark rooms, post-mortem rooms, and serve fume cupboards, autoclave hoods, &c.

Hot water:
> Storage cylinders supplied by 2 steam calorifiers with thermostatic control at the steam inlets.

Steam:
> Connexions to 5 plenum heater batteries, 14 autoclaves, 2 stills, and 4 steamers.

Air-cooling refrigeration plant:
> 3 motor-driven compressor units with induced draught evaporative condensers.

Town gas:
> Connexion to 69 outlets plus 2 twin outlets.

Compressed air:
> Connexion to 57 outlets.
> Compressor.

Vacuum:
> Connexion to 57 outlets.

Deep-freeze room:
> 1 room cooled to −20° C.

Cold rooms:
> 9 rooms cooled to +2° C.

Incubator rooms:
> 8 rooms at 37° C. with recirculating electric heating units.

Electrical services:
> Tunsten lighting throughout.
> Electrical installations in cold rooms, and incubator rooms.
> Air conditioning.
> Wiring to ancillary equipment, e.g. air compressors, vacuum pump, calorifiers, drying ovens.
> Intercommunication telephones.
> Public address system.
> Lifts.

Clock installation:
> 1 master and 26 slave clocks.

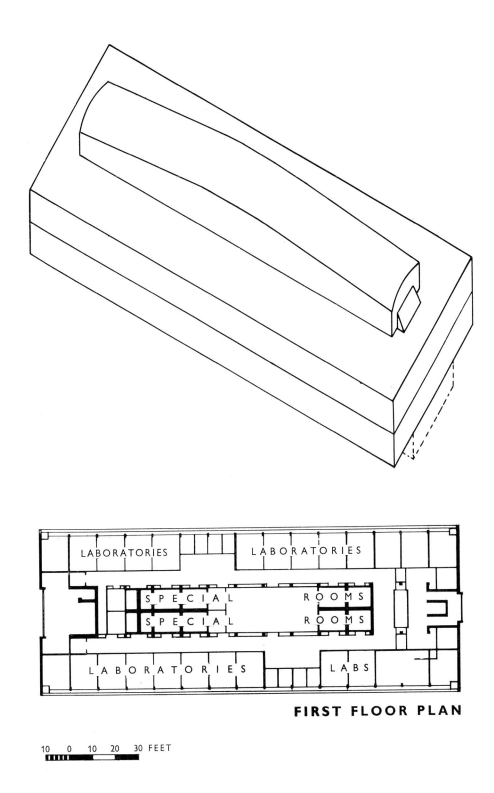

FIRST FLOOR PLAN

10 0 10 20 30 FEET

Fig. 95. Plan and block isometric of the Therapeutic Substances Laboratory at the Ministry of Agriculture, Fisheries and Food Veterinary Laboratory, Weybridge.

Cost Analysis

Based on superstructure area (28,213 sq. ft.) for groups 1 and 2 below. Total area (29,750 sq. ft.) used to obtain cost per sq. ft. of remainder.

Total cost (as at 31 March 1957)

	£
Building work	120,213
Engineering services (including builders' work, &c.)	74,303
Laboratory and other fittings, furniture, &c.	21,582
	£216,098

Gross floor area 29,750 ft. sup. Cost per ft. sup. gross £7. 8*s*. 0¼*d*.

Analysis by items:

	Per foot super gross		*Percentage*	
	£ s. d.	£ s. d.		
1. Work below ground-floor level	13 3		8·9	
Total		13 3		8·9
2. Superstructure:				
Structural frame including floors, stairs, roof, roof covering, flashings, and rainwater goods .	1 2 6		15·2	
External walling including facings	3 2		2·2	
Windows and external doors including glazing and ironmongery	10 0		6·7	
Internal structural walls	2 8		1·8	
Total		1 18 4		25·9
3. Partitioning and internal doors:				
Internal partitions	1 4¼		0·9	
Internal doors and borrowed lights	2 0¾		1·4	
Total		3 5		2·3
4. Finishes and decorations:				
Internal finishings to walls, floors, and ceilings	9 6¾		6·5	
Decorations—internal and external	4 10¾		3·4	
Total		14 5½		9·9
5. Services:				
Normal plumbing and sanitary services	3 4		2·2	
Laboratory ditto	1 9¾		1·2	
Engineering services:				
Mechanical				
Heating services	4 9		3·3	
Hot water services	1 8		1·2	
Steam services	1 4½		0·9	
Plenum input and extract system	17 0¾		11·6	
Ancillary ventilation services	3¾		0·2	
Air-cooling refrigeration services	5 4½		3·6	
Compressed-air installation	1 11¼		1·3	
Vacuum services	1 1¼		0·7	
Gas services	5¼		0·3	
Deep-freeze room insulation refrigeration equipment	5¾		0·3	
9 Cold rooms ditto	5 9½		4·0	
8 Incubator rooms insulation and electrical equipment	2 8¼		1·8	
Electrical				
Lighting installation	2 5¼		1·6	
Socket outlet installation	10¾		0·6	
Electrical installation in cold rooms	1½		0·09	
Ditto incubator rooms	1		0·06	
Ditto air-conditioning system	2½		0·1	
Ditto air-compressor system	0¼		0·03	
Ditto vacuum pump	0¼		0·03	
Ditto calorifier chamber	0¾		0·05	
Drying ovens	2½		0·1	
Electrical services to oven, peeler, water bath, &c.	2		0·1	
2 lifts	2 0		1·3	
Heating service controls	2¼		0·1	
Public-address system	2		0·1	
Intercommunication telephones	0½		0·04	
Clock installation (including clocks)	4¼		0·2	
Total		2 15 1¼		37·1
6. External works and services:				
External services including fencing, roads, paths, drainage, landscaping, &c.	7 11¾		5·4	
Total		7 11¾		5·4
7. Fittings and furnishing:				
Laboratory benching fixed including built-in cupboards	8 2		5·5	
Laboratory furniture:				
Laboratory tables, micro cabinets, laboratory chairs and stools, apparatus cupboards and units	1 0¾		0·7	
Blinds	10		0·6	
Lino (part *in situ* floor)	10		0·6	
Stores racking	1 3		0·8	
Changing-room equipment	3¼		0·2	
Office furniture	6½		0·4	
Canteen equipment including cooker, refrigerators, kitchen fittings, &c.	8½		0·5	
Total		13 8		9·3
8. Sundries:				
Sundries including fittings, balustrades, and minor items of daywork	1 9¾		1·2	
Total		1 9¾		1·2
Total cost per ft. sup. gross		£7 8 0¼		100·0

ANALYSIS No. 5

National Vegetable Research Station,
Wellesbourne.

Ministry of Agriculture, Fisheries and Food

Cost information supplied by the Ministry of
Agriculture, Fisheries and Food

National Vegetable Research Station, Wellesbourne

The building houses all types of research into vegetable growth and protection; disciplines include plant pathology, plant physiology, and entomology. The plan is H-shaped, the central block being slightly longer than the two wings. Laboratories and special rooms are placed on either side of a 6 ft. wide corridor and are 16 ft. 3 in. deep, giving a total building depth of about 40 ft. Rooms are 10 ft. 6 in. high on the ground floor and 9 ft. 6 in. high on the first floor; there is a fairly large basement. The building is planned on a 12 ft. structural grid but a number of internal partitions are not on the grid.

Proportion of primary space is fairly high (46·8 per cent.) with a moderately high ratio of general laboratories (30·5 per cent.); offices and stores take up 22 per cent. of the total area, and circulation space is about average (20·6 per cent.).

The building generally is reinforced concrete framed, with infilling of alternate brick and patent glazing panels. Steel roof trusses and purlins carry insulating panels and the roof finish is copper. Structural floors are of 4 in. precast prestressed units, screeded and finished generally in P.V.C. tiles. Hardwood strips are used in chemical laboratories, terrazzo in entrance, lavatories, &c., and granolithic finish in stores and basement. Internal walls are structural only in the staircase linking blocks and are in 13½ in. brickwork. Partitions are of light-weight blocks, plastered and painted. The upper floor has a 'Frenger' ceiling combining ceiling heating and acoustic treatment,

the ground-floor ceiling is rendered directly on the floor slabs above. Laboratory benches have teak tops.

Hot and cold water, demineralized water, bottled gas, electricity, and vacuum are piped to benches.

Items included under services (element group 5) are

Heating:
    Oil-fired sectional boiler.
    Oil tanks.
    Frenger ceiling coils.

Hot water:
    Calorifier heated by primary circulation.

Gas:
    No town gas available.
    Central bottled gas station in main store.
    Piped distribution to benches.

Vacuum:
    Connecting to existing compressor only
    Distribution pipes.

Rainwater and demineralized water system:
    Underground cistern.
    Roof tanks.

Electrical services:
    Fluorescent and tungsten.
    Bench outlets.

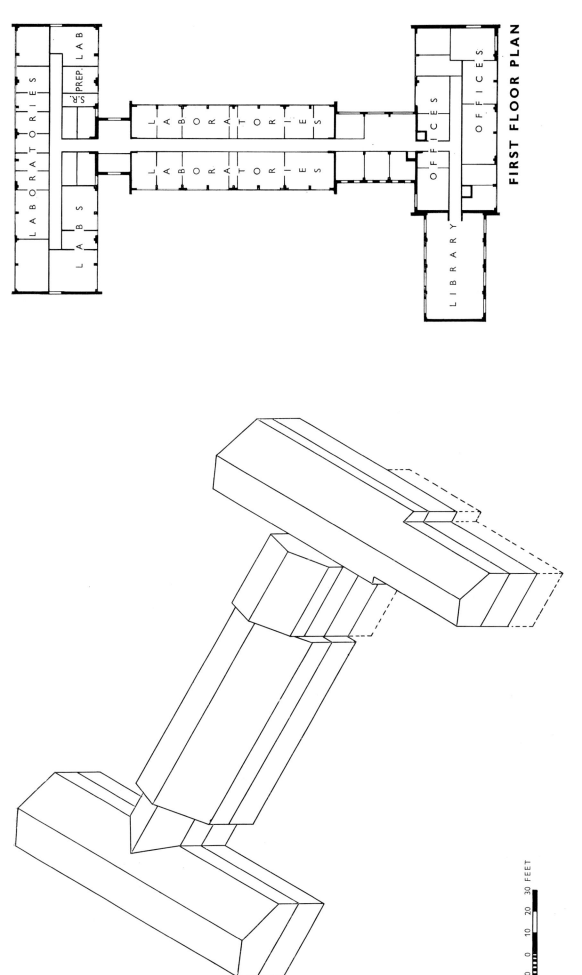

FIRST FLOOR PLAN

Fig. 96. Plan and block isometric of the National Vegetable Research Station, Wellesbourne.

10 0   10   20   30 FEET

187

Cost Analysis

Based on superstructure area (29,940 sq. ft.) for groups 1 and 2 below. Total area (33,766 sq. ft.) used to obtain cost per sq. ft. of remainder.

Total cost (as at 31 March 1957)

		£
Building work	. . . .	119,909
Engineering services (including builders' work, &c.)	. . .	39,463
Laboratory and other fittings, furniture, &c.	. . . .	13,823
		£173,195

Gross floor area: 33,766 ft. sup. Cost per ft. sup. gross: £5. 7s. 11¼d.

Analysis by items:

	Per foot super gross		Percentage	
	£ s. d.	£ s. d.		
1. Work below ground-floor level (including basement) . . .	9 11		9·1	
Total		9 11		9·1
2. Superstructure:				
Structural frame, roof and rainwater goods, upper floors and stairs, external walls	1 8 5¾		26·4	
Windows and external doors and roof lights . . .	9 10½		9·1	
Internal structural walls	9½		0·7	
Total		1 19 1¾		36·2
3. Partitioning and internal doors:				
Internal partitions	1 4		1·2	
Internal doors	3 3½		3·1	
Total		4 7½		4·3
4. Finishes and decorations:				
Internal finishes to walls, floors, and ceilings	12 3½		11·4	
Decorations	2 4½		2·2	
Total		14 8		13·6
5. Services:				
Normal plumbing and sanitary services	1 0¼		0·9	
Laboratory ditto	3 0¾		2·9	
Engineering services:				
Mechanical	13 11¾		12·9	
Electrical	9 5		8·7	
Total		1 7 5¾		25·4
6. External works and services:				
Paving and external works, cost of associated building (acid store), drainage adjacent to building	3 11		3·6	
Total		3 11		3·6
7. Fittings and furnishing:				
Laboratory fittings and built-in equipment	6 2½		5·8	
Furniture	1 2½		1·1	
Other built-in equipment	9¼		0·7	
Total		8 2¼		7·6
Total cost per ft. sup. gross		£5 7 11¼		100·0

ANALYSIS No. 6

Laboratories and Administration Block.
Fisons Limited Research Station, Levington.

Cost information supplied in the *Architects'
Journal*, vol. 127 (March 6), 1958

Laboratories and Administration Block, Fisons Limited Research Station, Levington

This research station has four separate buildings—a 'pot trials' building, a process laboratory and boiler house, a canteen block, and, sited in the centre, the main laboratory and administration building. The latter building is planned throughout on a 10 ft. grid and has three stories and a semi-basement used primarily for stores. On each floor, except the top floor (which contains the fume extract and ventilating plant), the laboratories are placed on either side of a central corridor and are separated from the administration wing by the main entrance and staircase. Rooms in the laboratory wing are 21 ft. deep and the corridor 6 ft. wide, giving an overall width of 53 ft. 6 in. In the administration wing, the rooms are 18 ft. deep and the corridor 9 ft. wide, giving an overall width of about 47 ft. Rooms throughout are 12 ft. high. The proportion of primary space (31 per cent.) is low, a good deal of space being allocated to offices and service accommodation.

The building has a concrete frame and precast concrete intermediate floor beams. Brick and timber cladding are used externally. The roof construction is of precast, prestressed slabs on *in situ* beams with concrete topping, vermiculite screed, and built-up felt finish. Windows are double glazed with soft wood frames. P.V.C. tiles are used for the main floor finish and the ceilings are finished with metal acoustic tiles throughout the laboratories and corridors. Linoleum floor covering is used in the offices and the ceilings finished with fibreboard acoustic tiles. Walls generally are plastered. The bench tops (teak) are of the cantilevered type and movable cupboard and drawer units are provided. The latter and the demountable partitioning are based on a 3 ft. 4 in. grid. Vertical ducts link up with horizontal mains in the corridor ceiling space and are easily accessible.

Services include hot and cold water, demineralized water, gas, compressed air, and vacuum. A plenum heating system is used. In-put air is filtered, and passed through sheet metal ducting to ceiling grilles in the laboratories, library, and conference room.

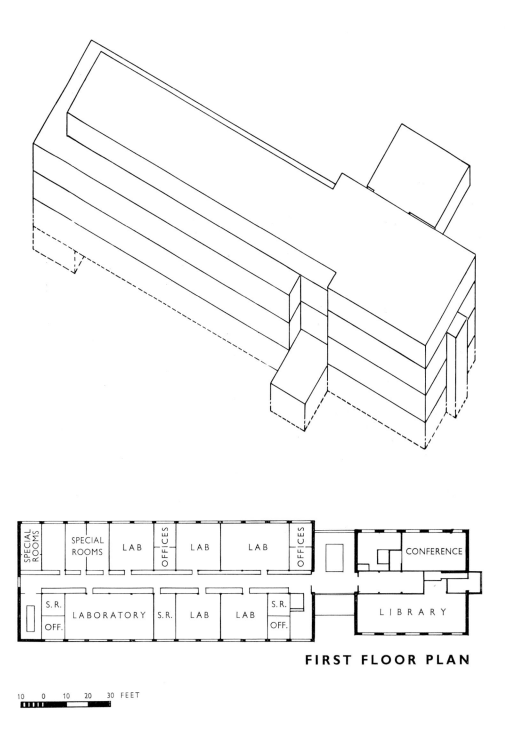

FIRST FLOOR PLAN

10　0　10　20　30 FEET

Fig. 97. Plan and block isometric of the Laboratories and Administration building, Fisons Limited Research Station, Levington.

Cost Analysis

Total cost (as at April 1957)

	£
Building work	115,923
Engineering services (including builders' work, &c.) . . .	85,180
Laboratory and other fittings, furniture, &c. . . .	35,212
	£236,315

Gross floor area: 38,780 ft. sup. Cost per ft. sup. gross: £6. 1s. 9¾d.

Analysis by items:

	Per foot super gross		Percentage	
	£ s. d.	£ s. d.		
1. Work below ground-floor level	4 10		3·9	
Proportion of preliminaries and insurances, contingencies . .	1¾		0·2	
Total		4 11¾		4·1
2. Superstructure:				
External walls and facings	5 3¼		4·3	
Frame or load-bearing element	2 11		2·4	
Upper-floor construction	4 4		3·6	
Staircases	1 10½		1·5	
Roof construction	2 7¼		2·1	
Roof lights	4¾		0·3	
Windows (cost includes sills and glazing)	5 4		4·4	
External doors (cost includes glazing)	2		0·2	
Proportion of preliminaries, insurances, and contingenices, &c. .	10		0·7	
Total		1 3 8¾		19·5
3. Partitioning and internal doors:				
Internal partitions	3 6¾		2·9	
W.C. doors and partitions	1½		0·1	
Internal doors.	1 2¾		1·0	
Ironmongery	8¾		0·6	
Proportion of preliminaries, &c.	2¼		0·2	
Total		5 10		4·8
4. Finishes and decorations:				
Internal finishes to walls, floors, and ceilings	10 0¾		8·3	
Decorations—internal and external	1 6¾		1·3	
Proportion of preliminaries, &c.	4¾		0·3	
Total		12 0¼		9·9
5. Services:*				
Normal plumbing and sanitary fittings	13 1¾		10·9	
Engineering services:				
Mechanical	1 10 4		24·8	
Electrical	13 7¼		11·1	
Total		2 17 1		46·8
6. External works and services not included in analysis				
7. Fittings and furnishing:				
Laboratory fittings	14 5¾		11·9	
Cloakrooms and other fittings, venetian blinds . . .	3 1		2·5	
Proportion of preliminaries, &c.	7¼		0·5	
Total		18 2		14·9
Total cost per ft. sup. gross		£6 1 9¾		100·0

* Proportion of preliminaries has been added to individual items, in the case of 5. Services in order to maintain consistency with Table 100.

ANALYSIS No. 7

Radio Research Station, Datchet, Bucks.

Department of Scientific and Industrial Research

Cost information supplied by the Ministry of Works

Radio Research Station, Datchet

The building consists of a two-story administration and office block (not shown on the plan), and a single-story block linking four wings, each intended to house a team or project, and comprising about 1,000 sq. ft. of office space, a small workshop, a store, two laboratories of about 350 sq. ft. each, and a large laboratory of about 1,300 sq. ft. at the end of each 'finger'. Covered bays attached to each of the large laboratories are for direct off-loading into the laboratory. The plan is based roughly on a 12 ft. module. The large laboratories are approximately 36 ft. square. The smaller laboratories are about 15 ft. deep on either side of a 6 ft. corridor and of various modular widths. The building, generally, is about 36 ft. in depth. Ceiling height in the larger laboratories is 12 ft. 6 in. and 9 ft. 6 in. elsewhere.

The space devoted to laboratories forms a lower proportion of total area than any of the other buildings studied. This is not due to the plan shape, which, unlike many plans of this kind is not extravagant in circulation space (14·2 per cent. as against an average of 20 per cent.), but because of the nature of the work, which requires more office space than usual (for computing, &c.). The provision of office and workshop space is fairly typical of the needs of physical research. Experimental work is also carried on outside the building at remote points on the site. The extensive distribution of services to these points is less typical.

Virtually the whole of the single-story building is concrete portal framed, with cavity brick non-structural walls between the frames. The two-story building is of load-bearing cavity-brick construction; internal structural walls are of 9 in. brickwork. Walls generally are finished in plaster and painted, those of the workshops, boiler room, &c., fair-faced brickwork with distemper finish. The floors are of concrete and have linoleum finish on screed. Flat roofs are of metal decking with insulating layer and bituminous-felt covering, generally with decking exposed internally and painted. Windows are metal side-hung casements except in canteen, library, and two laboratories, where hardwood frames and double-glazing are used. Laboratories have benches of the cantilevered type with a few under-bench units, cupboards, and loose tables. Workshop benches and storage fittings, blinds, kitchen, canteen, and office furniture are all included in the building cost.

Items included under services (element group 5) are:

Heating:
Two boilers.

Ventilation:
Supply of filtered air to entrance hall, dining-room, annexe, and kitchen.

Hot water:
600-gallon storage cylinder.
Distribution to benches.

Town gas:
Connexions to laboratories, kitchen, cooking appliances, and 3 water heaters.

Compressed air:
Compressor.
Connexion to 16 outlets in workshops.

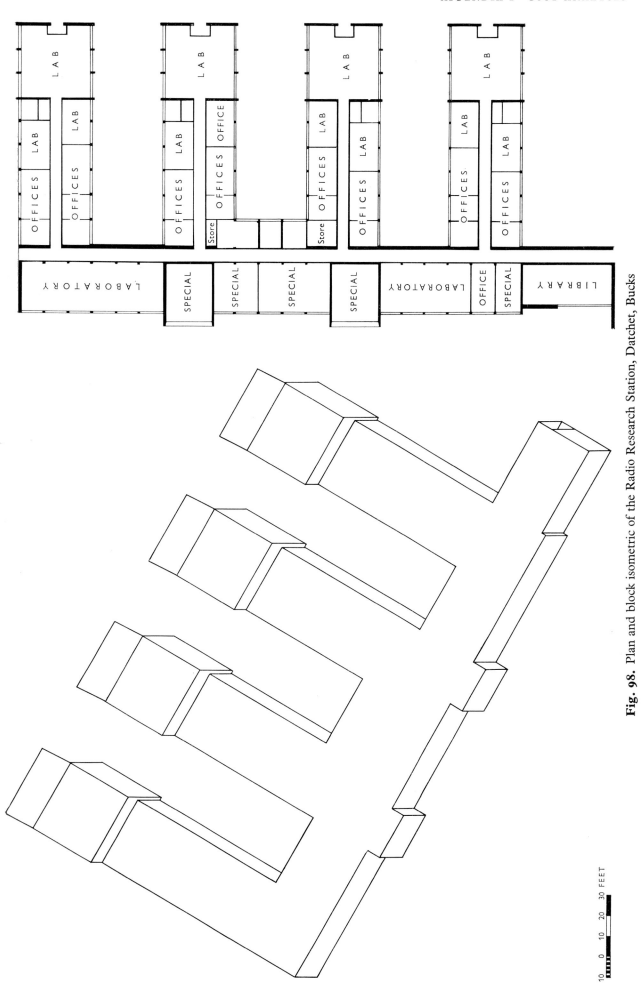

Fig. 98. Plan and block isometric of the Radio Research Station, Datchet, Bucks

Cost Analysis

Total cost (as at 31 March 1957)

	£
Building work	171,179
Engineering services (including builders' work, &c.)	55,863
Laboratory and other fittings, furniture, &c.	38,695
	£265,737

Gross floor area: 54,295 ft. sup. Cost per ft. sup. gross £4. 17*s.* 11*d.*

Analysis by items:

	Per foot super gross		*Percentage*	
	£ s. d.	£ s. d.		
1. Work below ground-floor level	8 0		8·2	
Total		8 0		8·2
2. Superstructure:				
Structural frame including floors, stairs, roof, roof covering, flashings, rainwater goods	19 5		19·8	
External walling including facings	4 4		4·4	
Windows and external doors including glazing and ironmongery	4 0		4·1	
Internal structural	1 4		1·4	
Total		1 9 1		29·7
3. Partitioning and internal doors:				
Internal partitions	2 3		2·3	
Internal doors and borrowed lights	2 0		2·0	
Total		4 3		4·3
4. Finishes and decorations:				
Internal finishing to walls, floors, and ceilings	5 3		5·4	
Decorations—internal and external	2 10		3·0	
Total		8 1		8·4
5. Services:				
Normal plumbing and sanitary services	1 2		1·2	
Laboratory ditto	6		0·5	
Engineering services:				
Mechanical				
Boiler-house plant and associated equipment	6 0¾		6·1	
Heating services in buildings	4 9½		4·9	
Hot water services	1 1½		1·2	
Ventilation to entrance hall	9½		0·9	
Gas installation	2		0·2	
Compressed-air to workshop	4		0·3	
Cold water storage tank, blacksmith's hearth, &c.	2		0·2	
Electrical				
Main underground distribution	6½		0·5	
Lighting installation	1 6		1·5	
Lighting fittings	1 3		1·3	
Socket outlet installation	2 10¼		2·9	
Fire-alarm system	1½		0·1	
Emergency lighting	0¾		0·06	
Internal telephones	0½		0·04	
Impulse clock system including clocks	3¾		0·3	
Lightning protection	1½		0·1	
Ancillary electrical services from boiler-house controls, &c.	4		0·3	
Total		1 2 3		22·6
6. External works and services:				
External services including fencing, roads, paths, drainage, landscaping, &c.	10 3		10·5	
Total		10 3		10·5
7. Fittings and furnishing:				
Laboratory benches fixed and mobile, fume cupboards, apparatus cupboards, and workshops benching	6 2½		6·3	
Laboratory furniture—				
Apparatus racks, laboratory desks, stools, trolleys, cabinets, tool lockers	1 1¾		1·2	
Blinds	5¾		0·5	
Lino	1 7¾		1·7	
Stores racking	1 0¼		1·0	
Changing-room equipment	0½		0·05	
Library fillings including wall panelling	11¼		0·95	
Office furniture	2 6		2·5	
Canteen furniture	3¼		0·3	
Canteen equipment including cookers, refrigerators, kitchen fittings, &c.	6		0·5	
Total		14 9		15·0
8. Sundries:				
Sundries—including fittings, balustrades, and minor items of daywork	1 3		1·3	
Total		1 3		1 3
Total cost per ft. sup. gross		£4 17 11		100·0

ANALYSIS No. 8

Acetate and Synthetic Fibres Laboratory
Courtaulds Limited, Coventry

Cost information supplied by Courtaulds Limited

Acetate and Synthetic Fibres Laboratory, Courtaulds Limited, Coventry

The building was designed to house about 150 graduates and assistants: disciplines include Chemistry, Bio-chemistry, and Physics. An office and storage block is attached. Rooms 28 ft. deep are planned on either side of a 6 ft. 6 in. wide corridor, and services are carried in vertical ducts between corridor and laboratories. The ducts are 3 ft. deep, giving a total building depth of about 70 ft. An 11 ft. 9 in. planning grid is used and internal partitions normally follow the grid lines. Floor-to-floor height is 12 ft. 6 in. There are four floors and a large basement.

The proportion of primary space (40·5 per cent.) is about average, offices occupy 13·1 per cent., and service space 12·6 per cent. (which includes 7·4 per cent. taken up by vertical ducts). Circulation area is a little below average at 19·1 per cent.

The building is a steel-framed structure with 11 in. cavity brick infilling: windows span the full width between structural columns in the laboratories. Internal walls are of light-weight blocks and are non-structural. Walls and ceilings are plastered and painted, and floors generally finished in P.V.C. tiles.

Items included under services (element group 5) are:

Heating:
Horizontal heating mains at high level in basement with rising mains in service shafts along each side of the central corridors.
Steam/water calorifier.
Ray-rad circuit pump.
Panel circuit pump.

Ventilation:
Mechanical exhaust systems coupled to the fume cupboards. Plenum system comprises a fresh-air input plant located in the basement having a viscous type filter, air washer, main air heater battery.

Constant temperature and variable conditioned laboratories:
Supply fan.
Discharge and recirculation ducting.
Air heater and cooler batteries.
Dehumidification unit and steam humidification unit, &c.

Hot water services:
Storage calorifier.
Pumps.

Town gas services:
596 single outlets.

Compressed air:
General air-supply—
2 compressors (1 standby).
253 single outlets.
Instrument clean compressed air-supply—
2 rotary, water-sealed compressors (1 standby).
Receiver humidrier.
Ancillary piping.

Refrigeration:
Factory brine circulating system.

Vacuum:
2 rotary-type water-sealed vacuum pumps (1 standby).
281 outlets.

L.P. Steam and condensate:
Condense piping, tank, pump, and insulation.
Steam supply to 2 fresh-air plants including washers, 4 air-conditioning plants, 1 heating calorifier, 1 domestic calorifier, 98 service points.

Electrical services:
Daylight fluorescent lamps.
Tungsten filament lighting in basement.
Wiring on ancillary equipment—service plant in basement, extract fans on roof.

Clock installation:
Circuit and fuse for each clock.

Alarm system:
12-way indicator panel for fire alarms.
6-way indicator panel for emergencies.

Telephones:
Cabling run in vertical shafts and floor ducts.

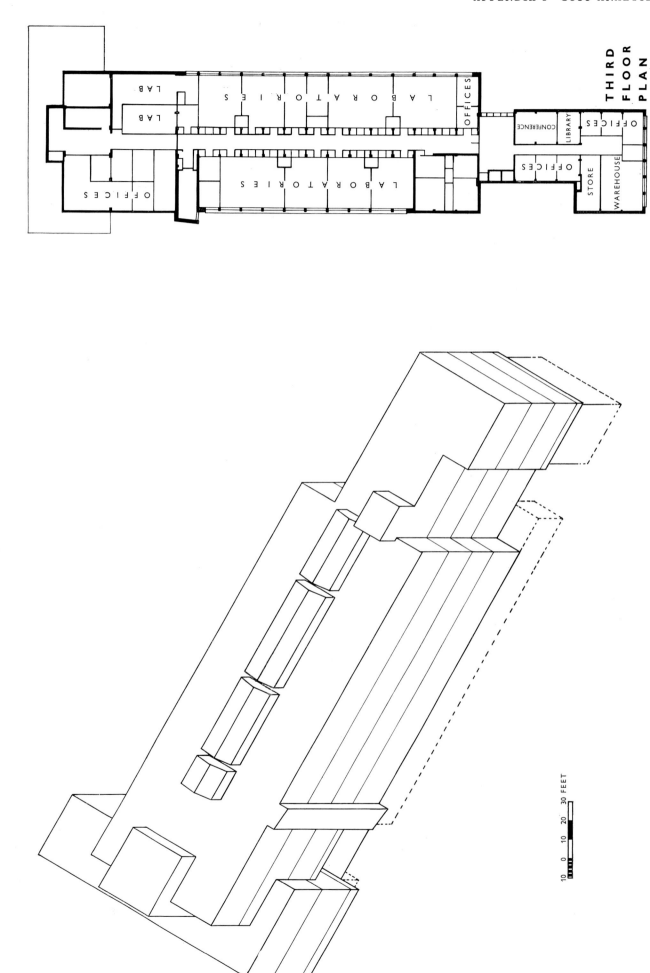

Fig. 99. Plan and block isometric of the Acetate and Synthetic Fibres Laboratory, Courtaulds Limited, Coventry.

Cost Analysis

Based on superstructure area (71,313 sq. ft.) for Groups 1 and 2 below. Total area (83,573 sq. ft.) used to obtain cost per sq. ft. of remainder.

Total cost (as at June 1957)

	£
Building work	258,692
Engineering services (including builders' work, &c.) . . .	211,965
Laboratory and other fittings, furniture, &c. . . .	71,149
	£541,806

Gross floor area: 83,573 ft. sup. Cost per ft. sup. gross: £6. 16s. 8½d.

Analysis by items:

	Per foot super gross			Percentage	
	s.	d.	£ s. d.		
1. Work below ground-floor area:					
Excavation footings, floor slab .	6	11¼		5·0	
Frame	1	6		1·1	
External walls	1	9¾		1·3	
Suspended ground floor and stairs	1	7		1·2	
Vertical duct		4¼		0·3	
Total			12 2¼		8·9
2. Superstructure:					
Frame	11	4½		8·3	
Roof	4	9		3·5	
External walls	4	9¼		3·5	
Floor and stairs	7	9		5·7	
Vertical ducts	2	5½		1·8	
Windows and external doors	4	6½		3·3	
Total			1 15 7¾		26·1
3. Partitioning and internal doors:					
Partitions	3	10¾		2·9	
Doors	2	5½		1·8	
Total			6 4¼		4·7
4. Finishes:					
To walls, floors, and ceilings	11	9		8·6	
Decorations	2	0		1·5	
Total			13 9		10·1
5. Services:					
Normal plumbing and sanitary services	1	11		1·4	
Laboratory ditto	3	4		2·4	
Engineering services:					
Mechanical					
Gas	1	0¼		0·7	
Compressed air	1	7½		1·2	
Vacuum	1	2¼		0·9	
Heating, hot water, and ventilation	15	3¼		11·2	
Refrigeration		3		0·2	
Steam	1	3¼		0·9	
Hydrants, &c.		11		0·6	
Electrical	13	10¼		10·2	
Total			2 0 7¾		29·7
6. External works and services:					
Drainage	1	1½		0·8	
Subsidiary buildings		6½		0·4	
External ducts and services	7	8½		5·6	
Roads and landscaping	1	8½		1·3	
Total			11 1		8·1
7. Fittings and furnishing:					
Laboratory benching, fume cupboards, cupboards	11	8		8·5	
Other fittings—built-in fittings, blinds, loose furniture, projector, &c., kitchen equipment	5	4½		3·9	
Total			17 0½		12·4
Total cost per ft. sup. gross			£6 16 8½		100·0

MATERIALS AND FINISHES

Introduction

It is outside the scope of this report to deal in great detail with all the finishing and structural materials used in laboratory construction. To cover every possibility would involve the consideration of almost the whole range of building materials. Materials are dealt with below only in relation to those special properties which are required in laboratories, but it must be remembered that the criteria which apply in all types of buildings (durability, ease of maintenance, quietness to the tread, &c.) also apply in laboratories. There are many publications dealing with the general properties of building materials, some of which have been listed in the selected bibliography at the end of this appendix. The physical properties of laboratory finishing materials (timbers, metals, and plastics) have been dealt with extensively in the recently published *Recommendations on Laboratory Furniture and Fittings* (British Standard 3202:1959). The latter contains tables giving the specific gravity, hardness, thermal conductivity, and normal temperature limits for most of the commonly used finishing materials.

The work carried out in laboratories varies so widely that there can be no simple panacea for the many problems involved in the choice of finishing materials. It has been suggested elsewhere in this report that the aim in laboratory design should be interchangeability and this may well be extended to the selection of materials. An ideal material for a chemistry or biochemistry laboratory may be quite unsuitable for other kinds of work and if the rooms are to be adaptable or interchangeable, this must be borne in mind when choosing floor and wall finishes and when designing the furniture and equipment.

Floors

Table 103 has been compiled to show in general terms the corrosion resistance and wearing qualities of the common floor finishes. It is based on a table published in *Building Research Station Digest*, no. 74, and has been extended to cover other properties. The price of floor finishes has a great influence on selection and the floor finishes may range in price from something less than 20s. per square yard for a granolithic finish, pitch mastic, or asphalt, through the medium price range for good-quality linoleum, P.V.C. tiles or sheet, to wood block or terrazzo (20s. to £3 per square yard). It should be noted that the price of hard floor finishes such as quarry tiles rises very considerably when laid in special cements.

Whilst Table 103 forms a good guide for the choice of materials in relation to chemical resistance, the choice may not always rest upon this, even in chemical labora-tories. The liquids which are spilled will only be highly corrosive on rare occasions, whereas water or very dilute solutions may be spilled quite frequently. The character of the material, therefore, is also of importance, for example, a surface finish made up of small units such as wood blocks or tiles, may allow liquid to penetrate to the structural sub-floor. With such materials, it is advisable always to place an acid-resistant, waterproof membrane between the floor finish and the sub-floor. This will of course add to cost. Acid-resistant asphalt and bituminous felt, tarred paper, and polythene films have all been used successfully for this purpose. It is essential to provide such protection to suspended reinforced concrete floors as slow seepage of corrosive liquids may go on unnoticed. In the case of ground floors some of the finishing materials will require a waterproof membrane for protection against rising damp: this is especially true of linoleum, P.V.C. sheet or tiles, cork tiles, and wood blocks.

It is probably because of the protection they give against spilled liquids that sheet materials, such as linoleum, have become popular for laboratory floors; linoleum is cheap, can be either washed or polished and is easy to replace. Linoleum is also used widely in laboratories for radioisotope work, where it is usually highly polished. Whilst it gives only moderate resistance to chemical attack, it is comfortable to the tread, wears well, and presents few joints through which seepage to the sub-floor may occur.

Bench tops

Complete information on the physical properties of timber, plastics, metals, and other materials, ranging from glazed earthenware to vitreous enamelled mild steel is given in B.S. 3202:1959. The most commonly used plastics are the laminated materials (phenolics and amino-plastics laminated with other materials), polyvinyl chloride and polythene. The laminated plastics are usually satisfactory up to about 100° C. whilst P.V.C. and polythene are usually given a temperature limit of about 70° C. Polytetrafluorethylene is one of the new plastics which has outstanding resistance to chemical attack and will withstand temperatures up to 250° C.

Table 104* shows the suitability of plastics materials against a large range of chemicals. Nylon and acrylic

* This table is reproduced from STANLEY, T. A., 'General aspects of the application of plastics to chemical plant' Society of Chemical Industry, *Materials of construction in the chemical industry*. London, 1950.

Table 103. The resistance of floor finishes and of bedding and jointing material to various liquids and solutions.

Material	Resistance to substances likely to be spilled									Dusting	Wear	
	Water	Weak acid	Strong acid	Dilute caustic alkali	Sulphates	Mineral oil	Animal or vegetable oil	Sugar	Organic solvents		Foot	Trucks
Portland cement concrete	VG	P	VP	VG	VP	G	P	P	G	F	VG–F	G–P
High alumina cement concrete	G	F	VP	P	G	G	F	F	G	F	VG–F	G–P
Pitch mastic (properties depend on grade)	VG	VG–F (acid-resisting grades available)	VG–F (acid-resisting grades available)	G	VG	F	F	F (when hot)	Softened by coal tar and bitumen distillates	G	VG–G	G–F
Mastic asphalt (properties depend on grade)	VG	VG–F (acid-resisting grades available)	VG–F (acid-resisting grades available)	G	VG	P	P	P (when hot)	Softened by coal tar and bitumen distillates	G	VG–G	G–F
Rubber-latex cement	G	G	P	G	F–G	F–G	F	F–G	P	G	VG–G	G–F
Resin-emulsion cement	F	G	P	G	F	G	F	F	P	G	VG–G	G–F
Rubber sheet	G	G–F	F–P	F–P	VG	P	P	F–P	Swells with petroleum	G	VG	G
Linoleum	G–F	F	P	P	G	P	P	P	Softened by ketones	G	G	P
P.V.C. sheet	G	G	F–P	G	G	G	G		Softened by chlorinated hydrocarbons	G	VG	G
Vinyl asbestos tiles	F–G	P	P	G	G	G	G		Softened by chlorinated hydrocarbons	G	G	G
Thermoplastic tiles	G	P	P	G	G	P	P	F–P	Softened by many solvents	G	F	P
P.V.C. tiles	G	G	F–P	G	G	G	G		As P.V.C. sheet	G	VG	G
Cork tiles	P	F–P	F–P	Stain or bleach		Stain	Stain	Stain	Not attacked but absorbed	G	G	Not used
Hardwood block	G	G–F	F–P	F–P	G	G	G	G	Not attacked	G	F–VG	VG if the right type
Clay tiles	VG	VG–G	VG–F	VG–F	VG–G	VG–F	VG–F	VG–F	Not attacked		G–VG	F–VG
Bedding and jointing materials for clay tiles or bricks												
Portland cement mortar	As above for Portland cement concrete but attack proceeds more slowly in thin joint											
Supersulphate cement mortar	VG	VG	VP	G	G				G			
High alumina cement mortar	As above for high alumina cement concrete but attack proceeds more slowly in thin joint											
Silicate cement	P	VG	VG	VP	VG	G	G		G			
Sulphur cement	VG	G	VG		G	G	P					
Resin emulsion cement and Rubber-latex cement	As above for the same materials, but attack proceeds more slowly in thin joint											
Phenol-formaldehyde resin cement	VG	VG	VG	F	G	G	G	G	G–P			
Cashew nut cement	VG	VG	G	G	G	P	P	G	P			
Furane resin cement	VG	VG	VG	VG	G	G	G	G	G			

KEY: VG = Very Good   F = Fair   G = Good   P = Poor

Table 104. Resistance of plastics to various chemicals.

Agent	Concentration	Polythene		P.V.C.		Acrylic sheet		Nylon		Polytetrafluoroethylene	
		20° C.	60° C.	20° C.	60° C.	20° C.	60° C.	20° C.	60° C.	20° C.	60° C.
Acetic acid	10%	S	S	S	S	S	S	S	A	S	S
		A	U	A	U			U		S	S
Acetone		U	U	U		U		S		S	S
Ammonia	100% dry gas	S	S	S	S	S	S	S		S	S
	0·88 s.g. solution	S	S	S	S	S	S	S		S	S
Amyl acetate	100%	U	U	A		U				S	S
Benzene		U	U	U		U		S		S	S
Bromine		U	U	A	U	A	U			S	S
Calcium chloride		S	S	S	S	S	S	S		S	S
Calcium hypochlorite	'Bleach' solution	S	S	S	S	S	S	U		S	S
Carbon disulphide		U	U	A	U	U	U			S	S
Carbon tetrachloride		U	U	A	U	U	U	S		S	S
Chlorine	Dry gas	A	U	S	A	U	U	S		S	S
	Liquid	U	U	U	U	U	U			S	S
Chlorsulphonic acid		U	U	A	U			U		S	S
Chromic acid including plating solution		S	S	S	S	U	U	U		S	S
Cider		S		S		S		S		S	
Citric acid		S	S	S	S	S	S	S		S	S
Cyclo-hexanone		U	U	U		U		S		S	S
Dibutyl phthalate		A	A	A	A	A	U			S	S
Diethylene glycol		S	S	S	S	S	S			S	S
Ethyl alcohol	100%	U	U	S	A	U	U	A		S	S
Ethyl acetate		A	U	U	U	U	U	S		S	S
Ethyl butyrate		A	U	A	U	U	U	S		S	S
Ethyl ether		U	U	U		U				S	S
Ethylene dichloride		U	U	U		U		S	A	S	S
Ferric chloride		S	S	S	S	S	S	S		S	S
Ferrous sulphate		S	S	S	S	S	S	S		S	S
Fluorine		S	U							S	S
Formaldehyde	40%	S		S		U				S	S
Formic acid	50%	S	S	S	S	S	S	U	U	S	S
Fufuryl alcohol		U	U					S		S	S
Glycerol		S	S	S		S				S	S
Hydrogen peroxide	40 vols.	S	S	S	S	A		A		S	S
	100 vols.	S	A	S	S	U		U		S	S
Hydrobrombic acid	50%	S	S	S	S			U		S	S
Hydrochloric acid	10%	S	S	S	S	S	S	U		S	S
	35%	S	S	S	S	S	S	U	U	S	S
Hydrofluoric acid	conc.	S	A	S	A			U		S	S
Iodine in KI solution	conc.	A	U					U			
Lactic acid	10–90%	S	S	S	A			S		S	S
Linseed oil		A	A	S	S					S	S
Magnesium chloride		S	S	S	S	S	S	S	S	S	S
Magnesium sulphate		S	S	S	S	S	S	S	S	S	S
Methyl bromide		A		A						S	S
Milk		S	S	S	S	S		S		S	S
Mineral oils		A	U	S	S			S		S	S
Nickel sulphate		S	S	S	S	S		S	S	S	S
Nitric acid		S	S	S	S	S	A	S		S	S
Nitric acid	70%	A	U	S	A	A	S	U		S	S
	95%	A	U	U		U	U	U		S	S
Octyl cresol		A	U	A	A	U		U		S	S
Oleic acid		A	U	S	S			S		S	S
Ozone		S	A	S	S	S	S			S	S
Petrol		U	U	S	S	A		S		S	S
Phosphoric acid	30%	S	S			S	S	U			
	90%	S	U	S	S			U		S	S
Photographic fixing solution		S	S	S	S	S	S	U		S	S

(continued)

'S' indicates satisfactory.

'A' indicates some attack or absorption (may be considered where alternative materials are unsatisfactory).

'U' indicates unsatisfactory.

A space indicates not applicable or information lacking.

Note: The inorganic salts listed above can be taken as being in aqueous solution of any concentration.

Table 104 (*continued*).

Agent	Concentration	Polythene		P.V.C.		Acrylic sheet		Nylon		Polytetra-fluorethylene	
		20° C.	60° C.	20° C.	60° C.	20° C.	60° C.	20° C.	60° C.	20° C.	60° C.
Potassium borate		S	S	S	S	S	S	S		S	S
Potassium chloride		S	S	S	S	S	S	S		S	S
Potassium cyanide		S	S	S	S	S	S	S		S	S
Potassium dichromate		S	S	S	S	S	S	S		S	S
Potassium hydroxide		S	S	S	S	S	S	S		S	S
Potassium nitrate		S	S	S	S	S	S	S		S	S
Potassium permanganate		S	S	S	S	S	S	U		S	S
Sea water		S	S	S	S	S	S	S		S	S
Silic acid	any	S	S	S	S	S	S	S		S	S
Silver nitrate	10%	S	S	S	S	S	S	S		S	S
Sodium benzoate		S	S	S	S	S	S	S		S	S
Sodium bisulphite		S	S	S	S	S	S	S		S	S
Sodium chlorate		S	S	S	S	S	S	S		S	S
Sodium chloride		S	S	S	S	S	S	S		S	S
Sodium hydroxide		S	S	S	S	S	S	S		S	S
Sodium sulphide		S	S	S	S	S	S	S		S	S
Stannous chloride		S	S	S	S	S	S	S		S	S
Starch solution	common	S	S	S	S	S	S	S		S	S
Stearic acid	100%	S	S	S	S	S	S	S		S	S
Sulphuric acid	10%	S	S	S	S	S	S	U		S	S
	70%	S	A	S	S			U		S	S
	98%	A	U	S	A			U		S	S
Tallow		S	A	S	S	S	S	S		S	S
Tartaric acid	10%	S	S	S	S	S	S			S	S
Toluene		U	U	U	U	U		S		S	S
Transformer oil		A	U	S	S	S				S	S
Trichlorethylene		U	U	U	U	S	S	A	U	S	S
Turpentine		A	U								
Vegetable and animal oils		U	U	S	S	S	S	S		S	S
Vinegar		S	S	S	S	S	S	S		S	S
Xylene		U	U	U		U		S		S	S
Yeast		S		S	A			S		S	
Zinc chloride		S	S	S	S	S	S	S		S	S
Zinc sulphate		S	S	S	S	S	S	S		S	S

' S' indicates satisfactory.

'A' indicates some attack or absorption (may be considered where alternative materials are unsatisfactory).

'U' indicates unsatisfactory.

A space indicates not applicable or information lacking.

Note: The inorganic salts listed above can be taken as being in aqueous solution of any concentration.

sheet have been included in this table as well as polythene and P.V.C. Laminated plastics have only a fairly good resistance to attack by dilute acids and alkalis but give good resistance to the common organic solvents. They have been chosen for use in laboratories where extreme cleanliness is essential, but have given some trouble due to failure of the adhesives when used around sinks and elsewhere under wet conditions. Under severe mechanical wear the surfaces of laminated plastics will break down.

Teak is of course the most stable of the hardwoods and is still chosen as the best bench top material by many authorities, but it does depend for its chemical resistance upon careful and constant maintenance. A number of other timbers have been used with some success for laboratory bench tops, notably Iroko, Kokrodua, and Afzelia.

Linoleum bench tops have been used with great success in laboratories where conditions of wear and exposure are less stringent, and it is very suitable in physics laboratories and in special instrument rooms. Public authorities have used it extensively, even in chemical laboratories where, when it is stained or damaged, it can be easily and cheaply replaced. This is a further example of the use of cheap replaceable materials: another example is the use of polythene film or tarred paper stretched over softwood bench tops in laboratories where radioactive materials are handled. The coverings are removed and destroyed when they become contaminated. Table 105 is reproduced from B.S. 3202: 1959 and shows the suitability of a range of materials for use as draining-boards. Table 106 gives similar information on materials for sinks.

Fume cupboard floors are also dealt with in B.S. 3202,

Table 105.[1] Materials for draining-boards and suitability for laboratory purposes.

Materials	Suitability
Asbestos cement and fireclay	Very limited application.
Lead	Dark rooms, &c., integral with sink. Costly.
Polythene and rigid P.V.C.	Obtainable by fabrication. Also available in moulded form. Cheap and easily replaceable. Kind to glassware.
Porcelain enamel	Subject to chipping. Not recommended.
Stainless steel	Good quality readily available. Hygienic and robust.
Teak	Generally satisfactory but regular waxing is desirable.
Glass, annealed or toughened	Moderately costly but easy to install and replace. Not conventional pattern. Substantial thickness recommended to provide rigidity of assembly and strength.

Table 106.[1] Materials for sinks and suitability for laboratory purposes.

Material	Suitability
Aluminium (anodized)	Only suitable for specific projects.
Glazed fireclay	General purpose use. Moderately inexpensive. Easily damaged and stained.
Chemical stoneware	Suitable for all purposes, highly resistant except to hydrofluoric acid and concentrated alkalis. Costly in comparison with glazed fireclay.
Copper-nickel alloy	Suitable for strong caustic soda, sulphuric acid, and salts. Expensive.
Lead	Dark rooms, &c., where the sink is integral with the remainder of the bench top. Costly.
P.V.C. or P.V.C. lined	A flanged lined outlet is required to provide a continuous lined surface.
Polythene or polythene lined	Polythene dipped only suitable as it tends to shrink from steel container. Robust, easily repaired and kind to glassware. Not suitable for solvents.
Porcelain enamel (pressed steel or cast iron)	Subject to chipping and attack by strong acids. Not recommended.
Stainless steel	Domestic sizes to B.S. 1244* may be suitable, but not suitable for hydrochloric and sulphuric acids, &c. Robust and hygienic.
Wood, zinc lined	Subject to chemical attack. Expensive and suitable only in paint and colour laboratories.

* B.S. 1244: 1956. 'Metal sinks for domestic purposes.'

[1] Tables 105–107 are reproduced from British Standard 3202:1959. *Recommendations on laboratory furniture and fittings.* Copies of the standard may be obtained from the British Standards Institution, 2 Park Street, W.1.

Table 107.[1] Materials recommended for service piping.

Service	Materials
Cold water	Lead, copper, polythene to B.S. 1973,* P.V.C., medium or heavy galvanized steel tube to B.S. 1387.†
Hot water	Copper, or medium galvanized steel to B.S. 1387,† for normal domestic or industrial purposes. Heavy galvanized steel tubes to B.S. 1387† for special cases (underground).
Heating (hot water or steam)	Medium black or galvanized steel tube to B.S. 1387† for normal installations, heavy for special cases. Copper.
Steam	Medium or heavy black steel tube to B.S. 1387.† Copper.
Condensate	Copper.
Gas (town or petrol)	Light or medium black steel tube to B.S. 1387.† Copper or aluminium.
Liquefied petroleum gas	Copper.
Compressed air	Medium or heavy black or galvanized steel tube to B.S. 1387.† Copper or aluminium.
Vacuum	Copper or aluminium. Medium steel to B.S. 1387.† Chemical lead to B.S. 334‡ for corrosive conditions.
Distilled water	Stainless steel, glass to B.S. 2598,§ P.V.C., polythene to B.S. 1973,* aluminium, pure tin.
Drains and wastes	Stainless steel. Chemical lead.
Suitable for gravity flow	Cast iron. Silicon iron (spun). Chemical stoneware. Vitreous enamel. Rubber lined. Glass lined. Hard rubber. Glazed fireclay. Copper. Glass to B.S. 2598.§ Polythene to B.S. 1973,* P.V.C. Chloroprene canvas hose.
Demineralized water (hot or cold) suitable for normal laboratory work	Stainless steel, glass, P.V.C., polythene to B.S. 1973,* aluminium.

* B.S. 1973, 'Low density polythene tube for general purposes, including chemical and food industry uses'.
† B.S. 1387, 'Steel tubes and tubulars suitable for screwing to B.S. 21 pipe threads'.
‡ B.S. 334, 'Chemical lead (types A and B)'.
§ B.S. 2598, 'Glass pipeline and fittings'.

which lists compressed asbestos cement board, lead, stainless steel, slate, toughened glass, and vitreous tiles. The asbestos cement boards are satisfactory but usually stain badly. Lead is liable to mechanical damage. Stainless steel is expensive but is often used for fume cupboards in radioactive work. Slate is a satisfactory material but may crack with heat or mechanical shock.

Service lines

Table 107 is reproduced from B.S. 3202: 1959, and gives suitable materials for the various kinds of piping used in laboratory services.

Electrical installations

There are four main types of installation suitable for laboratories:

1. Heavy gauge screwed welded conduit.
2. Fully insulated conduit.
3. Steel trunking.
4. Mineral insulated copper covered cable (M.I.C.C.).

1. HEAVY GAUGE SCREWED WELDED CONDUIT

This is a commonly used system and has a tremendous weight of contractors' experience in installation behind it. Sufficient space can be left for pulling through extra cables at a later date. It is not easy to add or change outlets within the length of a run of conduit. The normal finish as supplied, is black painted, but galvanized conduits and fittings are available.

2. FULLY INSULATED CONDUIT

Plastic tubing is screwed to moulded plastic fittings in the same way as for metal conduit. The system should be used in preference to metal in laboratories where above average concentrations of acidic fumes are expected, where its higher initial cost will be offset by reduced maintenance. The need for a separate earthing cable leads to higher material and installation costs than for metal conduit.

3. STEEL TRUNKING

Although more expensive than screwed steel conduit, gain in flexibility and neatness will often make the use of trunking worth while. Extra cables can be added for increased loads, and outlets can be added or moved with little difficulty.

4. MINERAL INSULATED COPPER COVERED CABLE

These cables are sufficiently resistant to mechanical damage to need no further protection. In atmospheres which are corrosive to copper the P.V.C. sheathed variety is preferable. The need to protect the mineral insulation where the cables are cut necessitates the use of glands at all junctions, so that the price for this kind of installation will be little different from one in screwed steel conduit. The installations are fire-, moisture-, and oil-proof.

Metal-insulated copper-covered cables have good heat resistance and are useful in positions where normal cables would have to be de-rated.

Cable types

P.V.C. cable should be used in laboratory installations, as it has superior corrosion resistance to the normal V.R.I. cable.

Cable is also available insulated with polythene, neoprene, alkathene, or kappathene, all of which have high resistance to chemical attack. Owing to the high insulation value of the materials, the overall size of the cable is reduced. They are, however, 20 per cent. to 30 per cent. more expensive than P.V.C. cables.

Laboratory wastes

The introduction of plastics piping and fittings has simplified the provision of suitable laboratory waste lines. Such pipes have almost universal application. The principal exceptions occur where mechanical rigidity is essential or where hot liquids must be carried continuously. In Europe P.V.C. has also been widely developed, but in this country manufacturers have concentrated on low-density polythene, and more recently on high-density polythene.

The thermal movement of polythene is about seven times that of copper. High-density polythene will retain its rigidity towards the temperature of boiling water, but will lack flexibility to absorb movement, while low-density polythene at this temperature becomes soft enough to 'snake' and takes the movement without damage, but in consequence needs almost continuous support to avoid sagging. As the two materials are quite compatible, a logical approach is to use high-density polythene traps which will take the heat shock without distortion, coupled to low-density pipe runs laid on battens in order to keep down thermal stresses.

The effect of organic solvents is to make polythene more brittle until it cracks due to thermal or mechanical movement. Whilst polythene pipes should not be used for carrying these liquids in large amounts, small quantities washed down a sink are not a serious hazard as the attack is slow, and the eventual failure would almost certainly occur in a trap rather than in a pipe run. Replacement is quick, easy, and inexpensive if compression joints are used. Where larger quantities of organic solvents are in use, recovery apparatus should be installed for the working liquids, so that the quantity going into the drains is small. Chemical lead pipes may be needed in such positions.

Of the other more traditional materials, steel pipe should be galvanized as a basis for a good paint system including a rust inhibiting primer. Copper pipes are not usually acceptable for laboratory use.

Glass pipes and traps are coming into more common use, but are still expensive. The danger of breakage is not so great as might be expected, as glass is naturally treated with respect. Glass traps are very suitable for laboratory use and may be successfully combined with other materials used in the waste disposal system generally.

Paints

In most laboratories, painted surfaces (i.e. walls, ceilings, &c.) are exposed to conditions which are only corrosive to a very mild degree. Fume extraction and ventilation are usually designed to maintain the atmosphere at reasonable levels of concentration for reasons of comfort and safety. For such conditions, the greatest danger of attack occurs when condensation is likely, and ample protection is given to walls and other surfaces by an exterior grade, good quality lead-free alkyd gloss paint. Alkali-resistant primers should, of course, be used on cement or lime surfaces.

More stringent measures must be taken to protect areas exposed to heavy concentrations of fumes or where corrosive liquids may be spilled. Metal surfaces such as the exposed parts of lighting fittings, furniture, fume cupboards, and similar components may be protected by paints based on epoxy resins. These paints give good resistance to most forms of chemical attack, but are not suitable for external use. Clear epoxy resin varnishes and other clear plastic sealers provide a renewable method of obtaining an impervious surface on wood and linoleum bench tops.

'Strippable' paints are widely used on fume cupboard floors, &c., especially in radioactive work. The paint is removed and destroyed when contaminated.

Condensation may occur on pipes carrying cold services. Epoxy resin paints have been used successfully on pipe runs: they may also be lagged. Polythene service and waste pipes do not need painting. If colour-marking is necessary it will usually be better to use a coloured P.V.C. wrapper.

In laboratories where high standards of cleanliness are required, exterior-grade alkyd gloss paints give a continuous impervious surface which is non-dusting and which will withstand much washing and scrubbing.

If impervious wall panels are used, for example in movable partitions, great care must be taken to ensure that the mounting adhesive or jointing compound has a comparable standard of moisture resistance to the panels.

Many special paints are available, e.g., anti-fungus and anti-insect paints, and paints designed to resist other specific forms of organic or inorganic attack. Paint manufacturers are usually willing to give detailed advice on individual problems, and guidance of this kind should be sought before using such paints. Excellent results under conditions of heavy chemical attack have been obtained with chlorinated rubber paints, for example, but great care is needed in their application, and the manufacturer's advice must be closely followed.

Plastics coatings are becoming common for laboratory fittings such as taps and valve handles. The application of such coatings is a factory process, and cannot easily be carried out on the site. Sprayed plastics wall finishes are, however, being developed, and have been used in a number of recent buildings; they may be suitable for certain laboratory wall surfaces, and have good wearing qualities. Application is usually carried out by a specialist firm.

BIBLIOGRAPHY

HANDISYDE, C. C. *Building materials, science and practice.* 3rd edition. London, Architectural Press, 1958.

McWILLIAM, J. A. 'Methods of fabrication of stainless steels as materials of construction.' *Materials of construction in the chemical industry.* London, Society of Chemical Industry, 1950, pp. 139–47.

HODSON, G. N. 'Chemical stoneware as a material of construction.' *Materials of construction in the chemical industry.* London, Society of Chemical Industry, 1950, pp. 23–24.

GILLET, R. T. 'Corrosion resisting materials in plumbing and drainage for chemical wastes.' *J. Instn. sanit. Engrs,* **54,** 1955, pp. 202–35.

COOPER, E. B. 'Plastics used in building construction. Plastics in building.' *Report of a conference conducted by the Building Research Institute, Washington D.C.* Washington, Building Research Institute, 1955, pp. 3–10.

WAIDELICH, A. T. 'Plastics used in building construction. Plastics in structural panels.' *Report of a conference conducted by the Building Research Institute, Washington D.C.* Washington, Building Research Institute, 1955, pp. 51–56.

MARECHAL, J. C. 'Wear tests on taps and fittings.' *Ann. Inst. Bâtim.,* **9,** no. 97, 1956, pp. 78–86.

NATIONAL ASSOCIATION OF CORROSION ENGINEERS. *Selected bibliography on corrosion of lead, 1937–54.* New York, 1955.

DEPARTMENT OF SCIENTIFIC AND INDUSTRIAL RESEARCH. *Thermoplastic flooring tiles.* London, 1953. *Building Research Station digest,* no. 57.

DEPARTMENT OF SCIENTIFIC AND INDUSTRIAL RESEARCH. *Floor finishes based on polyvinyl chloride (PVC) and polyvinyl acetate (PVA).* London, 1954. *Building Research Station digest,* no. 65.

DEPARTMENT OF SCIENTIFIC AND INDUSTRIAL RESEARCH. *Corrosion resistant floors,* pt. 1: Design considerations. London, 1955. *Building Research Station digest,* no. 73.

DEPARTMENT OF SCIENTIFIC AND INDUSTRIAL RESEARCH. *Corrosion resistant floors,* pt. 2: Materials for finishes. London, 1955. *Building Research Station digest,* no. 74.

DEPARTMENT OF SCIENTIFIC AND INDUSTRIAL RESEARCH. *Linoleum.* London, 1955. *Building Research Station digest,* no. 77.

DEPARTMENT OF SCIENTIFIC AND INDUSTRIAL RESEARCH. *Floor finishes for industrial buildings.* London, 1951. *National building studies. Special report,* no. 11. [Contains a bibliography and information for more severe laboratory conditions.]

DEPARTMENT OF SCIENTIFIC AND INDUSTRIAL RESEARCH. *A handbook of hardwoods.* London, 1956.

DEPARTMENT OF SCIENTIFIC AND INDUSTRIAL RESEARCH. *Hardwoods for industrial flooring.* London, 1954. *Forest Products Research leaflet,* no. 48.

DEPARTMENT OF SCIENTIFIC AND INDUSTRIAL RESEARCH. *Hardwoods for building and general purposes.* London, 1951.

BRITISH STANDARDS INSTITUTION. *Recommendations on laboratory furniture and fittings.* London, 1959. *British Standard,* 3202.

INDEX

Bold type denotes a Figure

Room height: continental practice, 22; scientists' opinions, 51; conclusions, 51; in chromatography rooms, 63; horizontal services, floor to floor height, 79, 81; ceiling heating, 96; ventilation, 97; and lighting, 111–12; cost studies, 168.

Room length, *see under* Room depth.

Safety: circulation gangway, 49, 143–53; glass-blowing, 69; records of laboratory accidents, 144; design factors affecting safety, 32, 146–9; escape routes, 146–7; protective and first-aid equipment, 151–3.

Serviced benches: nineteen-twenties, 15; nineteen-thirties, 17, **17**.

Services: survey observation and recording. 32; survey method of analysis, 32–33; in balance and instrument rooms, 60; in dark rooms, 62; in centrifuge rooms, 62; in inoculation rooms, 66; for media preparation, 67; for washing-up, 68; for glass-blowing, 69; for cage-washing, animal houses, 71

— Engineering services, 74–98; provision of services at bench position, 74; choice of piped services, 74–75; local units or centralized supply, 74–75; water, 75; steam, 75; town gas, 75; inert gases, 75–76; oxygen, 76; compressed air, 76; vacuum, 76; electrical supplies, 76; identification of services, 76, 149; scale of provision, results of survey, 85–95; use of cold-water taps, 85; use of hot-water taps, 88; use of gas taps, 88–90; electric services, use of current, 90–93; — use of electric points, 93–94; — use of points in relation to supply of current, 94–95; position of bench outlets, 95, 148; drainage and waste disposal, 149; electrical installations safety precautions, 149; gas cylinders, 151; emergency showers and eye-spray fittings, 152; fume disposal, 149; *See also under* Cost Studies and Material and finishes.

Services, methods of distribution, 76–84, **79**; nineteen twenties, 15, 16; exposed, 22, 79, **80**; electrical, 22; current practice, 19, 20, **21**, 22, 27; comparative costs, 37, 82–84, **83**; vertical metal channels to carry service pipes, 56; fire protection, 141; vertical sub-mains, 76, 77, 79, **79**, 83, 164; horizontal sub-mains, 79–81, **78**, 82, 164; drainage, 81; fume disposal ducts, 82; perimeter sub-mains, 83; and fire hazard, 142; and site planning, 154; and lighting, 104.

Services, space required, 49–50.

Shape of rooms, nineteen-twenties, 16, 29.

Sink length: survey method of analysis, 32–33; survey results, 42–43.

Sinks: analysis of survey results, 33; application of survey data, 48; for washing-up, 69; in animal rooms, 72.

Sites: planning for development, 154; single-story and multi-story buildings, 164.

Sound insulation and absorption, 123–4.

Space, per worker, *see* Floor area.

Special rooms, 58–73; conclusions, 165.

Staircases, minimum dimensions, 140.

Sterilization, 66–67; steam sterilizers, 66; autoclaves, 66; ovens, 66; glassware, 66; in animal houses, 71–72.

Storage space: in the laboratory, 53, 142, 147; in chromatography rooms, 64; in media preparation, 67; washing-up, 68; for cylinders, 75; in corridors, 140; poisons, 148; inflammable and explosive materials, 148; general bulk storage, 148; radioactive waste, 150; protective and first aid equipment, 151; floor-area, 160; near the laboratory, 160.

Sunlight penetration, 19, 116–18; sun control louvres, 110, 114, 117; solar heat gain, 116, 117; discomfort glare, 116–17; percentage solar heat transmission for various types of blinds, 117.

Survey of user requirements: purpose of the survey, 29; allocation of space, 29; provision of services, 29; the pilot survey, 29–30; assessment of lighting criteria, 29, 102–4; visual characteristics of work, 99, 102; the main survey, 30–33; classification of scientific staff, 30; A.R.C. research stations included in the survey, 30–31; industrial research laboratories included in the survey, 31; survey, conducted by I.C.I. Ltd., 31; data collected, 31–32; techniques of observation and recording, 32; method of analysis, 32–33; bench length, 39.

Tissue culture, *see* Inoculation rooms.

Unit benches, 22.

Unit of space: space requirements, 38–39; laboratory space, 47–53; scientists' opinions, 50–51.

University of Munich, Institute of Chemistry and Pharmacy, vertical servicing, 22, 79, **80**.

Ventilation, 95; room height, 51; in the A.R.C.'s radiobiological research laboratories, 54; chromatography rooms, 64; in inoculation rooms, 66; in sterilization rooms, 67; in glass-blowing rooms, 69; in animal houses, 72; the general laboratory area, 95, 97–98; fume cupboards, 97–98; noise in ventilating systems, 122; sound insulation, 124; fire protection, 142.

Vibration, 125–30; balance table, 59, **59**; and noise reduction, 119; isolation of machinery, 126; isolated piers, 127–8; anti-vibration mountings, 128, 129–30; principles of vibration isolation, 128–9.

Washing-up, 68–69, **67**; drying rack, **68**.

Water systems and noise, 121–2.

Windows: double glazing, 97, 117; design of, 113; roof light design, 113, **114**; clerestory lighting, 113, **116**.

Wyeth laboratories, Radnor, Pennsylvania, U.S.A., site plan, 154.